# SCANNERS 2

# SCANNERS 2
# INTERNATIONAL
## VHF/UHF Communications Guide

Peter Rouse GU1DKD

**ARGUS BOOKS**

Argus Books Limited
Wolsey House
Wolsey Road
Hemel Hempstead
Hertfordshire HP2 4SS

First published by Argus Books 1988
© Peter Rouse, 1988

ISBN 0 85242 924 X

Phototypesetting by En to En, Tunbridge Wells
Printed and bound by Whitstable Litho

# Contents

# Preface

Even before Scanners I (now into a second print and updated) was published it was obvious that there was high demand for a book on this fast growing hobby. In the course of researching material for the first book it also became apparent that there were many scanner owners who were not technically minded but who still wanted to have a better understanding of VHF/UHF communications in order to get more out of their equipment. I also came in contact with many professional, but non-technical users, who wanted to know more. As a result, the first book set out to explain some of the basics of scanning and communications generally as well as providing basic lists of who uses what frequencies. This book on the other hand is aimed at those scanner owners who have a little more technical knowledge and who can build simple accessories to add onto their equipment. We also look in more detail at some topics such as scanners under computer control, which were only lightly touched on in the first book. However, the non-technical reader has not been forgotten and again there are some useful lists which should provide valuable reference sources.

I make no apologies for a lack of theoretical detail throughout this book; as far as possible I have kept away from theory and stuck to practice. Readers who want to know more about things such as antenna or electronic theory should find a host of books on these subjects in any good book shop or be able to obtain them through amateur radio organisations such as the American Radio Relay League or Radio Society of Great Britain.

I must thank those many people who wrote to me after the first book was published. Some of them have made valuable suggestions for the contents of this book and in some instances have even provided material. Others have provided me with some very interesting data and I am indebted to them. If their names do not appear in these pages it is simply because they have requested anonimity.

Finally I would ask readers to bear in mind that we live in a fast changing world and it is inevitable that by the time this book is published some of the reference material may have changed. It is virtually impossible to stay completely up to date and if you take the hobby seriously you should always keep your own notes to record any new information or titbits that come your way.

PETER ROUSE 1987
Guernsey

## Acknowledgements

As was the case with Scanners 1, it would have been impossible to compile this book without the help of several individuals and organisations. In some cases the help has been in the form of permission to reproduce material which has been published before, in other cases several people have put in a lot of work on my behalf and some firms have either loaned or given me materials or equipment for assessment. I am indebted to them. They are:

Geoff Arnold G3GSR and Practical Wireless Magazine
Jane Berry and Radio & Electronics World
Paul Bennet and Cirkit Holdings Limited
Denis Goodwin and Icom (U.K.) Limited
Peter Turner G8TSY
John Wilson and Lowe Electronics (AOR scanners)
Peter Longhurst and Garex
Denis Reeves and Revco
Martin Ehrenfried G8JNJ
Mike Foster G8AMG
Peter Stonebridge G8ZQA
Paul Wiggins for help with the photography
Joan Bagley for the Apple Mac Laser printing of my artwork
Several other people who I know would prefer not to be named

# Home-built accessories 1

This chapter covers a variety of add-on projects which can enhance the performance of scanners from simple power supplies and NiCad chargers to sophisticated Hybrid IC broadband amplifiers.

In most instances the components should be available from regular suppliers including those who specialise in the mail order of components. Some devices may be a little difficult to come by but for the most part these will be the specialised ICs in some of the more sophisticated projects. Wherever possible the circuits have been designed to accept a wide tolerane of component values and in most cases many of the transistors specified can be substituted without making a great deal of difference to the performance.

Some of the circuits will need considerable care in construction and the choice of semiconductors and capacitors. For instance, in the circuits for pre-amplifiers, no specific details have been given to the all important considerations of layout. As a general rule all RF amplifiers should use the shortest possible interconnections with leads cropped as short as possible. Care should be taken where more than one inductor is incorporated in a circuit that these components should not have a damping effect on each other. Inputs and outputs should be well separated particularly where broadband circuits are concerned. Where possible double-sided circuit boards should be used and capacitors should be employed which are designed for use at VHF and UHF.

I do not recommend that the RF circuits be attempted by anyone with limited experience of VHF/UHF construction techniques. This is perhaps the trickiest area of home construction and it is far beyond the scope of this book to cover the subject in the kind of detail needed to get a grasp of the details involved. As I mentioned in the introduction, anyone wanting to learn more should get hold of some of the specialised books on the subject published by organisations such as the A.R.R.L. and R.S.G.B.

Having made those points I should say that most of the circuits involved in this chapter can be tackled by most people who can read a circuit diagram and solder properly.

## Safety

Before opening up any scanner to attach add-on circuits ensure that the equipment is fully disconnected from the mains power supply. If you must operated the equipment with covers off then this should only be done where the scanner is being fed with an externally supplied DC source from an isolated power supply. Remember, mains voltage can be lethal.

### Damage

The onus is on the reader to ensure that the circuits presented here do not cause damage to the equipment to which they are connected. You are strongly urged that unless you have the technical competence and suitable test equipment, do not attempt these projects. The misuse of some of these circuits or accidental wrong connections could seriously damage your scanner.

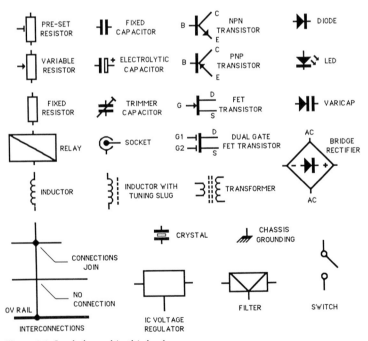

**Figure 1.1** Symbols used in this book

# Wideband amplifiers

The amplifier that will interest most scanner users is the wideband type which can boost signals over a wide range of frequencies. These days such amplifiers are not too difficult to construct as a large range of thick film integrated circuits are available. Most of these amplifiers are designed to be operated as television distribution amplifiers and they are easily adapted for use with scanners. The input/output impedance of these devices is 70 Ohms which is not a perfect match between either the IC and the antenna or into the scanner. In practice there is sufficient gain to overcome the slight losses caused by this missmatch.

First though why do we need an amplifier? In modern scanners the RF circuits are probably amplifying as much as possible with regard to signal to noise ratio and so it would seem that little can be gained from amplifying a signal yet further, bearing in mind that the amplifier itself will also introduce noise. In practice an amplifier can be used to make up for feeder losses and it is important to realise that even good quality low loss cable does attenuate signals and this effect becomes more apparent with increase in frequency. For an installation where say 10 metres of more of cable are used to feed from antenna to scanner, the losses can mean that some signals received at the antenna will not be heard on the receiver.

However, in order to use an amplifier to make up for cable losses it means we must install the amplifier at the masthead. This is not as difficult as it may appear as it is possible to feed the supply current to the amplifier up the existing coaxial cable. Although the examples that follow are limited to two specific devices there is no reason to believe that similar devices will not operate in the same way. The only point to watch is that some wideband thick film IC's include input/output coupling capacitors and others do not. If they do not then it would be inadvisable to couple D.C. current to the IC's output stage as damage could ensue.

## The drawbacks
An amplifier should only be used as a last resort and is not a substitute for good quality cable between the antenna and receiver. Amplifiers can add problems of their own particularly when the installation is in an area where there are strong signals. The signals can not only cause Intermodulation distortion, blocking and image problems (Bearcat 220 owners note) in the receiver, but some of these effects may become apparent in the amplifier itself.

## Construction and soldering techniques
With all thick film IC's the greatest care should be taken when soldering and the minimum of heat should be applied. Do not hold the

soldering iron onto the terminations for any longer than is necessary. These devices are not as rugged as normal IC's and it is possible to ruin the IC by excessive heat.

The IC's must be constructed on a double sided printed circuit board of the types shown. The combination of high gain and broad bandwidth is very susceptible to instability and only by using these construction techniques will problems be avoided. The input must be kept well away from the output and a further precaution can be taken by fitting a small inter-stage screen as shown in Figure 1.3. This can be made from a piece of copper sheet or may just be a small piece of PCB board soldered direct to the ground plane. If this screen is to be included it will require a fair amount of heat to solder to the board and so the IC should be fitted first but not soldered until all the other components have been connected.

## Masthead amplifier

This design can use one of several thick film amplifiers including the MC5229 and the OM 335. These devices are also available from different manufacturers under different designations. In the case of the MC5229 this is SH120A or HF 9091. The OM 335 is available in Great Britain as the RS Components 308–556.

Circuit diagrams are shown for each and the physical construction for both amplifiers is the same. However performance varies slightly as the MC5229 has a quoted gain of 17.5 dB whereas the OM 335 is quoted at 27 dB. Both devices have similar noise figures; 5 dB for the MC5229 and 5.5 dB for the OM 335. Both IC's are designed to operate in the range 40 MHz to 900 MHz but will in fact operate with slightly less gain above and below these frequencies. The practical upper limit appears to be around 1400 MHz and so the devices are suitable for use with scanners such as the AOR's and Regencies which have coverage up to 1300 MHz.

Simple low pass filtering has been included on the input stages of both amplifiers. these T-section filters have a Q of about 6 and are intended to attenuate signals below 30 MHz. Both devices in fact offer considerable gain down as low as 10 MHz and so it is wise to attenuate these frequencies so as to avoid blocking by strong HF broadcast transmissions. Capacitors C3/C4 are suppy decoupling components and the coil L2 is a choke which enables supply current to be fed to the IC without unduly affecting the output VSWR.

Whichever of the two masthead amplifiers is built, the circuit for the power supply is the same although component values will vary as the two IC's operate at different voltages. It is simply a question of using the appropriate transformer/regulator combination as shown. Some

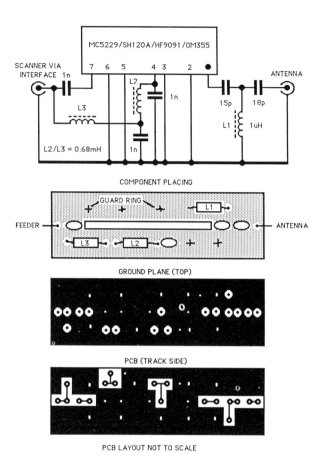

COMPONENT PLACING

GROUND PLANE (TOP)

PCB (TRACK SIDE)

PCB LAYOUT NOT TO SCALE

**Figure 1.2** Hybrid wideband amplifier with component layout and PCB data

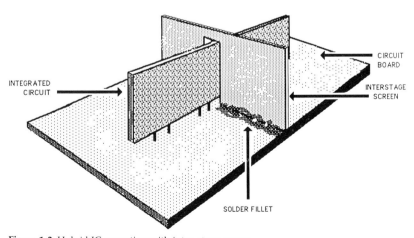

**Figure 1.3** Hybrid IC mounting with inter-stage screen

scanner users may be forced to use excessively long feeders in which case it may be necessary to experiment with different voltages to make up for high voltage drops.

## Construction and testing

Start by soldering the 'guard' ring on the double sided circuit board which should be well tinned before any work commences (this will ensure that minimum heat can be applied to make joints). This simply consists of silvered wire which is soldered both sides of the board. If you are going to fit an inter-stage screen (and it is a wise precaution to do so) then this must be fitted next. The screen need be nothing more than a scrap piece of double sided PCB which is cut to size with a slot for the IC. Before soldering it into place you will need to drop the IC into it's component holes but DO NOT at this stage solder it into

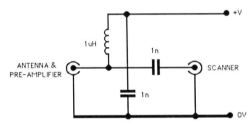

**Figure 1.4** Masthead pre-amp power supply interface

place. Solder the inter-stage screen first using fillets of solder between the screen and PCB ground plane. Then fit all the other components leaving the IC until last. Capacitors and coils which connect to earth should be soldered both sides of the board but the IC ground connections should only be soldered to the top of the board. A circuit board is not used for the power supply as all components are easily self-supporting. Once the amplifier and power supply have been constructed they should be bench tested to ensure that they operate correctly. It should be remembered that once the amplifier is installed there will be a slight voltage drop over its length. If possible a check should be made at the antenna end to ensure that this is not excessive and that the voltage appearing is within the operating range of the device.

It will be up to the individual to decide how best to house the amplifier circuit but whatever type of casing is chosen two considerations are paramount; the circuit must be electronically screened and it must be weathertight. Connection can either be with Flying leads or PL259 sockets. In the case of the former method, one amplifier was built and then encased in epoxy potting compound. The circuit was then wrapped in aluminium kitchen foil which had good contact with the braiding of the coaxial cable. The entire unit was then well wrapped in electrical insulating tape. Although this method of construction did not look very professional it worked perfectly and allowed the circuit to be housed inside the mounting pole of a Discone antenna.

Great care must be taken at the power supply stage. Remember that mains voltages can be lethal. The case used for the power supply should be made of metal and it should be grounded to the mains earth.

## Other devices

There are a number of other similar devices and although designs are not included here there is no reason why they should not operate in a

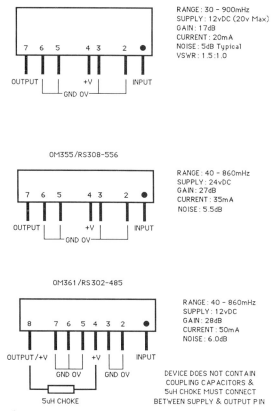

MC5229/SH120A/HF9091

RANGE: 30 – 900mHz
SUPPLY: 12vDC (20v Max)
GAIN: 17dB
CURRENT: 20mA
NOISE: 5dB Typical
VSWR: 1.5:1.0

OM355/RS308-556

RANGE: 40 – 860mHz
SUPPLY: 24vDC
GAIN: 27dB
CURRENT: 35mA
NOISE: 5.5dB

OM361/RS302-485

RANGE: 40 – 860mHz
SUPPLY: 12vDC
GAIN: 28dB
CURRENT: 50mA
NOISE: 6.0dB

DEVICE DOES NOT CONTAIN
COUPLING CAPACITORS &
5uH CHOKE MUST CONNECT
BETWEEN SUPPLY & OUTPUT PIN

**Figure 1.5** Hybrid wideband RF amplifiers

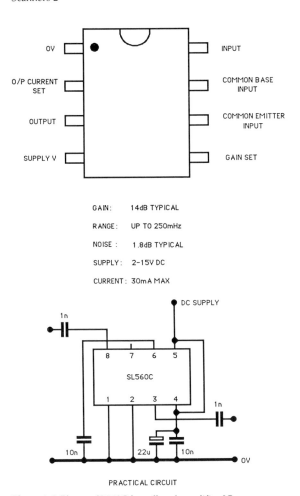

GAIN:      14dB TYPICAL

RANGE:     UP TO 250mHz

NOISE :    1.8dB TYPICAL

SUPPLY:    2-15V DC

CURRENT :  30mA MAX

PRACTICAL CIRCUIT

**Figure 1.6** Plessey SL560C broadband amplifier IC

similar way to devices mentioned above. Availability of these IC's will vary from country to country, for instance the MC5800 and MC5805 (used in the front end of the AOR 2002) do not appear to be generally available in the U.K. Likewise the Plessey SL560C does not appear to be listed in many hobbyist catalogues for some countries.

One interesting device is the EA5 which can be cascaded although note should be taken of the relatively low gain versus noise figure of this IC which will clearly limit the number of devices that can be stacked nose-to-tail.

All of these devices can be used as a basis for experiments either as masthead amplifiers or 'set-level' amplifiers to boost the performance of some earlier receivers which have poor sensitivity. They all have the added advantage that they require few external components but

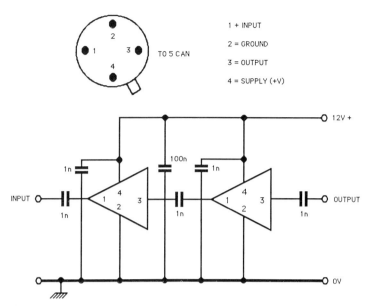

1 + INPUT

2 = GROUND

3 = OUTPUT

4 = SUPPLY (+V)

TO 5 CAN

**Figure 1.7** EA5 Cascadable RF amplifier

again be warned that the broadband/high gain characteristics can lead to instability if good VHF/UHF construction techniques are not employed.

## Discrete amplifiers

Hybrid circuits are expensive and not always easy to obtain. There is no reason why wide band amplifiers cannot be constructed from conventional bi-polar and Field Effect transistors. In fact given some limitations you may get more gain and less noise. The limitation is largely one of bandwidth. Two designs are shown: one for a dual-gate FET and the other for a pair of Bipolars. In each case some kind of matching or filtering has been included at the input without which we would run the risk of instability (oscillation) and blocking effects from strong HF signals. A look at the Bipolar pair first will reveal a fairly conventional arrangement. BF199s are shown but these can be substituted with similar VHF transistors. The particular circuit has fairly uniform gain of up to 20 dB across the range 30 to 200 MHz and higher. The capacitors and inductor at the input form a simple high-pass filter to cut off response rapidly below 30 MHz. Some care needs to be taken over layout and the usual rule of keeping short leads and input well away from output applies. A small PCB would be ideal and if this is double sided there should not be any problems with instability. A small interstage screen between the two transisitors will

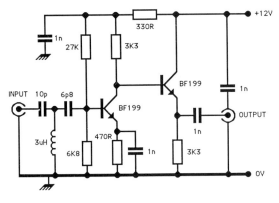

BIPOLAR TRANSISTOR AMPLIFIER (30 - 200MHZ +)

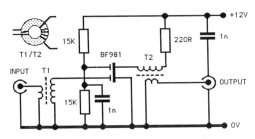

**Figure 1.8** Dual Gate FET amplifier (50–200 mHz+)

also help. With suitable de-coupling there is no reason why this pre-amplifier should not also be built as a masthead type.

The FET circuit is probably the simplest arrangement that can be made whilst retaining fairly good gain versus stability. The input output transformers need to be broadband and the prototype used small VHF toroids. T1 had a 2 turn input and 6 turn output, T2 had a 5 turn primary and 2 turn secondary. With those windings the amplifier

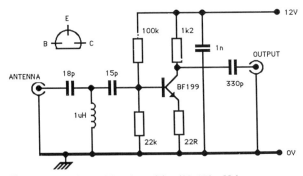

**Figure 1.9** Bipolar wideband amplifier (30–250 mHz)

tended to have peak gain at around 100 MHz of about 18 dB which dropped to about 12 dB at 50 MHz and 200 MHz. The amplifier actually proved a useful addition to an old airband-only scanner which was rather deaf by today's standards. The tuned amplifier discussed later is not really suitable because it does not have enough bandwidth.

Finally, for something really simple try to the single Bipolar design shown. (Figure 1.9). It really does work and I have even used this circuit with all sorts of strange transistors including humble AF types such as BC108's and BC109's. You can even get rid of the T-filter on the input and feed the transistor with a 100 pF capacitor.

## Narrowband amplifier

Although most scanner owners will want wideband amplifiers I have not forgotten that there are many single-band scanners and so a design is included here.

The amplifier uses a single Dual Gate MosFet and the basic configuration shown will cover many bands; it is simply a case of adjusting one coil and one capacitor to suit. For 144 MHz or similar bands, L2 should be tapped one turn from the ground end but for much lower frequencies where 8–10 turns are required on the coil, this may have to be increased to 2–3 turns from the ground end.

The use of a single input coil means the amplifier is relatively broadband with regard to this type of amplifier, and as such is capable of spanning several megahertz. In fact an airband version has been built and although gain was noticeably reduced at 118 and 136 megahertz, it was still usable. The transistor used can be any VHF/RF type but obviously the best results will be obtained with low noise types such as the BF981. Below 100 mHz, cheaper types can be used just as effectively and the BF961, BF963, 3SK81 or 3SK85 are suitable.

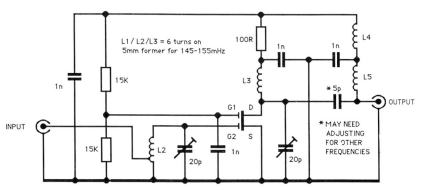

**Figure 1.10** VHF masthead amplifier — see text for coil selection

The usual warning is given regarding layout and short leads and the input should be kept well away from the output. A double sided PCB is the ideal method of construction but I confess that I have actually built one of these merely with self supporting components wired between two sockets and it worked well even at 156 MHz.

The version shown is for masthead use, which is where it should go but if you must use it at set-level then simply omit the two chokes L4/ L5 and the capacitor between their junction and ground. The supply then goes to the junction of the 100R resistor and the 15 k resistor. An additional decoupling capacitor should be connected to ground at this point.

## Tuneable preamplifier

The tuned preamplifier shown here can be built using almost any VHF dual-gate MosFET (BF961 is ideal). There is no need to employ expensive ultra low noise types unless the preamplifier is to be used above about 50 MHz. The circuit values shown are for the range 30– 35 MHz but simple adjustment to the coils shown on the input will enable this circuit to be used on a variety of bands.

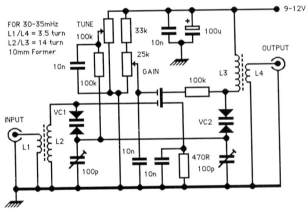

**Figure 1.11** Tunable pre-amplifier (30–35 mHz)

Tuning is accomplished by varicaps, (variable capacitance diodes). The choice of varicaps is not critical but they should have a maximum capacitance of around 40 pF dropping to at least 10 pF at 12 V. Typical examples are BA102 or BB109, or the varicap/trimmer capacitor arrangement can be substituted with dual types such as BB204B or KV1320. Some adjustments may need to be made to the circuit to get the tuning range you require and this may mean either adding fixed value capacitors in series or in parallel with the varicaps. This will largely depend on how wide a frequency swing you require and the particular varicaps you are using.

## Construction

Ideally a small printed circuit board should be made to hold the components although one 30 MHz version was made up on stripboard and worked perfectly. Only points to watch are the usual ones of keeping leads as short as possible and keeping the input well away from the output. A metal case should be used to house the circuit and the actual circuit board should be mounted as close as possible to the two potentiometers for tuning and gain. There is no need to use a multi-turn potentiometer for tuning as it is fairly broad and this is more of a peaking control than anything else. The trimmer capacitors are used to set the tuning range and tracking. With the trimmers set to low capacitance the tuning range will be quite wide and vice-versa. When adjusting for tracking it is best to use the tuning slugs to match the input to output on the low frequency end and the trimmer capacitors at the high frequency end. There will be a slight interaction between the two settings and so several adjustments may be needed for accurate tracking.

## Using the preamplifier

Once construction and testing are complete the amplifier is quite simple to use but do remember not to use any more gain than you have to. Some dual-gate MosFETs have considerable gain at these lower frequencies and because the input stage is relatively simple there could be some fairly hefty HF signals reaching the gate of the transistor. These can cause blocking, intermodulation and other undesirable effects so keep the gain backed off as much as possible.

## Power supplies and battery chargers

Many scanner owners often wish to use their equipment in an environment for which it may not have been designed. For instance the owner of a small pocket scanner which has internal 6 v cells may wish to use the scanner in a vehicle where the supply is 12 v or more, or may wish to use the vehicles supply to re-charge the internal NiCad Pack. Fortunately these days a large range of IC regulators are available and these can be configured to suit almost any custom design. They usually only require a small number of external components and so designs are simple and it is not usually necessary to bother with such things as printed circuit boards, IC regulators fall into two distinct categories; fixed or variable. There are also one or two tricks that can be done with fixed regulators to get them to work at slightly different voltages or to act as constant current generators for re-charging circuits. The devices featured in this section of the

**Photograph 1(a)** Hand portables can easily be used in a vehicle with a simple voltage regulator

book have been kept to a sensible minimum choosing only regulators which are available almost world-wide.

| Type | Output current | Output voltage | Quiescent current | Input range |
|------|---------------|----------------|-------------------|-------------|
| 7805 | 1 Amp | 5 volt | 4.2 mA | 7–25 volt |
| 7806 | 1 Amp | 6 volt | 4.2 mA | 8–25 volt |
| 7808 | 1 Amp | 8 volt | 4.2 mA | 10–27 volt |
| 7812 | 1 Amp | 12 volt | 4.3 mA | 14.5–30 volt |
| 78GU1C | 1 Amp | 5–30 volt | 5.0 mA | 7.5–40 volt |

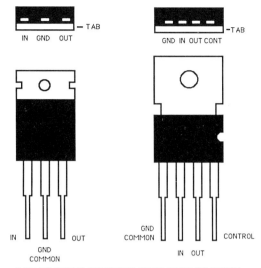

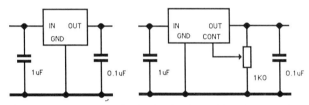

TABS ARE INTERNALLY CONNECTED TO THE GROUND/COMMON PIN

**Figure 1.12** Connections for the fixed and variable voltage regulators referred to in the book (note that other regulators may vary)

## 7805/7806
Several of the smaller pocket style scanners have power supply requirements in the range 4.5 to 6 volts and these particular regulators are ideal. They can be used not only to provide a suitable voltage from a vehicle or 12 volts mains adaptor but also to drop voltage from a 24 volts supply of the type found on some trucks.

## 7808
Ideal for scanners requiring a 9 volt supply. Most will happily operate from 8 volts but for the perfectionist a method is shown to 'jack' the voltage up to the required level.

## 7812
Cheap and simple, this regulator can form the heart of a home built mains power supply for 12 volt operation (circuit and notes follow).

### 78GU1C

Where an odd voltage is required this inexpensive and simple regulator can be used and a simple pre-set resistor is used to set the exact output voltage. The scanner owner will not need the full voltage range available from this device and so it is simply worth noting that whatever output voltage is required, the input voltage will have to be around 3 volts higher.

## Jacked-up regulators

Some readers may have difficulty in purchasing a regulator which conforms exactly to their voltage requirements. Where this is the case, it is possible to 'jack-up' the output voltage slightly by incorporating diodes in the common-to-ground connection. The slight voltage drop across the diode is used to increase the output voltage slightly. Two diodes connected in this fashion will raise the output voltage by

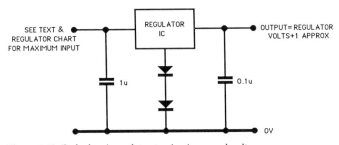

**Figure 1.13** 'Jacked-up' regulator to give increased voltage

slightly more than a volt. The same effect could be obtained with low value resistors but getting the exact value could be difficult and the devices would have to be power types, therefore it is easier, and indeed cheaper, to use diodes. One point to watch with this method of operation is that any heatsink connected to the tab of the regulator does not come into contact with ground. Although this will not harm the regulator clearly the diodes will be shorted and have no effect.

## Heatsinks

Although most 78 series devices can run quite hot when at a full 1 amp output, most scanners do not require this kind of current level: $\frac{1}{2}$ amp being a more typical figure. So for most uses the tab of the regulator will not need to be attached to a heatsink. However, for higher loads (or dropping from high voltages) it is a wise precaution to use a heatsink even if it only consists of bolting the device to the metal case of the project being built. Failing that, either a commercially available clip-on or bolt-on type can be used, or even just a small but thick piece of aluminium sheet.

## Construction

Ideally any mains power supply should be housed in a metal case which is connected to ground — always make sure that no exposed mains wiring can be touched. If a regulator is being used to drop voltage in a vehicle, it is a wise precaution to include not only a fuse but also a diode so that damage does not occur if the wiring is accidentally reversed. The capacitors on the input and output of these circuits not only provide supply smoothing but also de-couple the regulators. On no account should they be omitted as it is possible for the regulator to go into self-oscillation which can lead to excessive overheating and the eventual destruction of the IC.

## Power supply project

A simple 12 volt power supply is shown and this can be used either as a power source for a scanner or can be utilised with the masthead preamplifier interface shown elsewhere in the book — in fact it could be used simultaneously for both. The transformer should be rated at least 1 ampere output and have an input to suite the local mains supply (240 volt AC in most of Europe and 110 volt in North America). It will need a 12 volt secondary winding and on regulation and smoothing this will multiply by a factor of around 1:1.4 to give an output of 16.8 volt DC which falls within the input range of the 7812

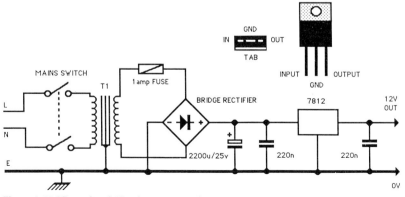

**Figure 1.14** IC regulated 12 volt power supply

regulator. The smoothing capacitor should be a good quality electrolytic rated AT LEAST 25 volt DC working. The bridge diode should handle 1 ampere and the fuse should be rated at the same current. With regard to type, remaining capacitors are not critical.

## Construction and safety

The project should ideally be housed in a metal case which is connected to mains supply earth. The mains input should be through a double-pole switch so that both neutral and live are disconnected when the power unit is switched off. The smoothing capacitor will need a clip either for horizontal or vertical mounting and this component and the IC regulator can be bolted direct to the base of the case. In fact all components can be free standing with interconnecting wiring being soldered directly onto the various contacts. It is a good idea to include sleeving on the connections if this method is adopted and as an added safety precaution sleeving should also be incorporated on the connections to the mains switch and transformer so that no bare wire is exposed. One of the neatest ways of doing this is to use heat-shrink tubing which is reduced to a tight fit by the use of a tool such as an electrical hot-air paint stripper. Caution should be used with this method though — do not try and shrink the tubing too quickly by applying a lot of heat as this can damage the components. The output of the power supply should be checked with a multi-meter prior to being connected.

## NiCad chargers

The majority of pocket or portable scanners are already supplied with a re-chargeable NiCad battery pack and charger. However, there are exceptions (such as some Realistic and Bearcat models). It is clearly far better to operate from NiCads particularly with synthesised scanners where the current drain can be quite high.

The NiCad charger project shown in Figure 1.15 consists of a charger 'block' or 'module' which can be used in a number of ways. There is nothing particularly unique about the circuit which utilises a 7805 voltage regulator IC configured as a constant current generator. Note the lack of any decoupling capacitors on the output line as these would increase the output impedance, whereas NiCads need to be charged from a low impedance source. The IN4001 is used to ensure that the device does not oscillate and so overheat. The value of the resistor RX must be calculated from the simple formula shown. Most NiCad cells have the required 14 hour charge current stated on their cases (for instance AA type cells are usually in the range 45–50 mA) and once the exact resistor value has been calculated it is necessary to

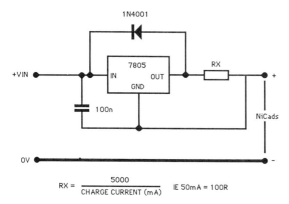

Figure 1.15 NiCad charge block

decide how the resistance value will be obtained in practice. It is safe to say that for values above 100 Ohms, using the nearest standard value will suffice and the device need not be rated any higher than half a watt. Below 100 Ohms it will be necessary to either use series or parallel configurations of resistors to get the correct value and resistors used should be rated at 1 watt down to 50 Ohms and 2.5 watts below that value.

## Using the module

Perhaps the most useful feature of this module is that it can be used to charge portables from the 12 V DC supply in a vehicle. Even those portables which are supplied with mains supply chargers do not have an accessory providing this particular facility. Used in this configuration the module will charge cells in the range 4–10 volts. The module can be simply fitted in a small case with flying leads and plugs to suit the charge socket on the scanner and the vehicle (a cigar lighter plug is ideal and easily removed). A printed circuit board has not been shown for this module because the components can be self supporting. However it must be noted that the tab of the IC regulator must be isolated from the ground line. The module can be used in one of two ways when it is required to charge cells from the mains supply: it can be built as a complete circuit with it's own transformer, bridge rectifier and smoothing capacitor, or can be used as a plug-in module with an existing mains/DC converter of the type used to power amateur and CB equipment. If the former method is used then the usual precautions should be taken to ensure that the mains supply does not come into contact with the casing or any of the output circuitry. The circuit shown can be configured to supply a charging current to virtually all known portable scanners and the only precaution that should be noted is the recommended charge rates and times issued by the manufacturer.

## Tape recorder switching

There can be several reasons for wanting to record signals (although it should be noted that in many countries it is illegal to record some kinds of communications). One of the main uses for recording is the gathering of data transmitted from satellites such as the weather types. Passes of these satellites may be at times when the scanner is not to hand. Some scanners, notably the SX200, do have some kind of facility for adding recorder switching. On the SX200 there is a pre-driver circuit fed by the scan-stop pin of the FM IF chip. All that is needed is an external driver transistor and relay (quite why the manufacturer chose not to fit these in the set is a mystery).

The methods that can be used to switch a recorder, fall into two broad categories; circuit or audio switched. The former, like the one on the SX200, relies on coupling the scan-stop circuit to a suitable relay driver and has the distinct advantage that when the scanner stops, the recorder turns on and when the scan starts again the recorder switches off. The disadvantage of using this method is that the scanner owner will need to modify his equipment to fit a suitable circuit and this may involve drilling holes in the casing for leads to go to the recorder. Modifications of this nature can affect the re-sale value of equipment. The second method requires no such modifications as the circuitry operates solely by connection to the external loudspeaker socket of the scanner. The circuit senses the presence of an audio signal and activates the recorder. The disadvantage of this method of operation is that the circuit might not respond to some AM signals where audio level is very low (the capture effect of FM tends to keep the audio fairly constant regardless of RF signal level).

## Automatic outboard tape switch

With the above limitations in mind a simple circuit is included here for an outboard tape switch. Figure 1.16 a simple three transistor circuit which will operate with almost any general purpose NPN and PNP transistors. Because the internal loudspeaker of the scanner will be cut out when a jack plug is inserted in the external 'speaker socket, it is necessary to provide a small external loudspeaker for monitoring. Operation of the circuit is quite simple. The loudspeaker audio is fed

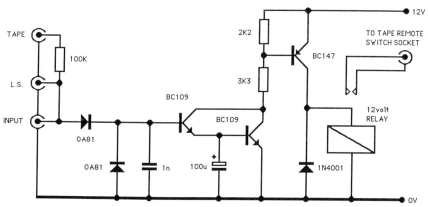

**Figure 1.16** Audio activated tape switch

to diode network D1/D2 which rectifies the positive going peaks of the audio. C1 decouples any remaining audio and the positive pulses switch transistor Q1 which in turn switches on transistor Q2. The capacitor C2 charges up on the switch-on cycle and holds Q2 on for a few seconds after a pulse. This stops the circuit from constantly cutting in and out on the audio peaks. Q3 is normally biased-off but turns on with Q2 and in doing so switches on the relay RLY1. The diode across the relay protects Q3 by soaking up the back EMF from the relay. Transistors Q1/Q2 can be any NPN devices with relatively high gain and Q3 is a general purpose PNP type with sufficient current handling to cope with the relay. The 100 k resistor merely serves to reduce the audio to a level which the auxillary record input of the tape recorder can handle.

### Construction
Layout is not critical and the circuit can be built using stripboard or similar material and then enclosed in a small box. My own version was built into the case of a small loudspeaker originally intended for use with a personal stereo tape player. The 12 volt supply can be taken from the supply for the scanner or provided by a separate circuit of the type shown on the section on power supplies.

### Using the circuit
The circuit requires a fair degree of drive. For instance on an AOR2002 the volume control will probably need to be at about the half way mark. This may cause excessive volume on the external monitor loudspeaker. If this is the case then the volume can be lowered by including a 10 Ohm/1 watt resistor in the positive lead to the loudspeaker. The output from the relay contacts are taken to a small jack plug to match the 'remote switch' socket found on the majority of

portable cassette tape recorders. The audio feed should ideally be taken to a high level input on the recorder. This is usually a 5-pin DIN socket but if only a microphone input is provided this can be used although there may be some distortion if the recorders circuit overloads.

### Scan-stop tape switching

Many scanners use the MC3357 FM IF chip (AOR, SX–200, Bearcats, etc) and included in this IC is a 'scan-stop' switch. In the case of this particular chip it is pin-13 of the IC which is normally held low when the squelch is open and swings high when it closes. In order to use this facilty for automatic tape recording all that it is needed is a simple inverter/relay driver circuit. A suitable circuit is shown and Q1 is a high gain NPN transistor and the voltage from pin 13 keeps it switched on whilst the squelch is closed. As a result Q2 is pulled low and so switches off. When the squelch opens on the MC3357 then pin 13 goes low and switches Q1 off. This means Q2 now biases-on via the 22 k resistor and so turns on the relay. D1 simply soaks up back EMF from the relay so protecting the transistor. The resistor R1 is included so as not to unduly load pin-13 of the IC as this will almost certainly be connected to other circuits in the scanner which could be upset if

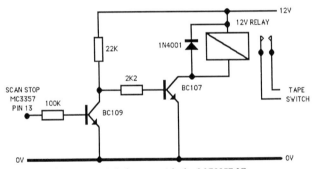

**Figure 1.17(a)** Tape switch for use with the MC3357 IC

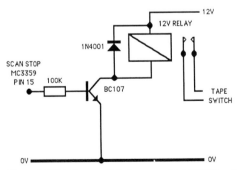

**Figure 1.17(b)** Tape switch for use with MC3359 or ULN3859

there was loading characteristics which had not been allowed for during the design of the scanner. If any problems are encountered in getting this circuit to work, the first step should be to juggle the value of this resistor, particularly if the scanner squelch circuits start to behave abnormally. The small size of this circuit means that it can easily be installed inside the scanner (even within the cramped confines of an AOR–2001/2) and can be fed from the set's 12 volt supply. A suitable audio tap for the tape recorder can be taken from the 'hot' end of the volume control via a small 0.1 mF capacitor.

### MC3359/ULN3859

This is a revamped version of the MC3357 and although I have yet to see it used in any scanner currently on the market it seems likely that future designs may well incorporate it as it has better performance than it's predecessor. On this particular IC the scan-stop works the other way round, i.e., the scan control pin (Pin-15) is held low when the squelch is closed but swings high when open. This means there is no need to invert and an even simpler arrangement is possible using a single transistor. Because we are likely to see this IC used in future I have included a simple circuit here. It may also be possible to use the same circuit with some other scanners which have different methods of IF demodulation, squelch and scan-stop. If the scanner owner has a circuit diagram and can spot the necessary parts of the circuit controlling the scan start/stop then they may be able to use one or the other of the above circuits to good effect.

### Using the circuits

There is very little to add to the above. A cassette recorder with remote start switch is connected to the relay contacts and the audio fed as described to the auxillary input. Ideally the recorder should have automatic recording level. Obviously the whole record sequence with these latter circuits operates completely independently of any volume control setting.

### Single sideband (SSB) adaptor

Although some of the more recent scanners such as the Yaesu and Icom have facilities for SSB reception, most scanners do not. It is possible to use a Beat Frequency Oscillator to resolve SSB, although the results will be largely dependent on the scanner concerned. The SX-200 works quite well on SSB with BFO injection whilst in AM mode. The circuit shown in Figure 1.18 was in fact designed originally for use with the SX-200 and has been published before (Radio & Electronics World July 1983) and is reproduced here by kind permission of Cirkit Holdings who can supply the module as a complete kit.

In order to re-insert the missing carrier of an SSB signal we need to inject a signal at the correct frequency, which in this case is slightly above or below the standard IF frequency of 455 kHz depending on whether the signal is Upper or Lower Sideband. It should be noted that BFO injection for SSB resolution does neet a bit of practice. Results with this kind of circuit will be far from ideal. First there is the problem that the relatively wide IF bandwidth (typically 12–15 kHz) of scanners such as the SX-200 and Bearcats means that on crowded bands several stations may be heard on top of each other. Sets designed to receive SSB usually have IF filters of around 2.6 kHz bandwidth. Secondly the scanner should have some kind of fine tuning control because with non-channelisation of SSB transmissions it is unlikely that signals will be found dead centre of the spot frequency steps tuned by most scanners. In the case of the SX-200 there is a fine tuning control and by using a combination of fine tune settings and BFO tuning it is usually possible to resolve most signals. I have tried the circuit presented here with a Bearcat 220FB and there were some stations which could not be resolved.

The circuit was designed for injecting a signal into the AM/IF stages of a scanner and although this will give the best results I have tried injecting BFO into an FM/IF stage as well. Limited SSB does sound a bit odd but signals are readable.

## The circuit

The circuit consists of little more than a modified Colpitts oscillator based on the FET Q1. Output is buffered by a simple amplifier, Q2, and the output is fed via a trimmer and fixed capacitor, the latter permitting a degree of control over the amount of signal level that is injected into the scanner. Conventional tuning capacitors have been avoided because the complete circuit is split into two modules. The active part of the circuit is housed inside the scanner and the control circuit is mounted in an external box. Clearly all sorts of problems would arise if we tried to run long leads from tuning capacitors, so varicaps (variable capacitance diodes) are used instead. These are diodes D1 and D2 and they change capacitance in proportion to the amount of voltage applied across them. The voltage is determined by a 100 k potentiometer and the tuning diodes and L1 vary the frequency of oscillation across the range 453.5 kHz to 456.5 kHz. The circuit is stabilised to avoid drift by the Zener diode.

The RF gain control circuit only applies to the SX-200 and it provides even more control where strong signals are concerned. For other scanners this part of the circuit is simply omitted.

## Components

Diodes D1 and D2 are BA102's. If any difficulty is experienced in obtaining these devices, it should be possible to substitute them with

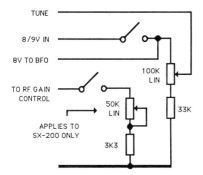

**Figure 1.18(a)** External controller for BFO

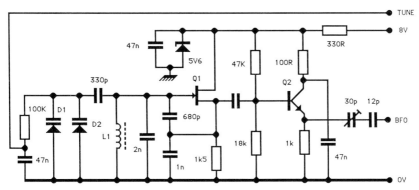

**Figure 1.18(b)** Beat frequency oscillator (BFO) for SSB reception (reproduced by courtesy of Cirkit Holdings)

something similar. At 2 volts they have a capacitance of around 40 pF which drops to about 15 pF at 8 volts. The coil L1 can either be home made or a standard coil from the Toko range. The KAN3333R or 154N8A6438 is ideal and the connection should be made across pins 1 and 3. If you cannot get this component then use an old 455 kHz IF transformer. The number of windings required may vary slightly according to the transformer but using 30 SWG enamelled wire it should be in the range 30 to 40 turns. The FET Q1 was a BF224 or TIS88 in the original circuit but any similar small signal RF FET should work. Transistor Q3 is a common BC108 type and again this component is not critical. The tuning potentiometer would ideally be a 'centre-click' type although this is not essential. Capacitors in the tuned circuits should be stable types such as polystyrene or Micas.

### Construction notes
The kit supplied by Cirkit uses a printed circuit board for the main module but there is no reason why stripboard or similar construction should not be employed as long as reasonable care is taken with layout

and you ensure that there are no long leads around the tuned circuit. Any unused track strips should be soldered to ground. The original article on this circuit made use of a small separate box connected to the SX-200 via a multi-way screened cable and Din plugs and sockets. This was because there is no room either on the front or back panel of the scanner in which holes can be drilled to fit additional controls and switches. A Din socket was fitted to the side of the case, which means drilling both the case and the chassis side panel. It may well be that a similar method will have to be employed with other scanners although in some instances the Din socket can be fitted to the rear apron. As a matter of interest I fitted this adaptor to my own SX-200 and managed to get away without drilling the case. There is a small tag-strip on the rear of the scanner for external tape control. I did not use this facility so I simply unscrewed it, taped the two wires up inside and used folded aluminium to make a small box that stuck out from the rear panel. The box contained a double-pole, centre off, miniature toggle switch. The RF gain control was ignored in this case but the board housing the electronics also contained two Varicap type multi-turn tuning potentiometers. The output from each of these was sent to the toggle switch and the remaining poles were used to switch 8 volts to the BFO board. This way the board was inactive with the switch centred but by switching either way the board was powered up and I was able to select either upper or lower sideband which were pre-set on the tuning potentiometers. It was not quite as flexible as the original circuit, with no gain control and no fine tuning of the BFO, just the fine tuning on the front of the scanner. However, I found it a reasonable compromise as I was not prepared to start drilling large holes in the side of the set.

Clearly if you can reach the back of your scanner, there is no reason why in the case of scanners such as the Bearcat 220FB, you should not put the switch and control on the rear panel. It is worth noting also of course that if you are using that particular model you will need to carry out the AM modification as well, because without it, AM is only selected whilst tuned to air band and you will not find any SSB transmissions there.

### Setting up and testing

It is a good idea to test the circuit before fitting it to the scanner. If you are lucky enough to own a digital frequency meter then this will be simplicity itself. Do not worry though if you do not have this equipment as the circuit can be set up using trial and error. With 8 or 9 volts feeding the circuit the first step is to ensure that some sort of signal is being generated. By placing a medium wave receiver close to the circuit it should be possible to hear the second harmonic around 910 kHz. Rotating the tuning potentiometer should cause the signal to shift up and down slightly. If all is well then the circuit can now be installed in the scanner. A suitable point will have to be found to pick up voltage but with most scanners a simple probing-around with a multimeter in the power supply stages will usually produce results (8 V in the case of SX-200 and 9 V on the Bearcat 220/250 series). The output of the BFO goes to capacitor C9 in the case of the SX-200. For other scanners I am afraid it is a question of trial and error and probing around the AM detector stage until a suitable point is found — you will hear quite a distinct drop in background hiss when successful. The BFO output trimmer capacitor is set to the maximum capacitance before the scanner's squelch opens. If you have a DFM, then with the tuning potentiometer at dead centre just tune the core of L1 until you get to exactly 455 kHz. Check that the frequency swings within the limits mentioned earlier when the potentiometer is swung to both end-stops. If a DFM is not available then you will need to inject some kind of signal into the scanner. Ideally this should be from a stable signal generator but as a last resort it can be an off-air signal. The only criteria is that you are tuned exactly on frequency. Once a signal is being injected or received, set the potentiometer to centre (and fine tuner in the case of SX-200) and switch on the BFO. Now use the tuning slug on L1 to get zero-beat — that's where no tone is superimposed on the signal. Once complete you should now find that by swinging the potentiometer to either end-stop you get a tone of approximately 1.5 kHz. If this is not the case, you may need to adjust the value of the 33 k resistor between the tuning potentiometer and ground (this will certainly be the case if you have substituted the tuning diodes or wound your own coil).

Now find an SSB signal to check that the adaptor is working properly. 27 MHz CB, 28 MHz amateur and the 2 Meter band around 144.30 MHz are the best frequencies to try. Do not be diasppointed if you cannot get the hang of resolving SSB signals straight-off. It takes practice to get used to using the BFO and do not forget that you may need to deliberately offset your scanner's tuning to get best results. This and the use of the BFO tuner should permit resolution of most SSB signals. As far as the SX-200 is concerned, use the fine tune control as well as the BFO tune and do not forget to wind the gain down a bit on strong signals. The 'hot' end of the gain control merely goes to the 'hot' end of the gain trimmer RV102 which is near IC 102.

## Automatic AM/FM switcher

The copyright of the following design is owned by Garex Electronics (Startop Communications Limited). The circuit was originally designed by Mike Foster G8AMG, and is reproduced here by kind permission of Peter Longhurst of Garex.

Owners of SX-200's and Revco RS-2000's, here is the answer to your prayer. Do not be put off by the complex look of the circuit, closer examination will show that it consists of only two inexpensive ICs. The circuit can be added to a host of VHF communications receivers, not just scanners, and the audio outputs from the appropriate AM and FM detectors are simply fed to the points marked and the selected audio is fed back to the AF circuits. Naturally, the circuit will only work with those scanners and receivers which have both detectors permanently switched on and where mode is selected by bringing into circuit the appropriate demodulated signal. Even receivers where this is not the case can probably be easily modified to work in this fashion.

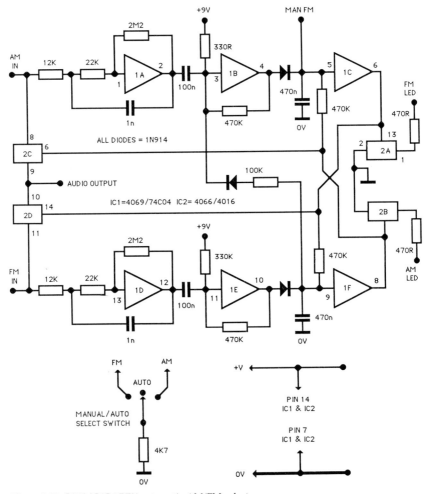

**Figure 1.19** G8AMG/GAREX automatic AM/FM selector

The circuit works by sampling both signals, seeing which looks the best and switching accordingly. Two spare gates on the c.m.o.s. bi-directional switching IC are used to power a pair of LEDs to indicate which detector is in circuit but naturally this part of the circuit can be ignored if not required. The LEDs connect between the resistor and supply line. The circuit works so well that it is not even fooled by FM signals which are slightly off frequency.

The following description is by designer, Mike Foster:

## Circuit

Audio from the FM and AM detectors is normalised to between 0.3 and 0.5 volts peak-to-peak and is then fed to a pair of single-pole active low-pass filters (IC1A and IC1D). The output of these is then taken to a pair of threshold detectors (IC1B and IC1D). The peak positive value of the output waveform is held by the 470 nF capacitors on the inputs of IC1C and IC1F. These form an astable switch and their outputs control the routing of the audio signals to the common audio amplifier (in the scanner) via IC2C and IC2D. There is simultaneous activation of the appropriate LEDs via IC2A or IC2B.

## Design notes

The low pass filters are designed to produce a roll-off above 1.2 kHz to eliminate residual I.F. leakage and to reduce the response to noise on weak signals. The main reason for this low frequency roll-off requirement is to provide additional protection in FM mode against double slope detection on AM. This can produce an audio component at twice frequency and the frequency modulated carrier sweeps over the lower and upper slopes of the AM filter. This effect is accentuated by the need to use a narrower bandwidth in the AM I.F. (on many scanners at least) to restore the relative signal to noise ratio between the modes.

The 100 K resistor and diode between IC1F input and IC1B input raises the threshold of the AM threshold detector to reduce the sensitivity to slope detected FM signals which are received off-channel. The result is that a genuine FM signal wil! still predominate even when it is off-channel.

The 470 K resistors which cross the gates of IC1C and IC1F together with the 470 nF capacitors form a latching delay which prevents the astable from switching over should there be a short noise burst from the unselected detector.

Manual mode selection is made by setting and holding the astable by an overriding ground signal applied to the required input.

## Additional notes by GU1DKD

Layout nor construction method is critical but do heed the usual
warnings regarding the handling of c.m.o.s. ICs and the need to
protect them against static. Strip-board is an ideal method of
construction and the circuit can be built small enough to fit in most
scanners. It will be difficult for the existing mode switching on the
SX-200 to be adapted for use in this circuit but in my own view the
automatic switch works so well that it can probably be just wired in to
work solely in automatic mode.

## S-meter

An S-meter is a useful addition to any scanner and really comes into
it's own where comparisons are made between antennas or
propagation conditions.

The S-meter described here is very simple and consists of nothing
more than a Buffer/IF amplifier, twin diode detector and meter
movement. The latter needs to be nothing more than an inexpensive
edgewise panel type often seen on small transceivers. The connections
shown apply to a typical MC3357 configuration where the output from
the final IF filter is also fed to an AM detector (as in the Bearcats,
SX-200, AOR's, etc.). However, there is no reason why the circuit

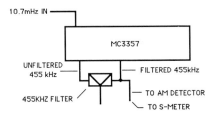

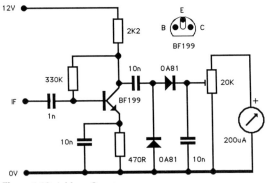

**Figure 1.20** Add-on S-meter

cannot be tried with other scanners which do not use this particular IF chip. The most obvious tapping point will still be the output of the final IF filter and if any noticeable loading effects occur, reduce the value of the 1nF capacitor feeding the base of the transistor. The 20 kOhm trimming resistor is used to set maximum deflection on the strongest signals.

Clearly the actual meter movement will not fit the front panel of most scanners and so some external arrangement will have to be made. It is advisable to build the circuitry into the scanner and just feed the detected output to the meter movement housed in a small case. It is not a good idea to start feeding IF signal out to a case which also contains the active circuitry. The two wire connection between the scanner and meter box can easily be made use of by a miniature jack plug/socket arrangement or could even be hard-wired if you do not want to drill the scanner's casing.

The circuit layout is not critical. A small P.C.B. could be used but the version I use with my Bearcat 220FB is built on strip-board and has not shown any signs of causing instability. It is of course essential that the connection between the board and the IF is as short as possible.

# 2 Modifications

## A warning

This chapter contains details and suggestions for a range of modifications to enhance or alter the performance of a number of scanners. Before any attempt is made to modify equipment, three very important factors must be taken into consideration; safety, guarantee voidance and equipment de-valuation.

First safety. Some scanners contain built in power supplies and under no circumstance should you expose circuitry on such a scanner when it is connected to the mains supply. Electric shocks can be lethal and if you need to work on 'LIVE' circuitry always operate the set from an external DC source.

Next is the question of guarantee voidance. You should be aware that any modification to a scanner will void the guarantee (warranty) and should the equipment need repair you will almost certainly be liable to pay for the work involved.

Lastly, many people contemplating the purchase of a second-hand scanner are reluctant to buy one that has been modified. Modifications, particularly those that involve drilling holes in panels or fitting extra switches, etc. will almost certainly affect the re-sale value of the scanner.

These modifications are presented here solely for those scanner owners who are technically competent and the author, publisher nor their agents will accept any liability for damage to equipment or the owner. Having clarified those points I must add that some of the modifications are quite easy to carry out and should be well within the capabilities of anyone who can find their way around a circuit diagram and recognise components.

## Bearcat 220 AM modification

The Bearcat 220FB, like many scanners, was originally designed for the American home market where all bands use FM with the exception of Airband. This can be a nuisance for European users as many communication bands contain a mix of both AM and FM.

However, like the SX-200 it is not too difficult to modify the set to provide AM on any of the bands. Unlike the SX-200 there is plenty of room on the back panel, and indeed the front panel, to fit a small toggle switch to bring the new facility into operation (see photograph 2(a)). Several modifications have appeared for providing AM on this scanner and the one shown has been tested on my own Bearcat 220 and works well. All you will need are two short lengths of connection wire, a single-pole single-throw miniature toggle switch and a small general purpose diode.

With the scanner opened-up, turn the set over so the component side of the main PCB is facing you. Locate the IC marked '91901' which is close to the mains input socket and you will see a PCB track going to pin-16. Use a sharp knife to cut the track but leave enough track so that you can solder a wire to it. Look at the diagram and locate the two resistors which have a short length of track connecting them and solder a wire to this track as well. These two wires now form the connection to the AM switch. This can be located on the back panel, the easiest option, or you can locate it on the front panel. There is enough room slightly to the right of the centre line between the volume and squelch controls. You will need to drill the front sub-frame and make a neat slot in the plastic front panel.

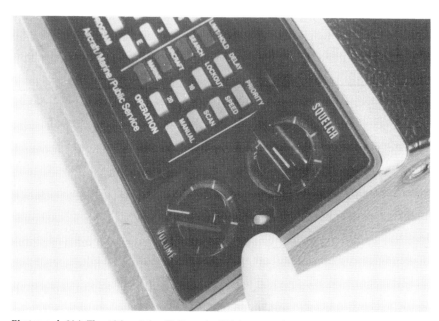

**Photograph 2(a)** The AM switch will fit on the 220 front panel

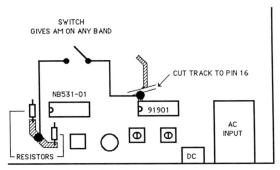

**Figure 2.1(a)** Bearcat 220 AM modification — component side.

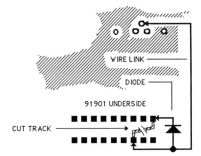

**Figure 2.1(b)** Modifications to the track side of the PCB

Now turn the set over and locate the underside of the same IC (91901) and you will see a short section of PCB track between pins 16 and 3. Cut the track and bridge the broken connection with a diode. From pin-3 you will also need a short wire link to the PCB pad shown. That completes the modification which now gives you simultaneous AM/FM reception when the switch is closed. With the switch in the open position the set will behave as normal.

## SX-400 SSB

It may seem obvious but I'll repeat the advice I gave in the original Scanners book about Single Sideband reception on the SX-400. The manufacturers have thoughtfully provided a 10.7 MHz IF output on the back panel of this set. Simply connect this output via screened lead to an HF communications receiver and tune it to 10.7 MHz. Turn the volume down on the SX-400 and use the SSB demodulator and audio stages of the HF set to receive sideband signals. The IF output of the SX-400 is quite meaty so you may need to back-off the HF set's RF gain control if there is any distortion.

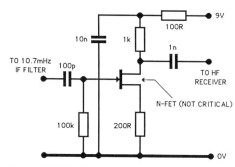

**Figure 2.2** IF buffer amplifier

There is of course no reason why sets such as the Bearcats, SX-200, etc, should not also be adapted for use in a similar way. A simple FET buffer amplifier after the 10.7 MHz filters could feed the signal out to the HF receiver. The advantage with this type of operation is that the SSB filters in most HF receivers will be far better suited to the narrow bandwidth required than the 'barn door' bandwidth of most scanners. This method of operation will certainly provide better results than simply injecting BFO into the scanner's AM demodulator stage.

This method of SSB demodulation will not work with AOR scanners because they use a pre-final IF of around 45 MHz which is well out of the tuning range of HF receivers.

### SX-200 modifications

In the days when I owned an SX-200 I was always a little frustrated at the fact that there was no S-meter on the scanner. Being someone who likes to play around with aerials and signal amplifiers I never had any means of comparing performance. Anyone who owns an SX-200 will know that there is no room on the back panel for a socket and no room on the front panel for a conventional moving coil meter. However, examination of the front panel assembly made me realise that a Bargraph S-meter could be fitted. A look in component catalogues showed that most factory made bargraphs were too wide for the available space. The answer would obviously be to make a bargraph assembly out of conventional miniature LEDs.

Driving the LEDs presents no real problem as these days a number of ICs are available which contain all the necessary electronics. I chose the LM3915 which has a Logarithmic response that closely approximates an S-meter in this application. The IC contains an operational amplifier and 10 comparitors which can drive the LEDs directly, without the need for either buffer transistors or current limiting resistors.

## Tapping into the SX-200

A look at the circuitry for the SX-200 will reveal that initial IF amplification at 10.7 MHz takes place in the usual MC3357 FM IF chip. Following second conversion down to 455 kHz the final IF appears at pin 3 where it is fed via a matching transformer, IFT 101, and thence to the Ceramic filter CF103. After this filter the signal goes simultaneously back into the MC3357 for FM and on to another IC for AM. The IF signal appearing at pin 3 is sufficient to drive the Bargraph driver IC with only simple rectification. The circuit shown here uses this method as it is simple but it does have the slight disadvantage that the meter can respond to adjacent channel signals. A better method would be to pick up the IF after the 455 kHz filter but at this stage insertion losses have reduced the signal level to the point where a small buffer amplifier would be needed to drive the Bargraph IC. I have never tried this arrangement but anyone experimenting with the circuit shown here may care to give it a go.

## The Bargraph Circuit

A look at the circuit (Figure 2.3) will show that the IF signal is fed in via the 270 pF capacitor feeding the two diodes. These should be small

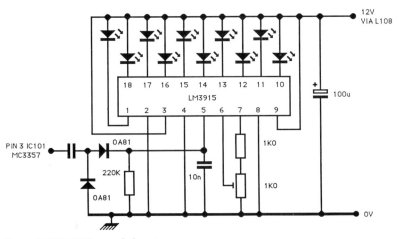

**Figure 2.3** SX–200 bargraph S-meter

signal types for efficient rectification and the resulting DC is matched to the IC by the 220 K resistor and any remaining IF is decoupled by the 10 nF capacitor on pin 5 of the IC. Pin 7 of the LM3915 provides an internally generated stabilised voltage which is used as a reference and fed to pin 6 via the pre-set resistor which controls the meter's sensitivity. Pin 9 of the IC can be used to set it in true bargraph or moving-dot mode. In the latter mode only one LED is lit at any one time. Taking pin 9 high gives bargraph whilst grounding the pin gives moving-dot.

**Construction**
Almost any method of construction can be used but whatever method is chosen, the board must be close to the MC3357 otherwise long leads carrying IF signal could cause problems. The PCB shown includes an area of bare board which is used as a mounting tab. This tab can be used to attach the PCB to the VCO box using double sided adhesive tape or sticky pads.

Assembly of the bargraph is more complicated. A PCB design is shown and if a small enough module is to be constructed it will have to be used. 3 mm LEDs will be needed and these can all be the same colour or mixed. I used 8 green LEDs, an amber one for S9 and red one for S9+ but the choice is yours. Prior to insertion in the board they will need to have their rims removed. These will shave-off quite easily with a sharp instrument like a modelling knife as shown in the diagram. Ensure that the LEDs are correctly polarised and mount

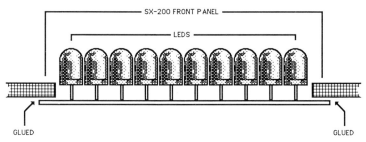

**Figure 2.4(a)** Mounting the display PCB to the front panel

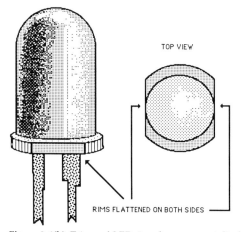

**Figure 2.4(b)** Trimmed LED rims for a compact display

them in the board and solder them. A loom consisting of eleven wires will need to be made up and soldered to the board and it is a good idea to test the entire circuit before proceeding to the next stage which is fitting the display.

Cutting a slot into the front of a piece of expensive equipment may seem a daunting prospect but in practice it is not as difficult as it may seem. I assume the SX-200 owner undertaking this project will have the skills and tools to be able to drill a row of reasonably straight lines and if that is the case then go ahead.

With the two sections of outer casing unscrewed, disconnect the loudspeaker by unplugging it. The entire front panel assembly of controls and keyboard is connected to the main circuit board by a plugged/wire loom arrangement and all the connections should be unplugged. After unplugging the 3 harnesses, remove the front panel's four retaining screws and move it away from the scanner.

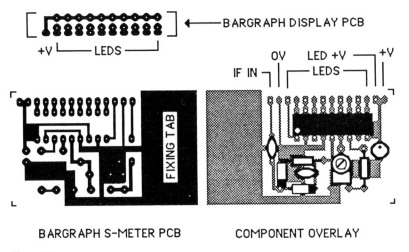

Figure 2.5

There is a small retaining bracket attached to the front panel on the power switch/mode selector switch side and this should be unscrewed. Using a scribe or marker of some sort mark out a 30 mm long vertical line that is half way between the edge of the front panel and the row of push buttons on that side. The bottom of the line should be level with the centre of the on/off power switch. The front panel consists of a thin metal sheet stuck to a plastic base and it will drill quite easily. Drill a row of holes along the line using a bit that is slightly less than 3 mm in diameter so that any slight miss-alignment can be coped with. Use a flat needle file to file-out a slot which has a rounded top and bottom. Files can be easily obtained in either a hardware store or a modelling shop. By patient and careful work the

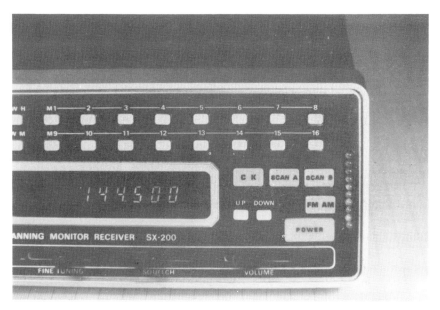

**Photograph 2(b)** The bargraph S-meter fitted to the right of the scan-B, FM/AM and power switches

**Photograph 2(c)** The bargraph driver board mounted with an adhesive pad on the V.C.O. box of the SX–200

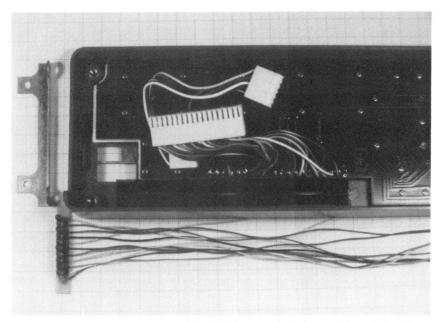

**Photograph 2(d)** With the front panel of the SX-200 removed, the bargraph is ready for fitting

slot should be neat and straight. Any slight score marks along the edge of the metal panel where the slot has been cut can be disguised with black felt-tip pen (the indelible types are ideal and can be used to hide scratch marks on all sorts of black equipment panels, black control knobs, etc.).

Once you are satisfied that the bargraph LED assembly will fit snugly into the slot you can now glue it into place. A small dab of strong glue applied to the overlapping edges of the miniature PCB will hold the display in place. Now reassemble the front panel and connect up. A short piece of miniature coaxial cable is used to connect to the MC3357. Voltage for the bargraph circuit is best taken from the back of the on/off power switch. It is easy to get at and has already been regulated by the time it goes to the switch.

### Setting up
Assuming everything is working correctly, calibrating the S-meter is easy. Swinging the trimming potentiometer should have most of the LEDs lit up at one extreme and all out at the other. Check that this is so, then tune the set to about 50 MHz. This is the centre of the VHF Low tuning head and you should adjust the trimmer potentiometer until the first LED just goes out. Check at 140 MHz and 450 MHz that the LEDs remain unlit with no signal present. Re-trim until it just goes out.

Now tune around for some signals and check that you get a reading on them. Do not be too surprised if the meter reads higher on FM signals than AM ones. This is really just an illusion caused by the quieting effect of FM making some moderately strong signals sound stronger than they really are. Comparison tests on the meter were carried out using a professional receiver with calibrated S-meter and results seemed to be fairly accurate.

One final point concerns flashing whilst scanning or searching; this is perfectly normal. Owners of sets like the AOR 2002 will tell you that it too has a flashing effect on the first two or three LEDs as the tuning stages chop from one frequency to the next.

**Simultaneous AM/FM**
My SX-200 had one feature which used to annoy me intensely. You could scan for FM signals or AM signals but not both. I decided to do something about it and the solution was remarkably simple, albeit a compromise. The IF signal inside the scanner splits up into two different stages, the FM and the AM and at any one time, regardless of switch settings, each is producing an audio output. The output that goes to the audio pre-amplifier is not physically switched at the front panel but via a set of switching diodes. So, if we cross couple the two outputs we can simultaneously receive the signal AM processed and FM processed. In practice we can choose which setting of the mode switch, AM or FM, will give us simultaneous reception. The MC3357 FM IF amplifier/demodulator is designed to reject as much AM as possible, so the obvious choice is to make the AM setting the one where we get simultaneous AM/FM. It works but AM signals are a little noisy. As I said at the start it is a compromise, therefore not perfect but good enough to satisfy many users and several SX-200 owners who heard the results on my own set asked me to do the modification for them. They have never asked me to reverse the process so I assume they are happy with the results.

**What to do**
There are no holes to drill, no switches to fit and like the very best modifications you can later remove it and no one would know it had ever been there. All you will need is a capacitor of 470 nF value, any type will do. Locate the small sub-circuit board at the rear of the set which plugs into the main circuit board. This is the board which carries the centre detector and AM demodulator. On it you will find switching diode D202 which is marked and you should solder the 470 nF capacitor across it — that is all there is to it.

You now have simultaneous AM/FM when switched to AM. The results are a little noisy but still far better than trying to listen to AM signals when the scanner is in FM mode. As a matter of interest the other switching diode is D201 and you could try fitting the capacitor across that diode and comparing results. Preference could well depend on which mode of signal you receive the most.

## AOR modifications

The two AORs, the 2001 and 2002 are not the easiest of scanners to modify as both have very crowded circuit boards which make it difficult to replace existing components. However, two well tried modifications have been done to these sets and these cover the scan rate on both models and the keyboard bleep on the 2001. Owners of the 2001 will know only too well that the bleep is far too loud and if the set is being operated manually for long sessions, it can become very bothersome. It is not possible to make the bleep's volume vary in accordance with the volume control in the way that the 2002 operates, but it is possible to reduce the volume to a level of your own choosing. With the top cover removed from the set you will need to locate R137. It is a 1 kOhm resistor, it is marked on the main board and is just forward of the 6 way plug and socket in the rear right-hand quadrant of the board. The bleep volume will lessen in proportion to an increase in it's value. Many owners have found that 10 kOhm provides a comfortable level.

**Photograph 2(e)** The AR-2001 can have the keyboard bleep reduced in volume, the scan rate can be increased, proper keyboard and S-meter added

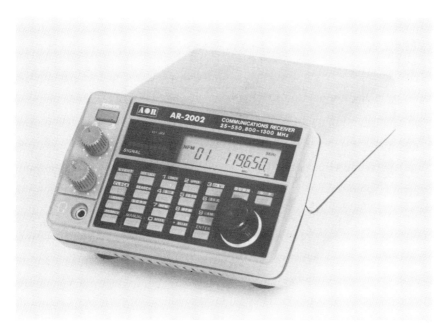

**Photograph 2(f)** The AR-2002 scan rate can be speeded up by changing just one capacitor

The AOR literature claims that the sets scan at a rate of 5 channels per second, but on both models, I have always found the rate to be 4 channels per second which is quite slow by today's standards. It is possible to increase the rate to about 6 channels per second, with a similar 50 percent increase in search rate as well. The modification only requires adjustment of one capacitor, but be warned that it is very difficult to get at and in the case of the 2002 it is a surface mounted component which is quite difficult to remove.

For both sets it is capacitor C3 on the main Microprocessor board which is directly behind the keyboard. With the case halves removed and the loudspeaker unplugged you need to remove a total of 9 screws which hold both the plastic front panel and metal sub-frame to the main chassis sides. Do not attempt to separate the front panel away from it's sub-frame as all the key contacts will fall out. Next unplug the two cable harnesses which go to the underside of the scanner board. You now need to gently pull the front panel assembly away from the main chassis — there are two points to watch: there will probably be a small strip of adhesive tape holding the front panel sub-frame to the chassis side and the insides of the sub-frame are indented where the plastic panel screws enter. One of the sides will need to be gently prised-off with a narrow screwdriver.

With all that done the entire front panel assembly can be moved away from the rest of the scanner. Looking at the assembly from the back you will now be able to see the microprocessor board in the case

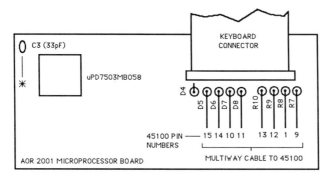

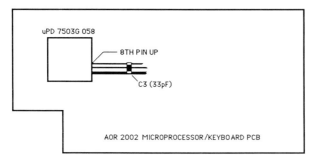

**Figure 2.6** Position of C3 (scan speed) on AOR scanners

of the 2001. For that particular model you now need to locate the 33 pF capacitor, C3 and change it for a 15 pF one. In the case of the 2002 you will need to unplug and remove the small printed circuit board mounted across the back of the keyboard and microprocessor circuit board. This will give you full access to the area around the square microprocessor IC. With it the right way up you need to count up 8 tracks from the lower right hand corner of the IC. Amongst the surface mounted components attached to that track will be the small brown coloured chip capacitor. Ignore the black chips with numbers on them, those are resistors. The capacitor can be seen attached to the 8th track up and at it's other end to a track that is thicker than the rest. Do not attempt to de-solder this component but crush it carefully with a small pair of side-snips. Using a sharp modelling knife, or small screwdriver, carefully scrape away the remaining parts of the capacitor, being careful not to damage the track that runs underneath the component. Using the two solder points from that component you can now fit a 15 pF device instead. It is possible to increase the speed even further by reducing the value of the capacitor down to 10 pF. However this can lead to the scanner skipping all but the strongest signals. There are some minor penalties to be paid for this increase in speed. the 'delay' time is proportionately reduced and on some sets there is also a reduction in the amount of time that the scanner will retain it's memory whilst completely disconnected from the power supply. I have seen one claim that this modification reduces the number of spurious signals found across the range. This is not so. It merely shifts them to other frequencies and so if you have made up a table of the spurious signals on your set then you will need to redo it.

## WFM changes

Much of the mail I get from scanner enthusiasts who own AORs has been about the possibility of changing the Wide Band FM circuitry for something better suited to weather satellite reception where we need an IF bandwidth of around 30 kHz. I have not attempted to modify either my 2001 or 2002 for such use so the notes given here are by way of experimental guidance only. They are based on service data and circuit diagrams for both the scanners.

A look at the circuit diagrams show that both narrow and wide FM are catered for by a separate MC3357s. IF input to both these devices is at 45.030 MHz that is where the similarity ends. The NBFM circuit (IC-4) mixes down to 455 kHz but the WBFM circuit (IC-5) down to 5.5 MHz final IF. The most obvious problem is that the 5.5 MHz filter is unusual and in Britain I have had no luck in obtaining a tighter filter of the same frequency. Changing the existing 39.53 MHz conversion frequency crystal to 34.33 MHz would give us a more standard 10.7 MHz final IF and 50 kHz roofing filters at this frequency would be ideal. No quadrature coil is used but instead a 5.5 MHz ceramic filter is used and once again this could possible be replaced by a 10.7 MHz equivalent (I assume the original filters are about 300 Ohms input/ output impedance as they are the same shape and size as existing filters in the range 6–27 MHz). The big question though is how does the MC3357's limiting amplifier and demodulator stage behave at this higher frequency. Sadly, even the full application notes from Motorola do not say. I have a sneaking suspicion that maximum performance at these frequencies cannot be guaranteed; I feel AOR would have used the more standard 10.7 MHz If if this had been the case. However, for the sake of the cost of a crystal and two inexpensive roofing filters (SFA.10.7MF) it may be worth trying. Of course even if this works, there is no AFC and so any Doppler shift will have to be manually tracked.

### 2001 S-meter

Unlike the 2002, the 2001 does not have an S-meter. There is no room on the front panel for such an indicator but there is nothing to stop an external meter being used — a suitable circuit is shown in chapter 3.

## Case screening

Both models have unscreened plastic cases and are prone to breakthrough of signals from such things as nearby computers. Quite a considerable improvement can be made by using Nickel screening spray paint on the insides of the case halves. Details of Nickel paint spray are given in Chapter 4 and should you wish to use the same spray on either of the AOR models then proceed as follows: remove the two plastic case halves and carefully use masking tape and paper to ensure that all outer surfaces are protected from spray. Take particular care around the loudspeaker grill as paint can work its way underneath any paper masking and appear on the outside of the case. Follow the manufacturers instruction and spray the insides of the casings with the paint and leave to dry. Once dry, remove the masking and re-assemble. Unless you have warped casings they will not need any connections to the scanner's ground because the inside of the cases come into direct contact with the chassis which is grounded.

Using an AOR 2002 near a BBC-B computer I found hash levels were better reduced by screening the scanner than by using similar spray on the computer.

## AOR-2001 computer interface

The following is an extract from an article by Martin Ehrenfried G8JNJ which appeared in the May 1987 edition of *Practical Wireless Magazine*. It is reproduced here by kind permission of the editor, Geoff Arnold.

AOR produce an interface board for use with the receiver, which bolts in place of the front panel and allows any computer with an RS-232 interface to control the receiver. However, examination of specifications for the interface does not give any indication of any extra facilities made available on the receiver other than a signal strength meter display on the computer. Almost the same facilities can be made available at a fraction of the cost providing the computer used has a parallel Input/Output port.

To achieve this, the receiver keyboard has a cross-point matrix format duplicated in part by a 45100 c.m.o.s. switch array. This accepts a 4-bit address word which selects each of the cross-points to be connected, and data and strobe inputs to be selected if the cross-point is opened or closed. The computer can then be duplicated by means of outputting the correct data to the c.m.o.s. switch, most of the keyboard commands. Note that not all commands are required, as the SEARCH, PRIORITY, LOCK-OUT and CLOCK functions can be achieved by the computer with suitable software. This permits the use of a single 4 × 4 matrix switch. Although a couple of extra ICs could be used to provide the missing functions if required. The circuit in

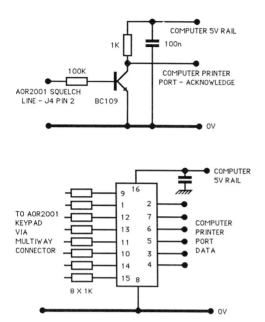

**Figure 2.7** AOR-2001 computer interface by Martin Ehrenfried G8JNJ (reproduced by kind permission of Practical Wireless Magazine)

Figure 2.6 shows the interface circuit and Figure 2.7 shows the connection details.

The best point to connect to the keyboard is just below the multi-way strip connector used to terminate the ribbon cable feed to the keyboard.

This is located on the control board at the rear of the front control panel. Miniature resistors are used as termination points for connections to the keyboard, again in order to provide a degree of protection to the receiver under fault conditions, and to help reduce re-radiation of 'hash' from the microprocessor control board. Beware when soldering near the ribbon connecting cable as it will melt very easily; it is best to hold it out of the way with some tape, or disconnect it completely when working on the PCB.

The facilities which could be provided by the receiver/computer combination are now only limited by the imagination and software writing ability of the user. Here are some suggestions:

Monitoring of channel occupancy with a bar chart style indication of usage
Providing extra memories
More than one PRIORITY channel
Intelligent scanning of memories
The most important frequencies being checked more often
Electronic logging of time and frequency information

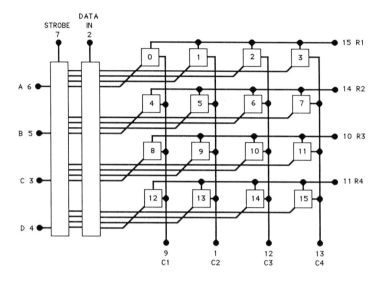

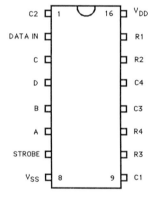

**Figure 2.8** 45100 connections and data

Selective recording of traffic on specific channels (with a cassette recorder also under computer control)

These are just a few of the more obvious ideas that spring to mind, each user may have their own ideas. The flow chart for a simple computer control programme is shown in Figure 2.8.

Note that the c.m.o.s. switch has to be commanded ON and OFF for each 'press' of the keyboard. Failure to do this leaves the keyboard 'locked-up', so it is important to include an initialisation routine at the start of the programme to 'switch-off' every location in the matrix. This prevents 'lock-up' occuring when the computer is first connected to the interface as spurious data may be fed into the switch. The rest of the programme consists of routines to convert computer keyboard

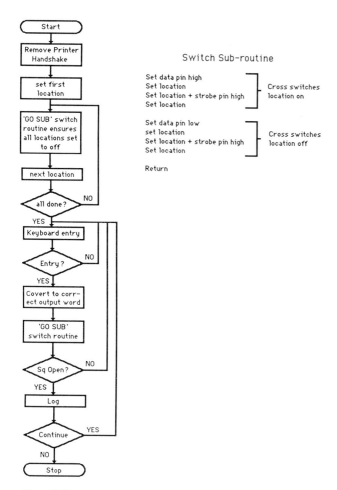

Figure 2.9

commands into the correct input/output format for control of the c.m.o.s. switch. A feed from the receiver squelch circuit to the I/O port allows the computer to determine when a signal is present, the results of which can be presented in a number of ways depending on the programme.

## AOR 2001 external keyboard

The external keyboard described here was developed by Peter Turner G8TSY and first appeared in *Practical Wireless* in March 1985.

Although the AOR 2001 broke new ground in scanner technology, its biggest weak-point was obviously the stiff and sluggish response from the membrane keyboard. The manufacturers obviously realised

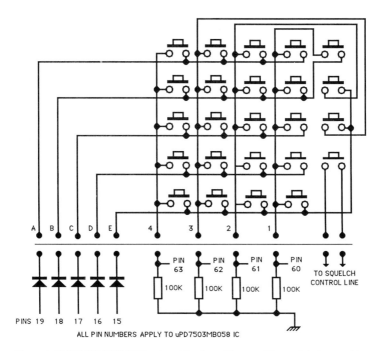

**Figure 2.10** G8TSY AOR-2001 external keyboard key positions relate to panel layout

this because the successor, the AOR 2002, had proper keys. However, it is not particularly difficult to build a remote keyboard using proper press-keys. Peter Turner's design follows the original keyboard fairly closely but splits the 'Delay' and 'Speed' buttons off onto keys of their own. The unit also incorporates a very useful 'squelch stop' function.

The keys used in the original design were of the type which are used to fabricate computer-style keyboards. The keys are inexpensive and purchased individually but they do require to be mounted on a printed circuit board as they have no means of being fixed to a front panel. A design for a PCB has not been included because the pin-outs on keys vary between manufacturers. However, anyone capable of etching their own circuit boards should have no difficulty at all in designing a simple board for the job. The best keys, if you can obtain them, are the ones which have a detachable transparent cover which allows key markings to be made on small squares of paper or card. This can be done either on a typewriter or using rub-down lettering.

All the keys are normal momentary-on types with the exception of the squelch stop switch which should be a press-on-press-off type. This switch allows the scanner to be stopped at any time without upsetting the squelch control setting and gives quick access to re-programming of frequency, mode, etc. Releasing the key provides instant resumption of scanning. The keyboard assembly will need to be housed in a suitable casing and some of the inexpensive slope-fronted plastic cases with metal front panels are ideal. If a big enough case is used then other extras such as the S-meter described earlier could also be incorporated.

## Connecting up

The use of ribbon cable is recommended for connection between the keyboard and scanner. It can either be routed between the back panel and the casing (it is a bit of a squeeze but will fit) or you can use a sharp knife to cut away the cover hiding the blank socket in the back panel which is designed for the optional computer interface. This cut-out takes a 25-way D-type plug and the cable can be simply passed through the hole. Looking at the inside of the front panel of the scanner you will see the flexi-P.C.B. strip that goes from the keyboard to the black socket on the front panel P.C.B. Alongside this plug you will see the five diodes and four 100 K resistors shown in the circuit diagram and it is simply a question of soldering the appropriate wire from the remote keyboard to the appropriate diode or resistor.

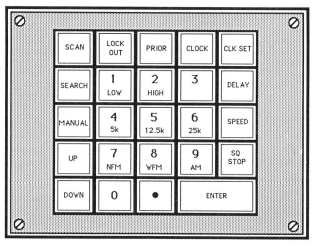

**Figure 2.11** G8TSY front panel layout for AOR-2001 external keyboard

To connect the squelch-stop switch, locate the small P.C.B. on the back of the volume control and you should find three wires; violet, black and yellow, which are all in a row. You have to break-into the black line so that the original connection on the PCB goes to the remote keyboard switch and the return wire connects to the black wire going to the main circuit board. If you are going to use a D-Plug for hooking-up your remote keyboard, you will need to fit a small toggle switch on the back panel of the scanner wired in parallel with the keyboard scan-stop switch, so that when the unit is disconnected the squelch line can be bridged for normal operation.

## ICOM R700

It may seem absurd to suggest that the R7000 needs any kind of modification as this is the receiver with just about everything. However, many owners may find that the Wideband FM facility is of little use and this particular part of the circuit could be used in a better way. I know a lot of scanner owners, myself included, who take the view that the scanner was not purchased to listen to broadcasting stations. With the advent of cheap digitisers and software to allow weather picture reception from satellites, it would seem that a circuit evolved for this use would be a more valuable facility. As has already been explained, the Narrow Band FM on scanners is far too narrow for reception and although some success has been achieved with normal Wide Band (100–150 kHz) reception this has only been on very strong signals.

The optimum bandwidth for weather satellite signals is about 30 kHz. However, few ceramic or crystal filters are produced specifically for this bandwidth and so a suitable compromise is a 50 kHz roofing filter. There is little difficulty in converting the existing 150 kHz bandwidth facility to a 50 kHz one. The relevant parts of the Icom's circuit are filters F11 and F12. These are standard ceramic filters fitted to a host of broadcast type FM receivers and they have 330 Ohm terminations. The originals are types SFE10.7-MMH/A and SFE10.7-MJ/A and can be directly replaced with a pair of SFE 10.7MFs which are identical in size and pin configuration. This particular IF section of the R7000 has no conversion down to 455 kHz and so these two filters solely determine the passband characteristic of the WFM mode. The filters are located on the main IF board close to IC2 (TA7303P). Close to that same IC is resistor R13 which is a 3.9 kOhm and some adjustment may have to be made to that resistor to optimise performance of the circuit with the tighter bandwidth. There are no holes to drill, and the scanner can easily be returned to its original state at any time.

Should any R700 owner feel inclined to attempt the modification I would strongly urge them to obtain a copy of the full service manual. This is a very useful publication and is one of the best manuals I have ever come across for a scanner.

## 10 channel FM scanner

In theory there is nothing particularly difficult about designing and building a crystal controlled scanner. In practice the availability of ready wound coils, miniature components and specialised VHF/RF devices makes the job somewhat harder. Presented here are a series of interactive circuits which provide the building blocks of a 10-channel FM, crystal controlled scanner. It is impossible to present a finalised do-it-yourself project because frequency coverage and the availability of components will all affect the finalised design. However, for anyone with reasonable knowledge of RF circuitry and some experience of VHF construction techniques, the circuits presented here should provide the basis for a practical project.

The circuit diagrams are presented in several separate stages to make the operation easy to follow. These are: RF amplifier/mixer/ crystal oscillator and multiplier stage — logic counter/clock and scan-stop-display/switching and crystal selection — IF amplifier and demodulator — audio amplifier and voltage regulation. The scanner makes extensive use of off-the-shelf components and is designed to work with inexpensive standard marine or amateur VHF crystals (45 MHz series types), although there is no reason why crystals cut for specific frequencies cannot be used for other bands. The set can be built to cover a bandwidth of about 4 MHz and with only slight adjustments to the tuned circuits shown, this band could be anywhere in the region 136–200 MHz.

I have deliberately made use of ICs wherever possible as they do cut down the amount of circuit complexity and construction time. All second conversion, IF amplification, demodulation, squelch and scan-stop functions are included in just one chip and even the scan logic requires only two standard ICs. All audio amplification is carried out by a single IC.

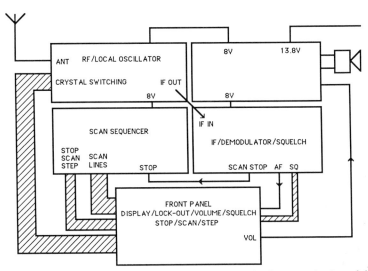

**Figure 3.1** 10 channel FM scanner showing interconnection between circuit modules

Although the circuits shown here are for a mobile or base station scanner, readers may be interested to know that this circuit (with only a change in the audio amplifier) has also been miniaturised down to a pocket scanner. Specific details are not given here because the degree of miniaturisation involved relies heavily on the availability of specialised components and I was unable to guarantee a regular and reliable source for such things as cases, switches and potentiometers. However, details are given at the end of this section on how to make a start on designing a cut-down version together with some hints and tips on such things as miniaturised LED displays and lock-out switching.

## RF amplifier, local oscillator and mixer

Q1 is a dual-gate MosFet transistor operated in ground-source mode with the two 10 K resistors on G2 detremining the gain of the stage. The incoming signal is matched to the device by L1 and its associated 20 pF trimming capacitor. The resultant output is fed via tuned circuits to the mixer transistor Q2. This is again a MosFet device with local oscillator injection being made via G1. The resulting output is fed to T1 which matches the now 10.7 MHz signal to the first IF filter, F1. This is a 2-pole crystal filter type 10M15A which provides initial selectivity having a 15 dB bandwidth of 15 kHz.

Now back to the oscillator injection and a look at the crystal oscillator and multiplier. Q3 is a standard Colpitts configuration with output and coupling to the multiplier stage via the network T2 and corresponding capacitors. The tuned output of the multiplier terminates in a secondary winding T3 and from there feeds to the gate of Q2.

The Scan-logic circuit is nothing more than a NE555 timer IC operated in astable mode with RX determining the pulse rate. The pulse is fed to a 4017B decade counter/divider IC. One point to watch with this IC is that it is c.m.o.s. and so the usual handling and soldering precautions must be observered otherwise the device can be damaged by static. Pin 13 is a clock inhibit and by taking the pin low the circuit counts but when pin 13 is taken high the circuit will stop. By using the scan-stop (high on signal) output of the IF chip, this pin is used to stop the scan sequence when a signal is received. The 1M resistor and 10 uF capacitor form a simple timing circuit which give a 'Scan Delay' of about 2 seconds. This facility of course can be removed entirely, simply by omitting the components or by feeding via a switch so that the delay can be brought in and out of circuit as desired. The 47 k resistor between pins 6 and 7 of the NE555 is used to set maximum speed relevant to consistent stopping — excessive speed will cause the scanner to 'overrun'. Slight adjustments may be necessary to the value of this resistor depending on the make and batch number of the IC but 47 k is a good starting point and should work in most instances. The output pulses from the 555 go via a Single-Pole, Double Throw (SPDT) toggle switch which has contacts configured as momentary-on, centre off, latched-on. In the normal switched-on position the receiver scans, in the centre off position it stops, and pushing it to the biased (momentary on) position moves the count on by one channel.

The outputs of the 4017B will directly drive LEDs and these are used to display which channel is active. When an IC output goes high, then the LED is forced into hard conduction, the crystal is grounded via it's capacitors and so the oscillator stage become active. Between the output of the IC and the LED/crystal stage are series switches which can be used to lockout any channels that are not required.

If the whole ten channels are not needed then the circuit can be configured for less channels. In order that the scan sequence does not waste time by the IC hunting through unused pins then the reset pin, number 15, should be taken to the pin after the last active output pin and not to ground.

All IF amplification, second conversion, demodulation, squelch and scan-stop functions are taken care of in just one IC. This is the MC3359 (also designated ULN-3859A) and is derived from the universally accepted MC3357. It does however offer several advantages over its predecessor. It has a more sensitive input, more audio output and is already matched to the new generation of crystal and ceramic filters. Neither the 10.7 MHz input filter nor the 455 kHz second IF filter require matching transformers.

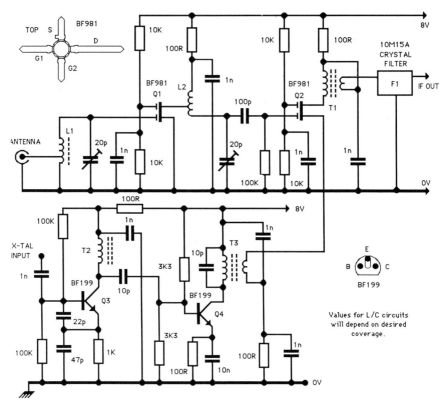

**Figure 3.2** 10 channel scanner RF/1ST oscillator/mixer

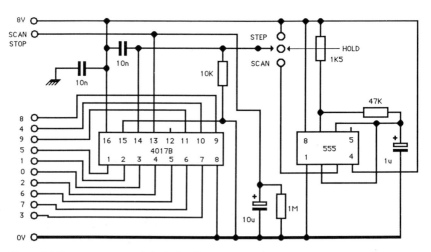

**Figure 3.3** Scan sequencer and clock circuit

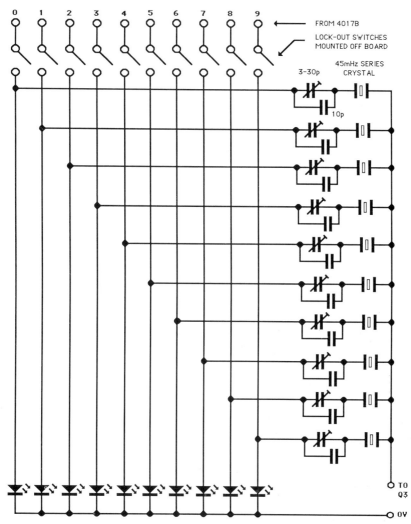

**Figure 3.4** Scanner display, lockout and crystals

The 10.7 MHz input is fed direct from the crystal filter to pin 18 which is the mixer input. The second conversion crystal of 10.245 MHz is connected to the internal oscillator via pin 1. Mixer output goes to pin 3 and is fed to a 455 kHz ceramic filter. This is an inexpensive device with 12 kHz bandwidth and its output goes to pin 5 where it enters a limiting amplifier inside the IC. That output is fed to an internal demodulator with its tuned circuit on pin 8. Although a particular component is listed for this transformer I have found in practice that almost any old 455 kHz IF coil will work — the only slight adjustment being to the damping resistor across the coil to achieve

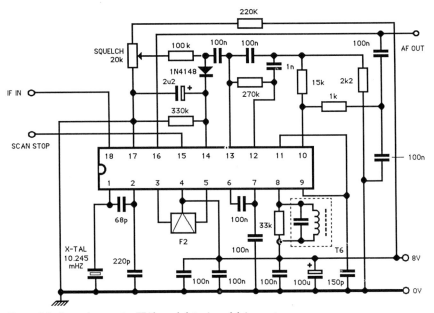

**Figure 3.5** Second converter/IF/demodulator/squelch/scan stop

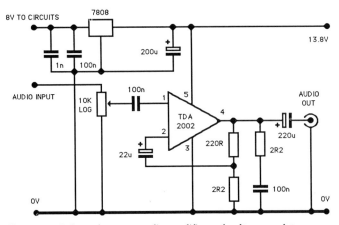

**Figure 3.6** 10 channel scanner audio amplifier and voltage regulator

best audio. Squelch control is achieved internally and only requires the external network of components based on pins 14 and 15. Pin 11 is for an AFC function which is not needed in this application but by connecting it to the demodulator filter on pin 9 we can double the audio output.

### Audio output and voltage regulation

All audio functions are taken care of by a single IC amplifier, the TDA 2002. In practice, in this circuit, the IC can provide around 4 watts of audio so making it deal for use in noisy environments such as automobiles. The network comprising two 2R2 resistors, 220R resistor and 100 nF capacitor are merely to ensure stability of this relatively broadband device. Even so, it is a good precaution to feed the output to the loudspeaker via screened cable as an extra precaution.

The scanner works with two voltages. The input, in the range 11–15 volts is fed directly to the audio IC but all remaining circuitry needs a stabilised voltage and this is provided by a 7808 three-terminal regulator. This device was chosen because it can operate from the voltage input specified whereas a 12 volt regulator would not, even though the higher voltage would provide greater 'headroom' for the MosFETs in the RF stages. Note that around the regulator are several decoupling and smoothing capacitors and throughout the scanner circuitry there are many such components. It is essential with these kind of circuits that RF is adequately decoupled if instability is to be avoided.

## Components

*Capacitors*
All are sub-miniature types and this is particularly important to note where the 100 nF decoupling ones are concerned around the area of the IF IC. 1 nF decoupling capacitors, of which there are several in the RF/Mixer/Oscillator stages can be ceramic plate types and those capacitors in the tuned circuits should be stable ones such as ceramic plate or polystyrene. All electrolytics must be sub-miniatures with a minimum of 16 volt working and there is no reason why tantalum types should not be used.

*Resistors*
All are $\frac{1}{4}$ Watt types.

*Coils*
The ones I used were Toko S18 types with L1/L2/T2/T3 being the 3.5 turn version for coverage of the Marine VHF band. Secondaries consisted of nothing more than single strand PVC coated wire which was looped twice round the main winding of the coil. T1 is a Toko type 119LC30099N. This is a 10.7 MHz IF transformer which has a ten turn primary in paralled with an internal 82 pF capacitor. The secondary is four turns. It may be possible to substitute this device with a 10.7 MHz transformer salvaged from other sources.

## Semiconductors

There is little to add to what has already been mentioned. My own scanner used BF981 transistors for the dual-gate MosFets and BF199's for the oscillator stages. These devices are the best choice but substitutions should be possible.

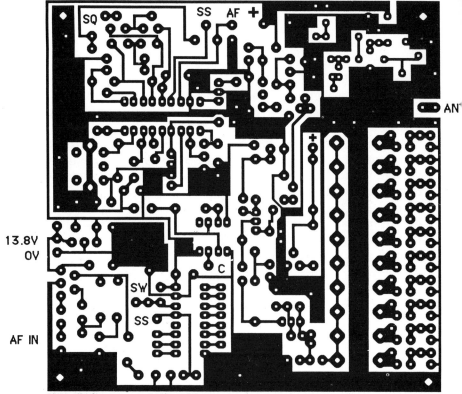

**Figure 3.7** 10 channel scanner PCB 1:1

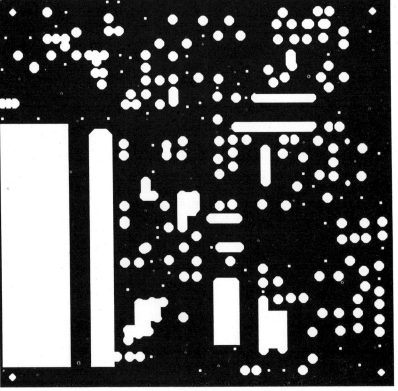

**Figure 3.8** 10 channel FM scanner PCB ground plane 1:1

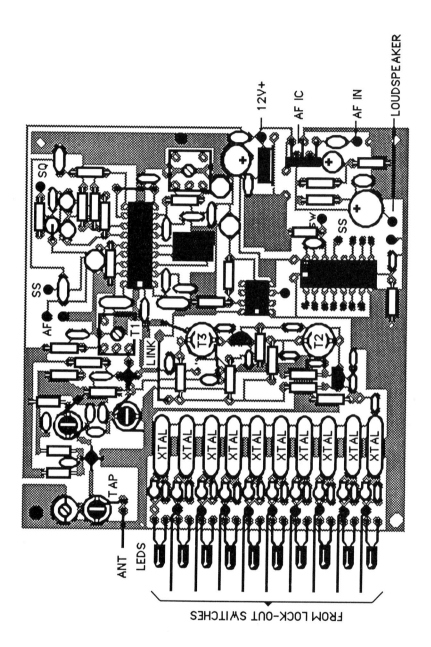

Figure 3.9

## Construction

A PCB design must be used and for the sake of stability it must be a double sided board with ground plane on the top. Note that arrangements have been made for Cirkit Holdings (address at the back of the book) to supply this scanner as a complete kit with Printed Circuit Board for coverage of the 2 metre Amateur or Marine VHF band. Great care must be taken with all soldering, particularly with ground connections which must be soldered on both sides of the board. All semiconductors and the LEDs should be soldered last of all.

## Casing the scanner

Much play is often made of only housing VHF equipment in metal cases. My own view is that this is not necessary and in fact many commercially made scanners are built into plastic housings with no ill effects. Any suitable size case can be used for this project and a suggested front panel layout is given in Figure 3.10

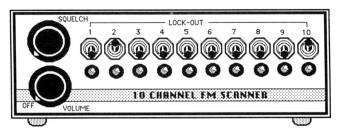

**Figure 3.10**

## Other options

The basic scanner design can be configured in two different ways: by removing the clock/sequencer circuit the receiver becomes a single frequency monitor, or by incorporating a rotary switch, a multi-frequency receiver. It is in fact possible to cascade the 4017 sequencer chips to gain extra channels but the cost of crystals then has to be weighed against the price of a synthesised scanner. The final option is to reconfigure the circuit for portable use. This has been done by simply compacting the circuit and using a smaller AF amplifier.

## Design considerations

I had originally intended including a complete design for a pocket scanner but supplies of miniaturised components could not be guaranteed. For instance at one stage I found a case that was the perfect shape and size. Within two months the manufacturer discontinued it and so I was back to square one. Manufacturers of scanners order components in such large quantities that they can afford to have special components such as volume controls and switches made to their specifications. The home constructor on the other hand has to rely on off-the-shelf components and it is often difficult to find miniature devices.

However, for readers with the skills to design their own printed circuits I have included some notes here to help them build a project based on components that should be obtainable.

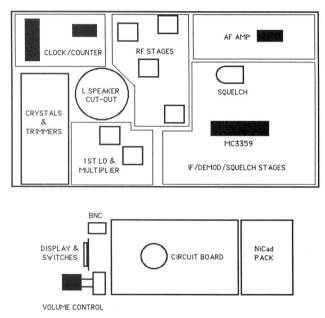

**Figure 3.11** Suggested layouts for a miniature version of the scanner

Firstly, you will not require as much audio volume on a pocket scanner and so a small IC amplifier rated at about half a watt should do. It will consume less current and be physically smaller. Two such circuits are shown, the ULN 2283B being the first choice because the all important component count is less. This is incidentally an excellent little amplifier for projects of this type, it costs no more than some IC Op amps and I always keep a small stock of them.

If you can settle for less channels on a portable, then the crystal count can be cut down to six and this allows us to cheat with the lock-out switching. In my own version I built a small PCB with 8-way DIL switch and miniature LEDs as a switch/display sub-assembly. DIL switches 1–6 were used for lockout, switch 7 for squelch override and switch 8 for power off/on. True, these switches are fiddly to operate

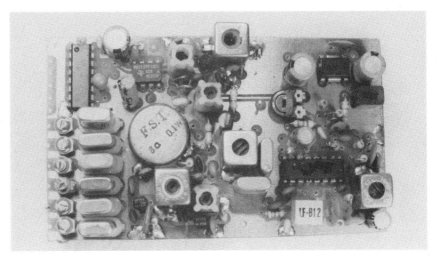

**Photograph 3(a)** A compacted prototype for pocket use

but the entire DIL switch is minute compared with even 8 sub-miniature toggle switches and costs far less. Once the set is operating, switch settings are rarely changed so the slight difficulty in actuating them is not really a problem. The tip of a pen or similar sharp instrument makes the job even easier.

As for the squelch, many commercially made portables rely on pre-set squelch anyway. In fact on a single VHF band there is rarely the need to keep readjusting the squelch setting.

**Photograph 3(b)** A pocket version of the scanner. Note the DIL switch used for lock-out, squelch override and on/off switching.

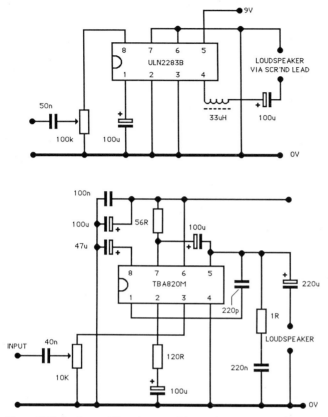

**Figure 3.12** Audio amplifiers for use with a pocket scanner

The IF stage will need some slight adjustment. The circuit for the MC 3359 shown in the service section of the book shows that the supply to the IC is stepped down to just over 5 volts. This is about the optimum for best performance versus low current consumption. This same stabilised voltage should be used in the first local oscillator as well. The rest of the circuit will work quite happily at around 9 volts and should be powered by suitable NiCad cells.

The block layout and photograph of my own pocket scanner show how the circuit was laid out (tuned circuits were different on this early prototype). This configuration worked well and despite the closeness of critical components such as inductors, there was no problem with stability. If you are using the ULN2283B, it is advisable to feed the loudspeaker through miniature coaxial cable (even for runs as short as a few centimetres) as the IC can get unstable when used around strong RF fields such as those generated by the two oscillators in the circuit.

The biggest problem will probably be the case. Slim upright cases such as those used on commercial scanners and small transceivers seem to be in very short supply from regular case manufacturers. The 'pocket-size' and 'hand-held' equipment cases designed by British manufacturers do not seem to consider the actual size of a jacket pocket! However, if you find one the right size and shape, do not worry whether it is metal or plastic; either will do. The antenna can be a helical type fitted to a BNC socket.

# Computer control 4

Computer control is one of the newest and most exciting aspects of advanced scanner operation. The average scanner, when all is said and done, is a somewhat stupid animal that can only work to a set pattern. Add a computer though, and suddenly you are in full command and can set up complex routines that can take into account a variety of situations. Let's look at one of the simplest examples: you are monitoring a split frequency simplex pair of frequencies, i.e. the base frequency and the mobile reply frequency. Under normal circumstances you would enter the first frequency in say memory 1 and the reply frequency in memory 2. Should the base frequency become active, when transmission ends, the scanner will move onto memory 2 and get the response. Fine, but of course when that transmission ends the scanner will then have to run through it's entire memory block to get back to the base frequency. At best you will miss part of any reply from the base and at worst you will miss it all if the scanner stops on another active channel.

However, under computer control, such situations can be coped with very easily. Using even simple Basic programming and 'IF' routines the scanner can be instructed to toggle back and forth between split-frequency pairs when they become active and only resume normal scanning after a pre-determined time where both channels have gone quiet.

That is just one of the simpler tasks that can enhance the operation of the scanner. There are far more sophisticated routines that can be catered for and even if you only have limited programming abilities you can still build up a suite of quite complex operations. Typical examples include automatic logging using tape recorders, printers and even computer memory to keep track of what is happening even when the scanner is unattended. Routines can be set up to search frequency segments and record any activity. Frequency, time, etc. can all be stored using a variety of means for later analysis. Some computer/ scanner users have developed quite complex programmes to incorporate such things as bargraphs to show the level of channel activity.

## Developing programmes

It is impossible to give specific programmes for all machines but suffice to say that a look at the programmes given in this chapter should provide a rough guide for what your computer will need to do when hooked to a scanner. In most cases a simple communications programme to send and receive data via a serial port is all that is needed. The programmes shown for the AOR machines demonstrate how a simple communications routine has extra lines added so that things such as a recorder can be switched on and off. Start with the basics and then just add routines bit by bit; in other words develop your programe to do what you want it to do. Whatever scanner you own, read through the sections dealing with all the scanners in this chapter because each one contains programming hints which you should be able to adapt to most scanners.

## Control methods

The link between the scanner and computer will fall into two broad categories; serial data port communications or keyboard access.

The former requires only communications software of the type already described and is the most common type of control. It can be subdivided into two distinct sections. The first is the type we find in the AOR's where the RC-pack is in fact a computer in it's own right even though it does not have a keyboard. The RC-pack contains additional control features in EPROM and these include the necessary communications software to send to and receive from the computer which will really be acting as a dumb-terminal. In the case of the RC-pack there is also ROM with power back-up to store additional memories and search patterns.

Other scanners though, typically the Icom-R7000, give your keyboard access to the internal microprocessor. For anyone with reasonable programming abilities this is by far the most powerful method of access and is quicker in terms of response time. It is possible to access the AOR's direct and the simple interface shown in the chapter on modification will do just that.

## Problems

Without a doubt the biggest problem in using a scanner with a computer is the amount of hash that is radiated from most computer circuits. The simplest and most obvious way to cut this down is to ensure that the scanner's antenna is sited well away from the computer. However, this will almost certainly not affect a complete cure. The problem largely stems from the fact that most home micro-computers are supplied with unscreened cases. American made equipment is generally better in this respect as the FCC has laid minimum radiation levels. In Britain no such legislation exists and so by and large equipment made here has no form of suppression at all and some computers radiate the most appaling hash. It has always struck me as somewhat ironic that one of the worst machines in this respect is the BBC computer, ironic of course because it is endorsed by the British Broadcasting Corporation. Still, broadcast it does (for several hundred yards) and it is not alone.

There are two ways of getting round this problem. The first, and by far the most expensive, is to re-build the computer into a metal case. Many of the larger component suppliers sell standard cases with ready cut-out keyboard panels and as most home computers are usually single PCB arrangements, it's not usually too difficult to rehouse the computer. Obviously the metal case must be earthed if it is going to act as an effective screen. However, although this method can cut hash dramatically it can be an expensive solution.

The other option is to fit screening to the existing plastic case. Two methods can be used; aluminium foil and Nickel spray. I have always been somewhat sceptical of the foil method which includes lining the plastic case with material such as aluminium cooking foil. I have seen this method recommended several times in various articles but my worry stems from the fact that wrinkles in the foil, or even the foil becoming detached, could come into contact with live circuitry with disastrous results. My preference is for the second method, Nickel spray, which in fact is used by some computer manufacturers.

Both methods of screening involve stripping the keyboard, circuit board and power supply out of the casing. This is not quite the daunting task it may seem; on the BBC for instance, the PCB comes free after a few screws have been removed and the only wire that has to be unsoldered is the one to the BNC video socket. The Nickel spray can be obtained from component suppliers and although it is quite expensive it is far cheaper than buying a new metal case. The outsides of the case must be carefully masked with tape and paper. Once this is done the inside is sprayed in accordance with the manufacturers recommendation on paint thickness.

Once the paint had dried there are two important points to watch. Carefully check the track side of the computer PCB to ensure that no tracks around the mounting holes are going to come into contact with the mounting pillars on the case. If this is so then you can either use insulating washers when you reassemble the PCB back in the case or you can scrape the Nickel coating off the top of the pillars. In other words, the once non-conductive plastic pillars are now conductive and you must act accordingly.

The second point is that the conductive coating on the insides of the casing have to be connected to ground to have any effect. It is possible of course that ground tracks on the underside of the PCB will come into contact via the coating on the pillars and that is fine. If not you will have to devise some method of connecting the case coating to ground. Solder tags mounted via a nut and bolt are ideal.

The reduction in hash levels will no doubt vary between machines, but on my own BBC-B the effect is quite noticeable. However, it is not perfect because there are various unscreened leads connecting the computer to the outside world, typically the video monitor, disc drive and printer. All these leads can radiate hash and ideally need to be screened. The easiest way to do this is to wrap them in metal foil. Again, take great care that whatever foil you use does not come into contact with any live connections and of course the foil will need to be connected to earth to have any effect. Baking foil and self adhesive copper tape are all suitable and I have been told that some of the chrome tape sold for embellishing bicycles will also work.

If you are re-building your computer into a metal case it may be worth making external connection via feed-through capacitors which will de-couple RF.

One further problem that can arise is where the scanner itself is not adequately screened. The AOR is a typical example and details were given earlier on how to use the same Nickel spray to good effect.

## AOR scanners under computer control

The AOR series of scanners, AR2001 and 2002, have proved immensely popular and with the addition of what's called an RC-Pack brings either of these machines under computer control and adds a whole new dimension to scanning.

First though a look at the two scanners themselves. The 2001 was the first receiver to appear on the market that allowed 'no-gaps' coverage from 25 to 550 MHz. It also scored over some of it's earlier competitors in that far fewer spurii appeared across it's tuning range. The 2002 (which also appears as the Regency MX8000) is a re-vamped version with the addition of an 800 to 1300 MHz tuning range, a bargraph S-meter, proper keypad buttons and a manual tuning knob. Interestingly the case is exactly the same shape and size as it's predecessor. Either machine offers 20 memory channels and each channel can be individually programmed for mode and delay.

### Tapping into the micro
The optional computer interface certainly is not much to look at; a plain grey box with an LED power light and a push-on-push-off

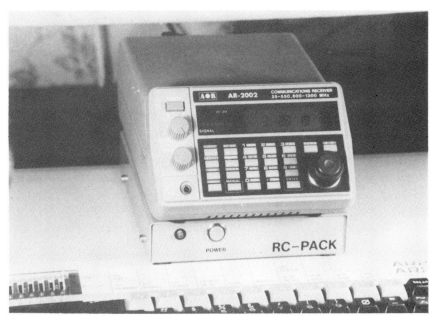

**Photograph 4(a)** The RC-pack sits neatly under the AR2002

**Photograph 4(b)** The AOR2002 connected to the RC-pack

switch. It comes with a short length of ribbon cable terminated in IDC plugs which connect directly to a socket on the back of the AR2002. In the case of the AR2001 an additional adaptor is required and connecting up is slightly more complicated. The set has to be opened up and the plug carrying the keyboard connection has to be disconnected from the main PCB. This means that the AR2001 can then only be used under computer control. There is no such drawback with the 2002 as switching the RC-Pack on automatically puts the scanner under computer control.

## AOR commands

The following is a list of commands available on the AR2002:

| | |
|---|---|
| RS xxx | Sets the response time from the Ar2002. xxx=1 to 255. Responds with "GOOD" |
| EC | Toggles the screen echo on or off (Only required if terminal program is being used) |
| WFM | Sets the mode to Wide FM |
| NFM | Sets the mode to Narrow FM |
| AM | Sets the mode to AM |
| SFxxx.xxxx | Set frequency (in MHz, SF is optional) |
| SQ | Returns "O" if squelch is on or "1" if squelch is off |
| LK | Returns "0" if PLL is unlocked or "1" if PLL is locked |
| AG | Returns a number from "000" to "255" which represents the signal input level. This is ONLY used on NFM or AM but not WFM. The following is a guide to indicate the returned numbers as voltages: |

">" equal Greater than and "<" equal Less than

| | | | | | |
|---|---|---|---|---|---|
| > 222 = | 5 uV, | 222 = | .5 uV, | 196 = | .6 uV |
| 170 = | .7 uV, | 156 = | .8 uV, | 142 = | .9 uV |
| 132 = | 1.0 uV, | 117 = | 1.2 uV, | 107 = | 1.4 uV |
| 100 = | 1.6 uV, | 95 = | 1.8 uV, | 90 = | 2.0 uV |
| 82 = | 2.5 uV, | 77 = | 3.0 uV, | 70 = | 4.0 uV |
| 65 = | 5.0 uV, | 55 = | 10.0 uV, | 51 = | 20.0 uV |
| 48 = | 50.0 uV, | 46 = | 100.0 uV, | 44 = | 200.0 uV |
| 41 = | 500.0 uV, | <41 = | >500.0 uV, | | |

On the rear apron of the RC-Pack is a 25-way D-series socket which provides a standard RS232 connection (8 bit, non parity, 1 stop bit) to the computer which can either control the scanner directly under constant control or can act as a dumb terminal just to get the RC-Pack programmed. Baud rates are set within the RC-Pack using dip switches. The factory set rate is 9600 baud but this can be changed to 4800 or 2400.

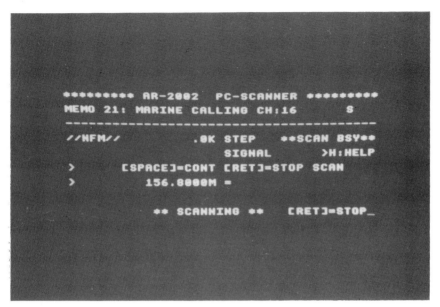

**Photograph 4(c)** Standard RC-pack screen output

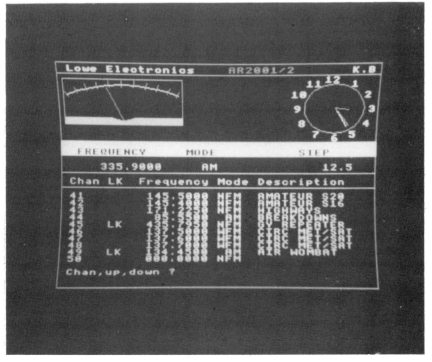

**Photograph 4(d)** Lowe's graphics on the RC-pack software for the BBC-B

**Photograph 4(e)** Inside the RC-pack switches set baud rates

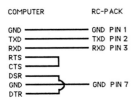

**Figure 4.1** AOR2001/2002 RC-pack connections

The pack contains its own 8-bit CPU and non volatile memory (capacitor style power cell that will retain memory for around a month without power applied). Using the internal software, a host of additional facilities are available. Now 50 memory channels can be used and notes can be written to identify the frequency user and these appear on screen when a signal is received. Additionally, 10 banks of search ranges can be set up and recalled at any time.

### Additional Features
Pre-set step rates for searches on the set are limited to hops of 5, 12.5 and 25 kilohertz but under computer control virtually any step rate from 100 hertz upwards can be programmed. During search sequences the arrow and plus and minus keys on the computer (assuming they generate standard ASCII codes) can be used for up/down tuning at a nominal 70 millisecond step rate (this can be altered). It is interesting to note that under computer control it is also possible to search outside the specified

limits of the receiver. The frequency can be set to anything below 25 MHz but performance tails off sharply around 10 MHz. The highest limit is 1355 MHz but despite this quirk it is not possible to programme frequencies between 550 and 800 MHz (TV sound). Naturally reception of stations between 10 and 25 MHz is far from perfect because of the relatively wide bandwidth of the I.F. filters in the set.

When it comes to scanning proper, a range of features are available which includes as many priority channels as you want and the ability to set the rate at which they are checked. Delay on scan channels is adjustable from 1-127 seconds.

## Software

So far my own experiments have been conducted solely with a BBC-B computer. On receiving the RC-Pack my first problem was to find a suitable 25-way plug to hook it to the RS432 terminal on the Beeb as one is not supplied. Fortunately I had one and a suitable Domino Din plug for the computer and a few minutes with a soldering iron meant I was able to plug the pack to the Beeb. With the RC-Pack switched on, the AR2002 went dead and just the time showed. I booted up the only communication softwear I had, Mini Office II, selected 9600 baud from the available rates and then typed in 'EC'; the command that 'kick starts' the interface. The system fired up perfectly. I will not go into detail on how things work from then on as it is simply a question of using a few new commands or following prompts. A Help facility fires up a description of all the available commands.

Once frequencies have been programmed into the memory channels and such things as priorities and delays have been set then the computer's break key can be hit. The scanner will carry on working and the computer can be returned to normal usage or even switched off.

Having used a commercial communications package to try out the equipment, I decided to develop a simple basic programme to do the job (it was a bit tedious having to set up the various options and protocols on the Mini Office II package).

### Practical programmes
Programme 1 is about the simplest possible software you can use to get the computer to act as a dumb terminal. It is fractionally slower than a proper communication programme written in machine code but in practice this does not cause any drawbacks. The programme automatically sets the response time between the RC-Pack and computer and once 'run' you just type in 'EC' followed by return. 'EC' will not appear on screen but that is perfectly normal. The RC-Pack is

then in 'Echo' mode and will start to write to the screen. The only point to watch is that if the RC-Pack has already been used with faster software it may not respond properly at first. Try giving it a slower response speed such as 'RS 50' and then re-run the software.

That simple programme will allow full programming of the RC-Pack and again once the scanner is under way the Beeb can be returned to normal usage. The beauty of this programme is that the thousands of people like myself who cannot programme in machine code can now start adding a few extras. Programme 2 is a slightly modified version that simply uses the internal cassette switching relay of the Beeb to turn a tape recorder on when a signal is received. This idea can be taken a stage further by using a stereo cassette deck so that audio is recorded on one track and screen information is stored as a file on the other track. This obviously allows the scanner to be left unattended and later playback will show who was transmitting what and on which frequency. Used in search mode it also allows new statons to be found.

```
5  REM COPYRIGHT PETER ROUSE 1986
10  REM *** PROGRAMME 1 ***
20  REM AOR 2001/2002 RC-PACK DUMB TERMINAL
40  REM RUN THEN TYPE 'EC RETURN'
50  REM BBC CAN BREAK AND RETURN TO NORMAL
60  REM PROGRAMMING AFTER SETTING RC PACK
70  CLS
80  *FX7,7
90  *FX8,7
100  *FX3,7
110  PRINT"RS 14"
120  *FX2,2
130  X=INKEY (1):IF X=−1 THEN 170
140  *FX3,7
150  VDU X
160  *FX3,0
170  *FX2,1
180  *FX3,0
190  x=INKEY(1):IFX=−1THEN120
200  VDU X
210  IFX=10 THEN VDU X
220  GOTO 120
```

```
10  REM  COPYRIGHT PETER ROUSE 1986
20  REM  2002/2001 KEYBOARD/TAPE CONTROL
30  CLS
```

```
40  MODE1
50  COLOUR 1
60  *FX7,7
70  *FX8,7
80  T=0
90  *FX3,7
100 PRINT"RS 14"
110 *FX2,2
120 X=INKEY(1):IF X=-1THEN 160
130 *FX3,7
140 VDU X
150 *FX3,0
160 *FX2,1
170 *FX3,0
180 X=INKEY(1):IFX>0 THEN250
190 IFT<20 THEN 280
200 *FX137,0
210 IFX=-1THEN110
220 VDU X
230 IFX=10 THEN VDU X
240 GOTO 110
250 *FX137,1
260 T=0
270 GOTO220
280 T=T+1
290 GOTO210
```

Having said all that, do note the laws concerning recording of transmissions.

### Commercial programmes
There is only one programme specifically designed for the AOR RC-Pack available in Britain and that is supplied as a plug-in ROM by Lowe Electronics who are the importers of this equipment. It is much faster to use than a conventional communication package and bypasses much of the internal software of the RC-Pack so giving more control to the Beeb. Once memory channels have been selected these are stored on disc (channels stored in the non-volatile memory of the RC-Pack remain unaffected by use of Lowe programme) and the various functions are assigned to the programmable keys on the computer (Keystrip provided).

A pleasing colour graphic display provides a clock and mock up of a conventional moving coil type S-Meter. The ROM is accompanied by a tape which contains an instruction file and a sample programme of what can be done to provide extra features. These include tape recorder switching and hard copy log on a printer of the details and time of signals received. The programme is written in assembly language and a detailed description is included of what is doing what so those with the necessary programming skills can start adding their own features.

## AOR RC-PACK/LOWE ROM

### The keys and function keys used

*The ESCAPE key*   Use this to escape from any of the functions, i.e. entering memories, searching, scanning. If in doubt press the escape key a few times.

*The UP/DOWN arrow keys*   You can use these to increment or decrement the frequency by the step.

*The LEFT/RIGHT arrow keys*   Using these keys will single step through the memories.

*Shift f0*   Will ask you for a new step frequency in KHz. This can be from .1 (100Hz) to 999.9 KHz. RETURN or ESCAPE will go back to the normal display mode.

*f0*   Will ask you for a new frequency in MHz and will accept 25 to 550 MHz and 800 to 1300 MHz. RETURN or ESCAPE will go back to the normal display mode.

*f1*   Is used for adding or altering the scan memories. You can use the UP or DOWN arrow keys to look through the 50 memories or enter a channel number 1 to 50. If you enter a single number, i.e. 2 you will have to press return after it — alternatively, you can type in a two digit channel number, i.e. 02 or 23.

Pressing RETURN for any of the following questions will take the existing part of the memory as a default.

*LOCK Y/N?*   Y will lock out the memory channel. N will unlock it.

*Enter Freq?*   Enter a valid frequency or press f0 to use the display frequency and mode.

*Mode?*   Press f7, f8 or f9 to select mode for this channel.

*Description?*   Will allow you to enter a 13 character description. You can then either enter another memory or press escape.

*f2*   Is used for setting the search bands — first enter the low frequency and then the high frequency. Pressing return for either will leave existing frequency.

*f3*   Is used as a toggle switch for the priority on/off. Channel 1 is used for the priority channel and will work whether the channel is locked out or not. When the priority is on, it will continue to interrupt whatever you are doing in the program, i.e. while you are entering memories.

*f4*   Enters scan mode. You can press the space bar to hold any frequency you wish to temporarily stop on, and will remain until you

press the space bar again. Press the escape key to exit from scan mode.
*f5* Enters search mode. You can press the space bar to hold any frequency you wish to temporarily stop on, and will remain until you press the space bar again. Press the escape key to exit from search mode.
*f6* Toggles the delay on/off, and is set to a default of 3 seconds.
*Shift f6* This will save all 50 memories, search frequencies and the display frequency, mode and step.
*f7* Sets the mode to Wide FM.
*f8* Sets the mode to Narrow FM.
*f9* Sets the mode to AM.

## Other computers
Any computer which either has or can have added to it an RS232 interface can be used with the RC-Pack — it is simply a matter of using communications software which has selectable baud rates. Many computers such as the Dragon 64, Sinclair QL, etc, have suitable ports.

## Sinclair Spectrum dumb terminal software
The following program was written by Peter Stonebridge (G8ZQA) for the 48K Spectrum and operates via the optional ZX RS232 adaptor. According to him, it suffers a minor problem in that because the RS232 is operated directly under the control of the Spectrum's CPU, it occasionally locks up. This is no major problem as typing-in 'continue' will get the process going again.

```
3  REM AOR 2002 BY G8ZQA
5  LET LINE=0
10 OPEN #4;"t"
20 OPEN #5;"t"
25 PRINT #5;"rs35"
30 GOSUB 100                    :REM send
40 GOSUB 200                    :REM receive
50 GOTO 30
100 LET K$=INKEY$
110 IF K$="" THEN RETURN
120 IF K$<>"" THEN GO SUB 500
200 LET K$=INKEY$#4
210 IF K$=CHR$ 13 THEN LET LINE =LINE+1: POKE 23692,255
                                :REM to keep scrolling
240 PRINT K$;
250 RETURN
500 IF K$="1" THEN LET K$="ML"  :REM "MEMORY LIST"
510 IF K$="e" THEN LET K$="EC"  :REM "ECHO ON/OFF"
```

```
520  IF K$="c" THEN LET K$="CL"    :REM "RESET RC TO START
                                         CONDITION"
530  IF K$="s" THEN LET K$="SC"    :REM "SCAN"
540  IF K$="d" THEN LET K$="DL5"   :REM "DELAY 5 SECONDS"
550  IF K$="p" THEN LET K$="PR"    :REM PRIORITY OFF/ON"
560  IF K$="a" THEN LET K$="PA L " :REM "PASS FREQUENCY
                                         LIST"
570  IF K$="m" THEN LET K$="M"     :REM "MEMORY MODE"
580  IF K$="h" THEN LET K$="SE"
1000 PRINT #5;K$;
1010 GOTO 200
```

### MSX commands and software

According to the manual supplied with the RC-Pack, connection can be made direct to those MSX machines which have a communications port. The following commands and programme lines are all that are necessary to get the set-up working.

```
SCREEN 0
WIDTH 39
10  CALL COMINI ("0.8N1NNNNN",9600,9600)
20  CALL COMTERM ("0:")
```

Once you have run the above, type in 'EC' followed by 'RETURN' and then 'RS 5' again followed by 'RETURN'.

Their handbooks give details on how to receive and send via them. It should not be difficult to develop suitable basic programs along the lines of the one shown here for the BBC B.

### Conclusion

There is a bug in the internal software of the RC-Pack which manifests itself as one of the information lines being overwritten on the screen and then appearing in the wrong place. It does not effect the performance but it is slightly annoying. The command to kill delay is supposed to be 'DL X' which in fact has no effect whatsoever and it is necessary to use 'DL 1' and put up with a 1 second delay as minimum.

AOR provide no information at all on what order the data is sent back and forth nor how to use the RC-Pack in any way other than with the computer acting as a keyboard. The result is that it will be difficult for someone with only average programming abilities to write software that does away with such things as the unecessary refreshing of the entire screen every time a signal is received. Without some better means of control, setting up the RC-Pack is rather edious as instructions have to be entered one at a time with a complete screen refresh sequence between each one.

The set-up will appeal to two groups of scanner users: The first being those scanner buffs who want to be able to do such things as auto-log and the second being those people like myself who are compulsive fiddlers. I must confess to having had hours of fun finding out what I could and could not do with the computer hooked to the scanner. I suspect I have only just scratched the surface and hours more fun are in store as I play around with different programmes.

## Practical problems

Nearly all home micros generate dreadful signals from their internal clocks and the harmonics from these stretch well up into the VHF bands. My own system is unusable if the antenna system is anywhere near the computer and in fact even with the aerial 10 metres away from the Beeb the squelch has to be set slightly harder than normal.

The obvious answer to this is to fit the computer into an earthed metal case which might not be as silly as it sounds. There is no reason why a cheap computer should not be permanently connected to the scanner. Older computers and ones that have failed commercially can often be obtained quite cheaply either second hand or even new. I have seen MSX machines being sold new at bargain basement prices and according to the AOR manual these machines can be hooked directly to the RC-Pack and the computer's internal softwear for communications can be called up with just a few simple commands. The added advantage of all this is that you need not then tie up an expensive machine like a BBC-B on a dedicated operation.

Another way of screening a computer is to use Conductive spray paint. This is a Nickel coating which can be sprayed onto plastics. The spray is rather expensive but appears to be quite effective. I have already used this spray (which looks like dark grey matt finish paint) on the two halves of my AOR 2002. The two halves were removed from the scanner and the loudspeaker was unscrewed. Masking tape was carefully applied to all outer surfaces to ensure that the Nickel coating did not spoil the outside appearance of the scanner. Take particular care where the loudspeaker grill is concerned otherwise the coating can leak through. The coating is only an effective RF shield if connected to ground, but once the AOR is re-assembled it would appear that the insides of the case halves do come into contact with the chassis. My otherwise unscreened AOR now seems to be less prone to picking up hash from two computers in the same room. A similar process of dissassembly, masking and spraying has also been done to the BBC computer and hash levels have dropped noticeably. The results are not perfect and I suspect remaining radiation comes from unscreened leads to the printer and disc-drive. A further improvement could possibly be made by using Ferrite Chokes on these leads. Such chokes can now be bought which strap onto these leads.

One final tip is to try earthing different items of equipment. For some strange reason I noticed that hash levels dropped when I tried jumper wires between the casings of things like the disc drives, monitor and RC-Pack; it was just a case of finding the right combination.

## SX-400 computer control

The SX-400 requires an external interface and in Britain a suitable device, designated SX-232, provides a serial interface to the computer. The SX-232 is manufactured by Garex Elecronics and the following description and software was written by Garex director, Peter Longhurst.

### Control programs for SX400 receiver with SX232 interface

The SX232 is an intelligent device which requires quite simple control programs in the host computer.

Examples of simple control routines written in BASIC are given; they were written for the IBM PC, but should run with slight variations on most common machines which support BASIC.

The author makes no apology for the low tone of these notes and programs, since he believes that there are others, like himself, who claim talents in directions other than computer operation and programming.

### Getting started

Firstly, it is essential that the computer has a Communications port in RS232 or RS423 format. A Communications port is standard on a few machines and an optional extra on most. The industry standard connector for the Communications port is the 25 way "D" series. Three connections are normally employed: quite simply, SEND, RECEIVE and GROUND. The SX232 is supplied fitted with a 25 way "D" socket wired to the normal convention. Check the SX232 and computer handbooks to confirm that they are compatible. Other connections to the Comms port may be employed, they can generally be disregarded, but see the handbooks in case of difficulty.

The easiest way to test the system is to use a "Terminal Emulator" or "Modem Program" which should be available for most computers. This may take the form of a few lines of BASIC or similar in the handbook, or is often supplied as one of the utilities on your system disc. These programs are usually "public domain" and easy to obtain. The author uses "PC-TALK" on the IBM.

Load the program, setting the Baud rate and other parameters to suit those of the SX232 (see page 4 of the SX232 handbook). Set Position 4 of the selector switch inside the SX232 to OFF, corresponding to TERMINAL MODE. Initial programming is much easier in this mode. Note that the keyboard must output capital letters only ("CAPS LOCK").

Connect the SX232 signal lead to the computer and power up the SX232. Run the program and the screen should display the SX232 copyright message; if it doesn't display, try interrupting the SX232 power supply for a moment. Sending a 'Z' from the keyboard should also return the copyright message.

If garbage is displayed, then the most likely explanation is incorrect Baud rate. If nothing is displayed, then check all connections, and see P4 of the SX232 handbook.

On the assumption that all appears well, connect the SX232 to the SX400 and power up. The act of connecting the SX232 may require that the SX400 needs resetting.

Refer to the SX232 handbook and test the keyboard functions.

**Control programs**
If you do not have a 'Terminal Emulator' or 'Modem Program' for your machine, then the best advice is to get one! They can be very useful. However, we will not be using these programs for subsequent operations, as it can be quite difficult to 'get inside' these programs to write the control routines for the SX232. The first thing we need to do in order to communicate with the SX232 is to find out from the computer handbook the required format for addressing the Comms port.

It is likely to be something like "OPEN COM 1 . . . . . . . (followed by characters which set the communications parameters).

This is how we go about it on the IBM:

```
10  CLOSE              :REM — put this in as a safety precaution
20  OPEN "COM1:4800,E,7,1,CS,DS" AS £1
```

This sets a Baud rate of 4800, Even parity, 7 data bits, 1 stop bit, and disables the Clear To Send & Data Set Ready lines. "£1" in effect means 'the SX232'.

We can add three more lines:

```
30  PRINT £1,"R";
40  INPUT £1,A$
50  PRINT A$
```

30 sends 'R' to the SX232 which causes it to interrogate the SX400 display; 40 returns that display string and 50 displays the result on the VDU. Note that the built-in 'R' routine in the SX232 simplifies programming.

## Sending data to the SX400

In the simple case, we wish to type frequencies, etc. on the computer keyboard and enter them into the SX400. We do this in the same way as we program the SX400 direct: key in the frequency followed by ENTER, or <RETURN>. The data is held in the keyboard buffer until <RETURN> is pressed then the control program has to send the data one character at a time to the SX400, ending with <RETURN>.

Starting as above:

```
10 CLOSE
20 OPEN "COM1:4800,E,7,1,CS,DS" AS £1
30 INPUT A1$
40 F=LEN(A1$)          :REM F characters in the buffer
50 IF F<1 GOTO 30
60 FOR A=1 TO F        :REM Sends one char. at a time
70 B$=MID$(A1$,A,1)
80 PRINT £1,B$;
90 INPUT £1,C$
100 NEXT A
110 PRINT £1,           :REM <ENTER>
120 INPUT £1,D$:PRINT D$
```

The last line reads back the finished display of the SX400. This routine is used extensively in the Control Program and you should make sure you can run it without difficulty.

Add another line:

```
130 GOTO 30
```

and the program will continue to request data for the SX400; you can select the mode (AM of FM), SCAN A or B, etc. See the SX232 book of the control codes.

## Logging mode

The EPROM in the SX232 has a built-in Logging Mode; sending of a "+" and "−" from the keyboard will automatically start and stop the process. All frequencies which trigger the squelch of the SX400 while scanning or searching will be listed. The use of these single keystrokes to control this routine greatly simplifies the programming. The "+" can be sent as one of the control codes in the data sending process; but there is a slight snag with the interrupt: "−". You cannot just send it and hope to catch the SX232 unawares. But you can put it into the buffer and wait for the right opportunity to send it to the SX232.

```
85 IF B$="+" GOTO 200      :REM See data sending routine
200 E$=INKEY$ : IF E$="−" GOTO 250
```

```
210  IF LOC(1)=1 GOTO 200
220  INPUT £1,D$              :REM Logging
230  PRINT D$
240  GOTO 200
250  PRINT £1,"—"
260  INPUT £1,G$: PRINT G$ :REM "LOGGING MODE OFF"
```

**Memory processing**

If you study P2 of the SX232 handbook, you will see that the memories of the SX400 are accessed by using <CONTROL> followed by a letter, such that the Decimal Code of this combination corresponds to the required memory number; the only complication being that we cannot use <CONTROL M>. However, this is only a minor inconvenience, you just remember to add 1 to memory numbers 13 and above

"IF M>12 LET M=M+1", for example

The following routine will give you a screen listing of the current memory bank in the SX400:

```
300  CLOSE
310  OPEN "COM1:4800,E,7,1,CS,DS" AS £1
320  FOR M=1 TO 12
330  PRINT £1,CHR$(M);
340  INPUT £1,A$:PRINT A$
350  NEXT M
360  FOR N=14 TO 21
370  PRINT £1,CHR$(N);
380  INPUT £1,B$:PRINT B$
390  NEXT N
```

Note the slightly more verbose way of dodging "13"!

One small point which has not been mentioned so far: any of the lines containing "PRINT" can be written "LPRINT" to give a hard copy. Entering Memories: Start this routine by using the lines 10 to 110, above; this enters the frequency, then proceed:

```
120  INPUT "ENTER MEMORY NUMBER";M
130  IF M>20 GOTO 120              :REM Error trap
140  IF M>12 LET M=M+1
150  FOR Z=1 TO 200: NEXT Z        :REM Time delay
160  PRINT £1,CHR$(72);CHR$(M); :REM CHR$(72) = <CTRL>
170  FOR Y=1 TO 200:NEXT Y
180  INPUT £1,F$
190  IF LOC(1)>1 GOTO 180
200  PRINT F$
```

```
210  INPUT "ANOTHER MEMORY? (Y/N)";G$
220  IF G$="Y" GOTO 120
230  IF G$="N" GOTO xxx          :REM Resume as reqd.
```

This routine demonstrates another slight pitfall: sometimes you have to wait for the SX400 to catch up, hence the two delay loops in the above. The programmer should always be aware that timing is potentially critical, and there is one very good way of finding out when delays are needed. If an experimental routine does not work and errors and system seizures result, insert delay loops of 2 or 3 seconds duration between each of the active lines and watch what happens to the SX400 display. The above routine miraculously worked as soon as these diagnostic delays were inserted!

It is then a matter of systematically discarding the unwanted delays and pruning the necessary ones to a minimum safe length. Be warned that the required delays may depend on Baud rate and the machine in use. Experienced programmers will be aware of better ways of coping with this program ("OUT" and "WAIT" statements, for example).

Another simple and useful diagnostic tool is to insert a "PRINT x$" (or "LPRINT . . ") so that you get a screen display of the process; if you couple this with the "diagnostic delays" the errors are often resolved. "x" = the string variable in the current operation; in the data sending routine try:

```
35  PRINT A1$
```

This diagnostic was found to be useful in checking data loading from a data store, which we go onto next.

### Data handling

To really begin to unleash the power of the computer controlled SX400, we need to be able to store data collected by the SX400 (in "Logging Mode", for example) or to instruct the SX400 to follow a pre-determined operation; e.g. to monitor and report given frequencies.

Let us begin with a simple example, loading a pre-listed frequency, together with the required mode.

We start with a slightly amended version of the standard data entry routine (see lines 10 to 120):

```
1010  CLOSE: OPEN "COM1 . . . (etc)
1020  DATA 97.6,F,W
1030  READ A1$              :REM Note the change here
1040  F=LEN(A1$)            :REM The next few lines are familiar!
1050  IF F<1 GOTO 1040
1060  FOR A=1 TO F
1070  B$=MID$(A1$,A,1)
1075  ON ERROR GOTO 1120 :REM Detects end of frequency
```

```
1080  PRINT £1,B$;
1090  INPUT £1,C$
1100  NEXT A
1110  PRINT £1,
1120  FOR Z=1 TO 300:NEXT Z
1130  READ E$ : PRINT £1,E$
1140  FOR Y=1 TO 300:NEXT Y
1150  READ F$ : PRINT £1,F$
1160  PRINT "THIS IS CHILTERN RADIO ON 97.6MHz!"
```

This routine was originally devised to amuse the casual onlookers, but it does have a practical application. Many users of this system may not know the actual frequency of the station they wish to monitor; they will know the name, callsign or channel number. Write a simple preamble to the above:

```
900  PRINT "WHAT STATION DO YOU WANT TO LISTEN TO";X$
910  IF X$="CHILTERN RADIO" GOTO 1010
920  IF X$<>"CHILTERN RADIO" PRINT "TRY AGAIN":GOTO 900
```

The above frequency becomes more useful if we can pre-load more than one array of frequency/mode information.

Each array has to be labelled with a number:

```
1020  DATA 1,97.6,F,W,2,145.5,F,N,3,128.6,A,N
1022  READ Z
1024  IF Z=N GOTO 1030
1026  READ W$,X$,Y$
1028  GOTO 1022
1030  READ A1$
1040  F=LEN(A1$)
```

and so on . . .

In the preamble to this, 'N' in line 1024 would have been set to '3' if the user had requested 'VOLMET' (the aircraft weather service). The data array is read until the required label is encountered, whereupon programming commences.

The above routine becomes verbose but none-the-less easy to write for an indefinite number of input situations.

We now progress to saving and loading our data using disc. Starting with the least complicated bit, saving data to disc:

```
2010  CLOSE
2020  OPEN "A:DATA1" FOR OUTPUT AS £2
2030  FOR M=1 TO 20
2040  INPUT "FREQUENCY (Enter x to finish)";A$
2050  IF A$="X" LET M=M−1:GOTO 2100
2060  INPUT "MODE (AM or FM)";B$
```

```
2070  INPUT "Wide or Narrow";C$
2080  WRITE £2,A$,B$,C$
2090  NEXT M
2100  CLOSE £2
2110  PRINT M "MEMORIES NOW SAVED"
```

This will result in a block of up to 20 frequencies ready for loading into the SX400 memories.

In line 2020, 'A:' defines the disc drive. "DATA1" is the filename, change these as required.

And now, to load this data into the SX400 memories we put together some familiar routines:

```
3010  CLOSE:OPEN "COM1 . . . ." (etc)
3020  OPEN "A:DATA1" FOR INPUT AS £2
3030  FOR M=1 TO 20
3040  IF M>12 LET M=M+1
3050  ON ERROR GOTO 3280
3060  INPUT £2,A1$
3065  PRINT A1$                        :REM diagnostic check on data
3070  F=LEN(A1$)
3080  IF F<1 GOTO 3070
3090  FOR A=1 TO F
3100  B$=MID$(A1$,A,1)
3110  ON ERROR GOTO 3150
3120  PRINT £1,B$;
3130  INPUT £1,C$
3140  NEXT A
3150  PRINT £1,
3160  FOR Z=1 TO 300:NEXT Z
3170  INPUT £2,K$:PRINT £1,K$
3180  FOR Y=1 TO 300:NEXT Y
3190  INPUT £2,L$:PRINT £1,L$
3200  FOR X=1 TO 300:NEXT X
3210  PRINT £1,CHR$(72);CHR$(M);
3220  FOR W=1 TO 300:NEXT W
3230  INPUT £1,F$
3240  IF LOC(1)>1 GOTO 3230
3250  PRINT F$
3260  FOR V=1 TO 400:NEXT V
3270  NEXT M
3280  CLOSE £2                  :REM Optional − CLOSE £1
3290  PRINT "MEMORY LOADING COMPLETE" M−1 "MEMORIES
LOADED"
```

## Icom computer control

The Icom R7000 is the easiest of all scanners to put under computer control. The interface unit is so simple that the actual circuit fits inside a 'D'-type plug. The actual interface and the software by Jaytee Electronic Services is in fact a control system that is common to the BBC-B computer and all Icom equipment that has computer interfacing. That means that an amateur with a modern Icom transceiver can use the same system as well and it is in fact possible to simultaneously control more than one scanner or transceiver.

The software is supplied in BASIC and the excellent manual by Jaytee not only gives a detailed description of each of the programme lines but also supplies hints on how to modify the programme to include customised options. The display is not as elaborate as the one used on Lowe's AOR controller but is stilll more than adequate for normal use.

Anyone not having a BBC computer will obviously have to write their own software. The interface is for standard serial RS-232 connection and simple communications write and read lines will be needed as a basis for control. Unlike the AOR RC-Pack, the communications software on it's own is not enough for full control. Although the R7000 will respond to standard RS-232 instructions, the data it sends back will have to be formatted to be useable. This is not quite as daunting as it may sound because Icom do supply a very detailed description of how data is sent back and forth.

The following details apply to the R7000 under BBC-B control but the facilities can be incorporated in programmes written for other computers. There are two connections to the BBC-B. The 'D'-type plug fits into the Joystick port (solely to pick-up power for the interface and provide a connection for the S-meter signal) and the 5-pin Domino DIN-plug goes to the serial port. On the R7000 there are two connections. The first is a 3.5 mm jack plug which goes to the serial port and carries the RS232 write/read signal. The other connection is slightly more complicated and involves opening up the set and connecting a wire between the cathode of diode D15 on the main board and the spare phono socket on the back of the scanner. The remaining yellow wire from the interface is plugged into the phono socket and it is this connection that sends the S-meter signal to the computer. Once the scanner/computer hook-up is complete, the trimmer resistor inside the 'D'-plug has to be adjusted so that the S-meter display on the computer corresponds to the reading on the scanner.

### Additional features
Latest versions of Jaytee's software (release 1.2) have two scan modes; Scan-P and Scan-W. Scan-P stops on a signal but resumes scanning

after a pre-set time lapse (as per FRG-9600). Scan-W operates in the normal way in that it stops on a signal but does not resume until the signal stops. All other features are as follows.

## Icom R700/BBC system

### Facilities
*Set select*   up to four sets, each provided with: frequency/memory/ mode/steps storage; fully independent memories; memory file storage; five user defined 'scan channels'; available mode information
*Mode control*   'step through' selection
*Frequency control*   direct entry; up/down control; step rate select
*Memories*   99 per set —frequency and mode; up/down by channel; direct entry channel number; vfo to memory transfer; memory write; memory clear; memory file read; memory write.
*Scanning*   frequency scan using 'scan channels'; memory scan; mode scan of memory channels; scan pause; scan wait.
*General*   analogue S-meter/bargraph select; channel occupancy display; speech (frequency/mode) requires Acorn speech; real time clock display.

## Icom R7000/BBC control keys

*f0 Frequency*   Allows direct entry of frequency to avoid unnecessary stepping. Input validation is not made, and frequency should be in MHz.
*f1 Mode*   Steps through the available modes for the selected set, and re-transmits the frequency, since mode changes will cause the carrier offset to affect the display of a set with parallel interface. this is nothing to do with the interface, simply the then prevailing cpu system.
*f2 Frequency/memory scan*   With VFO selected, you will be prompted for a scan channel number (0 to 5). Selecting 0 you will be prompted for Upper and Lower frequencies (to be input in MHz). Numbers in the range 1 to 5 will cause scanning in the specified range, at the step rate selected. BEWARE, scanning is possible in transmit mode and is of course ILLEGAL! With memeory selected, scanning proceeds through all non-blank memories, changing mode as necessary.
*f3 Mode scan*   Memories will be selected, if not already, and scanning proceeds, selecting only memories of the appropriate mode. If none exist, scanning stopes.
*f4 VFO->Memory*   Transfers the current VFO frequency and mode to the currently indicated memory channel. No check is made as to whether the memory channel is currently programmed.

*f4 Memory write*  When in memory mode, updates the stored frequency and mode to those on the display.

*f6 Memory clear*  Clears the currently indicated memory channel. This is useful as unwanted frequencies would otherwise be included in memory scans.

*f7 Set 'SIG' level*  Presets, per set, on a scale of 0 to 40, the level at which the SIG indicator lights. This also, unless deselected, is the S-meter level at which scanning will be halted, and where the cassette relay (if selected — see R below) is operated.

*f8 Memory file read*  Prompts for filename which, in a disc system will be in directory 1 to 4 depending on set number, and reads that file, if it exists, into the memories and VFO for currently selected set. This will not work until you write a file (f9 below).

*f9 Memory file write*  As f8, but write operation.

*H HELP*  Presents a help menu page. Press any key to clear.

*< --> Frequency steps (cursor keys)*  Cycles through the KHz per step entries, controlling the rate at which the up/down keys operate.

*/ \\*  Frequency control (up/down cursor keys).

*M*  Select memory channel 1 to 99.

*,.*  Memory channel up/down.

*/ VFO*  Memory changeover (toggle).

*B*  Bargraph/S-meter changeover (toggle).

*@*  Occupancy on-off. Initiates a channel occupancy display, controlled by the SIG indicator across the top of the screen when in frequency scan mode. This is a very simple function, included merely as a starting point (toggle).

*:*  SCAN-P or SCAN-W select (toggle). SCAN-P pauses when a signal is detected and resumes scanning after a preset period. SCAN-W waits when a signal is detected and does not resume scanning until that signal ceases.

*R*  Relay. Enable/disable option where cassette relay is controlled by SIG indicator (toggle).

*S*  Change current set. Selects between the currently enabled sets, retaining VFO/memory/frequency/mode information.

*<del>*  Speaks the currently displayed frequency and mode. This is a function of the computer, requiring the Acorn speech kit, and cannot be made to operate speech in the sets.

*Q*  Quit program and return to menu.

## Yaesu 9600 computer control

The Yaesu 9600 can be controlled in one of two ways. The first is Yaesu's own 'CAT' system which allows the scanner to be controlled by any computer with an RS232 port and suitable software and the second is a system developed separately for the BBC-B, BBC-B+ and BBC Master Computers.

The Yaesu system requires the 'CAT-FIF' interface which allows the computer access to the internal microprocessor in the scanner. It bears close similarity to the Icom system and data is sent back and forth as a series of blocks. This is quite a complex system and anyone wanting to write software for a specific machine will need to have quite a good knowledge of programming. It does mean though that the computer can be programmed to provide a whole range of functions not included on the FRG-9600, the internal processor merely acting as a frequency switcher.

The Yaesu service manual shows a sample programme and although most of it is written in microsoft BASIC there are Poke statements which obviously apply to a specific machine and unfortunately the manual does not say which make of computer this is designed to run on (I have strong suspicion though that it is the MSX).

## BBC system

The system designed to work with the BBC computers (all models except the Master Compact) does away with the need for the Yaesu interface. The system is supplied by Alan Hooker Electronics (42 Nether Hall Road, Doncaster. Tel: (0302) 25690 and was written by Andrew Jost and Peter Clappison. It has also been marketed by Ray Withers Communications and works with their specially modified version of the FRG-9600 which have extended frequency coverage.

### CAT FRG-9600 program

```
LIST
5  REM RESET FIF-65 I/O CHIP
10  POKE 49345,0: POKE 49345,0: POKE 49345,0
15  REM INITIALIZE FIF-65 I/O CHIP
20  POKE 49345,64: POKE 49345,207: POKE 49345,55
30  HOME : PRINT "INPUT (0) — (7) "
40  PRINT " (0).......FREQUENCY SET"
50  PRINT " (1).......FM-WIDE"
60  PRINT " (2).......FM-NARROW"
70  PRINT " (3).......AM-WIDE"
80  PRINT " (5).......AM-NARROW"
90  PRINT " (5).......USB"
100  PRINT " (6).......LSB"
120  PRINT " (7).......END": PRINT
130  INPUT " SELECT 1 — 7 >";A: IF A > 7 THEN 30
135  REM CALL −958 CLEARS ALL BELOW CURSOR
```

```
140  PRINT : IF A = 7 THEN HTAB 1: VTAB 1: CALL — 958: END
150  IF A = 0 THEN N0 = 10: GOTO 1000
160  IF A = 1 THEN N0 = 23
170  IF A = 2 THEN N0 = 22
180  IF A = 3 THEN N0 = 21
190  IF A = 4 THEN N0 = 20
200  IF A = 5 THEN N0 = 17
210  IF A = 6 THEN N0 = 16
220  GOTO 2000
1000 REM FREQUENCY SET
1010 PRINT "INPUT FREQ. (MHZ)"
1020 PRINT " FREQ. RANGE 60.0 — 905.0 (MHZ) ": PRINT
1030 INPUT FR
1040 IF FR < 60.0 OR FR > 905.0 THEN PRINT : PRINT " OUT OF
RANGE !": PRINT : HTAB 10: PRINT "INPUT AGAIN !": FOR I = 0
TO 1000: NEXT : VTAB 14: CALL — 958: GOTO 1020
1050 FR = FR * 10000
1060 M1 = INT (FR / 100000)
1070 M2 = INT (FR / 1000) — M1 * 100
1030 M3 = INT (FR / 10) — M1 * 10000 — M2 * 100
1090 L1 = M1 * 100000:L2 = M2 * 1000:L3 = M3 * 10
1100 M4 = FR — L1 — L2 — L3:M4 = INT (M4 + .5) * 10
1110 N1 = INT (M1 / 10) * 16 + M1 — INT (M1 / 10) * 10
1120 N2 = INT (M2 / 10) * 16 + M2 — INT (M2 / 10) * 10
1130 N3 = INT (M3 / 10) * 16 + M3 — INT (M3 / 10) * 10
1140 N4 = INT (M4 / 10) * 16 + M4 — INT (M4 / 10) * 10
2000 REM SEND 5BYTES VIA FIF—65 to RCVR
2010 POKE 49344,N0: POKE 49344,N1: POKE 49344,N2: POKE
49344,N3: POKE 49 344,N4
2020 GOTO 30
```

The system consists of a programme ROM, interface lead and manual. The ROM is inserted in the usual way and the lead connects between the joystick port of the computer and 6-pin DIN socket on the scanner. The program controls both frequency and mode, provides automatic and manual frequency scanning as well as programming from pre-set stations in the memory. Those pre-set stations can be stored on either tape or disc. The program will also carry out search patterns and can be commanded to do such things as time the duration of signals. Facilities are included within the program for the user to include separate BASIC or machine code routines to carry out specialised operations.

On start-up the standard screen offers a range of options and when any particular one is selected a menu appears requesting the various parameters. These include:

*On screen 'Help'*   Command Summary
*Signal strength*   Bargraph type
*Tape*   on/off
*Frequency*   Input frequency (current frequency is displayed)
*Status*   Shows current program and scanner status
*Mode*   Select, USB, LSB, AM-Narrow, AM-Wide, FM-Narrow, FM-Wide
*Manual Search*   Set start frequency, input stepping rate (increment)
Store to memory, change mode.
*Priority*   Select up to 10 priority channels.
*Auto search*   Store active frequencies found in one pass, in continuous passes, set search range, scan all stations, scan between two stations, scan selected stations.
*Auto search*   Store active frequencies found in one pass, in continuous passes, set search range, scan all stations, scan between two stations, scan selected stations.
*Program from memory*   Program from frequencies stored on tape/disc
*Memory management*   Load, Save, Add new, change station, delete station, view/print stored information.

During the automatic storing routines and normal scanning, the program can be set to record the time of each transmission. Files stored on disc include frequency, mode and station name.

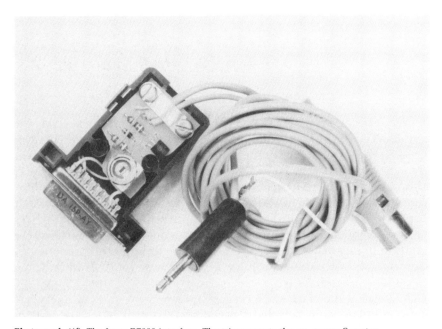

**Photograph 4(f)** The Icom R7000 interface. The trimmer sets the on-screen S-meter

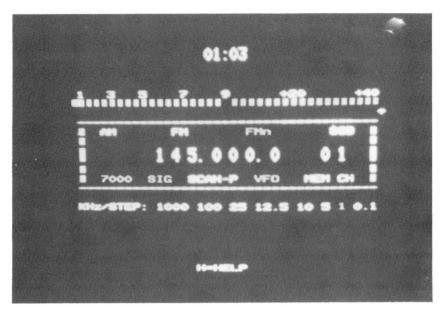

**Photograph 4(g)** Jaytees normal screen for the Icom R7000

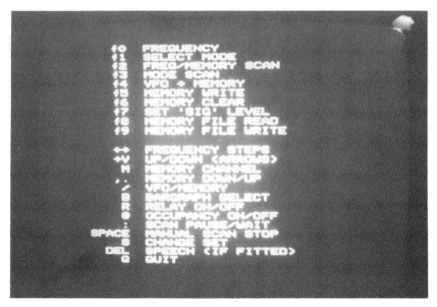

**Photograph 4(h)** Icom R7000 on-screen 'help'

**Photograph 4(i)** The Icom R7000. Simplest computer interface yet

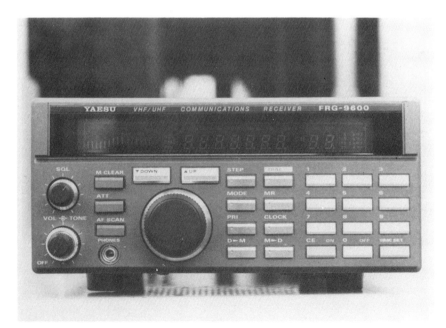

**Photograph 4(j)** FRG-9600. Two methods of computer control

## Conclusions

This is probably the least expensive system yet available commercially for connecting any scanner to a computer. It has very comprehensive facilities and considerable documentation on program parameters for users who can program in machine code or BASIC. However, for the average user, the weakness will be the manual. Something is obviously amiss when a manual has to run nearly 40 pages of A4 size paper. I suggest that programmers should not write their own manuals because they too easily drop into the use of computer jargon which is often baffling to the average user.

# 5 Common faults

## Basic servicing

The majority of the scanners on the market these days are fairly reliable and by and large common faults are known to importers and their agents who can usually be contacted if a problem arises. However, there will no doubt be those occasions when a scanner owner may need to carry out a repair without guidance. The normal rules of troubleshooting apply and the usual warning is given that complex repair work should not be attempted without at least a circuit diagram and test gear such as a signal generator and multi-meter with high impedance input and digital frequency meter.

One of the biggest headaches that can be encountered is trying to troubleshoot and repair devices in the circuit when no known equivalent can be found. The section at the end of this chapter gives a useful range of devices and often by comparing pinouts between those shown and circuit diagrams, a substitute device can be found. This is particularly useful with some ICs from the Far East which are marked with obscure code numbers and some early Regency and Bearcat scanners which have IC's identified only by the equipment makers part number.

## Re-alignment

This is the one area where many service engineers and hobbyists get into difficulties and often it is because complex re-alignment is attempted without good reason. Are you really sure the scanner needs re-aligning? Experience has shown that generally equipment leaves the factory in good alignment and it is rare for circuits to drift off tune unless some component in the tuned circuits has been replaced. All too often though, engineers decide to 'try a tweek here — try a tweek there'. With most synthesised scanners the results can be disastrous and it is then virtually impossible to re-align the circuits without detailed step-by-step procedures from a proper service handbook. It is also virtually impossible to re-align such scanners without proper communication test equipment. So it is a good rule to leave re-alignment alone until other troubleshooting has been carried out. Ask yourself why the set needs re-aligning? Is it because sensitivity seems to be down? If that is your reason then you can almost certainly rule-out re-alignment unless perhaps the set has been subject to violent shock which may have dislodged coils and their tuning slugs. Unless that is so, then a failing semiconductor or voltage regulator is more likely and so is the possibility of a broken or shorted connection in the aerial socket.

### Digital circuitry
The synthesis and microprocessor control circuits in most scanners require specialist repair techniques and many of the components used in these stages will be custom made for the scanner manufacturer. Unless you have a good knowledge of digital and microprocessor circuitry and are confident you can obtain replacement parts, it is best to leave servicing of this area to the manufacturer or their agent. However, do not overlook the obvious. Dry joints, poor connections and failing memory back-up cells can often cause problems which manifest themselves not only as failure to retain memory. Finally, do not forget that many of the IC's appearing in these stages now are CMOS devices which can easily be destroyed by static discharged by a finger. Always play safe and make sure you and your soldering iron are well earthed.

### SX-200 faults
There are several common faults on the SX-200, most of which are known to the manufacturers, their agents and importers. The most common complaints are of low frequency buzz and the centre detector causing the squelch to close on audio peaks. The following notes have been kindly supplied by Revco Electronics and Garex Electronics of Britain.

### LF buzz
The low frequency buzz, which can sound a bit like mains hum, can arise from two different sources which can occur separately or together. If this problem is apparent it is worthwhile affecting the cure for both sources whilst the SX-200 is opened up.
*Problem* Buzz apparent only when the scanner is tuned to the range 140–180 MHz and cuts out when the squelch is closed. This effect is usually caused by stray coupling into the 140–180 MHz VCO from the wiring to the memory back-up battery.
*Cure* Locate the wiring to the memory back-up cells and re-route it away from the underside of the 140–180 MHz box (see Figure 5.1). It may be necessary to actually remove the VCO box and tuck the wiring

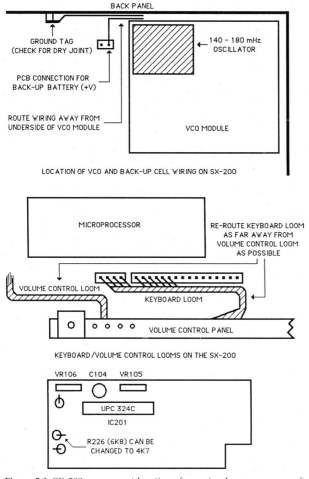

**Figure 5.1** SX-200 component locations for curing known common faults

between the box's end panel and the rear panel of the scanner case.

*Problem*    Buzz apparent at all frequencies and still audible whilst the squelch is closed. This effect is caused by stray coupling between the wiring loom to the volume control and the loom between the micro-processor and keyboard.

*Cure*    Adjusting the two looms as far apart as possible (see diagram). Note that if the squelch PCB is removed, the buzz will get worse because the ground connection to the volume control will be broken. On re-assembly though the buzz should disappear.

*Problem*    Squelch not opening on certain narrow-band signals or closing on audio peaks. If a signal generator is available this effect can be confirmed by tuning the generator through the passband at any selected frequency in any range. Inhibition of the squelch circuit should become apparent.

*Cure*   Re-adjustment of the centre detector should cure this effect and work should proceed as follows. Locate the pre-set resistor RV106 which is on a small plug-in circuit board near the rear panel of the scanner. Measure the voltage on pin 6 of IC201 which is located directly between the left pin of VR106 and the electrolytic capacitor C104. The fine tuning control on the front panel should be set to fully open the squelch on a signal.

By adjusting VR106 and monitoring the voltage on pin 6 of IC201 a voltage of 2.3 and 2.6 volts should be obtained where the squelch closes. Set VR106 to the midpoint between these two extremes. A similar effect to this can be achieved by rotating the core of transformer IF102 on the main circuit board. There should be a span of around 90 degrees between the points where the squelch closes and the core should be set at half way between these points. This should effect a complete cure but if not, one other remedy can be tried. Locate resistor R226 on the sub-board which has IC201 and VR106 on it. The resistor has a value of 6K8 which gives a detector bandwidth of 12 KHz. By changing the value to 4K7 the bandwidth is increased to 20 KHz.

*Problem*   Memory failure. this problem manifests itself as failure to retain memory even with new back-up cells. This problem is associated with poor connections to the back-up cells and particularly affected early (pre-N series) models.

*Cure*   Use a voltmeter to check that there is 3.6 V on the end of the yellow lead which goes to the main circuit board next to the RAM IC D5101LC. If no voltage is present check backwards from this point for dry solder joints or poor connections.


## Bearcat faults

One of the more common faults on Bearcat 220/20–20 scanners is related to the power supply. What makes the problem even more frustrating is that the dual op-amp which forms part of the 9 and 11 volt regulated supply is a LM358 which can be difficult to obtain. Certainly in Britain few of the mail order firms who supply hobbyists seem to stock this device or an equivalent. The IC and the two transistors associated with it seem prone to failure and ironically the same IC is used in the scan-stop circuitry as a window detector and this too has been known to fail.

However let us deal with the commonest fault, the power supply. First of all it is usually very easy to spot the fault if it appears. Should either section fail then the scanner will appear to operate but not receive signals. In other words the display will work and audio will be heard from the loudspeaker but no signals will be present. It is then a

**Photograph 5(a)** Bearcat 220. Power supply problems are common but easily solved.

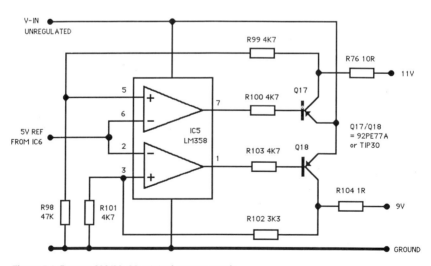

**Figure 5.2** Bearcat 220/20–20 original power supply

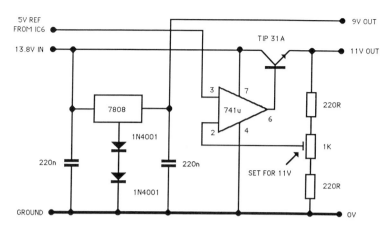

**Figure 5.3** Bearcat 220/20–20 Replacement Power supply

simple matter of checking with a voltmeter which section has failed. Check pins 1 and 7 of IC5 to see if voltage is present. If it is then you are lucky and it will be the relevant pass transistor which has blown. Simply replace the transistor with a suitable equivalent. On the other hand if either pin 1 or 7 shows no voltage then it can be assumed that the IC has failed. You are now left with two options. First you can replace the IC if you can get one. If not, do not despair as a new circuit can be built from readily available components. Refer to Figure 5.3 and you will see that the new circuit consists of two distinct sections.

The first is a 7808 regulator 'jacked-up' to give an output of 9 volts. The second is a simple IC/pass transistor regulator which uses the 5.4 volt output of IC6 as a reference. The whole circuit can be built on a small board and there is plenty of room inside the scanner to fit it with suitable input/output leads to the points marked on the circuit diagram. It is not possible to use an IC regulator for the 11 volt supply. The nearest IC is a 7812 and this requires a minimum input of 14.5 volts. When these scanners are used with their internal mains supply this is not a problem but it will become one if the scanner is used mobile or on a standard 13.8 volt mains power pack.

## Installation and testing

Before any attempt is made to connect the new power supply, certain components have to be removed from the scanner's circuit board. These are IC5, transistors Q17/Q18 and resistors 101, 102, 98 and 99. With the new circuit board mounted in a suitable location, connections are made to the points shown. Set the pre-set resistor on the new circuit so that the wiper is closest to the 220 Ohm resistor which goes to ground. Switch the power on and connect the voltmeter to the end of the resistor R76 furthest from the new power supply, i.e. the end that goes to the scanner circuitry. Now slowly adjust the preset resistor for a reading of 11 volts. Check that there are 9 volts on the end of the resistor R104 at the point where it goes to the scanner circuitry. Finally, it is possible of course to simply use either section of the new regulator circuit to replace whichever half of IC5 has failed. However for the sake of just a few components it is hardly worthwhile. The replacement circuit is more robust than the original.

### Squelch

As mentioned already, the same IC is used as a window detector in the squelch circuitry. The fault usually first appears as a shift in the normal position of the squelch control. Attempts to adjust the setting of the internal pre-set tight-squelch control has no effect and when the panel control is set to cut noise, only the strongest of signals will open up the circuit.

Again, the difficulty may arise in finding a replacement IC. In an extreme case (i.e. you either do something or drop the scanner in a dustbin), I can only suggest that you very carefully remove the power supply IC and use that. You will then of course have to replace the power supply with the circuitry described above. This may seem not only an extreme suggestion but one that also verges on the absurd. However, I know of at least two sets where in desperation, this method of affecting a cure was used — you do of course also end up with a better power supply.

Take great care when removing the IC. It is soldered on both sides of the PCB which means a proper solder sucker is a must if you are going to get it without causing heat damage.

### AOR faults

Both AOR models seem to be relatively free of any major problems but there are two quirks that are common to both the 2001 and 2002.

The first is a tendency for the set to either be slightly off tune right from purchase or this problem may occur a little while after the set has been purchased. I have serviced a number of sets with this problem and in all cases it was simply the VCO slightly off-tune. I can only imagine that some samples of the scanner are fitted with crystals that have not been aged properly. The cure is quite simple. On the PLL board you will see the 6.4 MHz crystal with a trimmer close to it (in fact it is one of the few trimming capacitors you will find in circuitry). Use a DFM to measure the output on the emitter of Q9 (2SC3355) and adjust for 6.4 MHz as closely as possible.

The second quirk concerns the BNC antenna socket. Surprisingly it is a relatively poor quality component with flimsy centre pin contacts. At best it gives poor UHF performance and at worst, the contact pins often break, particularly where aerial connections are regularly swapped. It is not very easy to change it and quite fiddly but well worth the effort. Replace it with the best quality component you can find.

## Ceramic and crystal filters

Although it is highly unlikely that a ceramic or crystal filter will fail, it is at least useful to be able to identify these devices so that the associated circuitry can be traced. There may also be occasions when a technically competent scanner owner may wish to replace these devices in order to improve or alter performance.

Nearly all scanners work on multi-conversion principles and at least one ceramic or crystal filter will be found somewhere in the IF stages. Some scanners such as the AORs have a relatively high 1st IF of around 45 MHz prior to final conversion down to 455 KHz. Many other sets though, such as the SX-200, most Bearcats and many Realistic models and hand portables use a conventional dual conversion based on frequencies of 10.7 MHz and 455 kHz.

Some of the more compact FM hand portables rely entirely on the 455 kHz filter to determine the bandpass characteristics, typically about 12 kHz. The filter included in the preceding IF usually consists of nothing more than a 50 kHz/BW ceramic roofing filter which does little more than make the job of the 455 kHz slightly easier by cleaning up strong signals from some of the adjacent frequencies to which the scanner is tuned. Many other dual conversion sets such as the earlier Bearcat models replace the rather broadband ceramic filter with a 2-pole crystal type with a narrower 15 kHz bandwidth. This generally gives better results by cleaning up adjacent sidebands a lot more effectively so giving the 455 kHz filter a better chance of rejecting unwanted signals.

One device that is easily mistaken for a filter is the 455D discriminator. It looks very much like a typical plastics cased 455 kHz ceramic filter, but is in fact solely a coilless discriminator and performs no function in determining signal bandwidth.

### 10.7 MHz filters

Two basic types will be encountered. The first is the small, three lead, ceramic type which has a non-metallic casing. It has a typical 50 kHz bandwidth characteristic and is produced by a number of manufacturers, typically Toko, Kyocera, NTKK, Murata, etc. The types

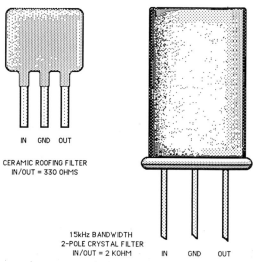

IN    GND    OUT

CERAMIC ROOFING FILTER
IN/OUT = 330 OHMS

15kHz BANDWIDTH
2-POLE CRYSTAL FILTER
IN/OUT = 2 KOHM        IN        GND        OUT

**Figure 5.4**

designated 10.7MU and SFA10.7MF are commonly found in hand portables and they have an input/output impedance of 300 Ohms. It is not possible to directly replace them with the better 2-pole crystal ceramic types unless some form of matching to the 3 kOhm impedance of the latter can be made. Missmatches of this magnitude will seriously degrade the passband characteristics of these or indeed any filters. The input/output connections of these filters are interchangeable, i.e. the filters are bi-directional.

The 10.7 MHz 2-pole crystal types offer considerably better performance and in the SX-200 the response is sharpened even further by cascading two of these devices. There is no reason why this system should not be adopted as a modification for other scanners but do note that there will be some insertion loss and it is advisable to include a 2 pF capacitor between ground and the output to input connection between the two filters.

## 2-pole crystal filter specifications

| Type | FCY MHz | BW kHz | Ripple dB | Stopband kHz @ −dB | SR dB | Insert loss dB | Zt kOhms |
|------|---------|--------|-----------|--------------------|-------|----------------|----------|
| 10M15A | 10.7 | 15 | 0.5 | ±25@18 | −18 | 2.0 | 3 |
| 10M08AA | 10.695 | 8* | 0.5 | ±25@18 | −18 | 2.0 | 1.8 |

*@6db

Like the ceramic types these filters are bi-directional. They are housed in a hermetically sealed metal case the same size as an HCU18 crystal.

### 455 kHz filters

The 455 kHz filters are limited to different sizes and there is a slight difference in their performance. Although they conform to a similar size, shape and pin configuration between the several manufacturers who produce them, their specification does vary and it is sometimes difficult to determine what bandwidth they are. The devices are not bi-directional and a look at Figure 5.5 will show that inputs and outputs are clearly marked. Despite their extensive use these filters will not directly match into the MC3357 and matching transformers are required. They will however match directly into the newer version of this IC, the MC3359/ULN3859.

### Ceramic filters for 455 kHz

| Part number | Bandwidth rank | 6dB bandwidth (kHz) min | Attenuation bandwidth (kHz Max) | Stop Band Att (dB) min. CFU CFW LFB LFG | | Insertion loss (dB) Max | In/Out impedance (kOhm) |
|---|---|---|---|---|---|---|---|
| CFU455B2/ CFW455B | B | ±15 | ±30 | 27 | 35 | 4.0 | 1K5 |
| CFU455C2/ CFW455C/ LFG12S/ LFB12 | C | ±12.5 | ±24 | 27 | 35 | 4.0 | 1K5 2K0 |
| CFU455D2/ CFW455D | D | ±10 | ±15 | 27 | 35 | 6.0 | 1K0 |
| LFH8S/LFB8 | | ±8 | ±15 | 27 | 35 | 6.0 | 2K0 |
| CFU455F2/ CFW455F/ LFH6S/LFB6 | F | ±6 | ±12 | 27 | 35 | 6.0 | 2K0 |

It can be seen from the above list that a lot of filters are interchangeable in order to increase or reduce the bandwidth characteristic. An important guide to the bandwidth of filters with an unfamiliar coding is the bandwidth rank letter. It seems to be the only standard identification amongst manufacturers and letters higher than those shown will usually indicate a narrower characteristic (6dB), G=4.5 kHz, H=3 kHz, I=2 kHz, etc.

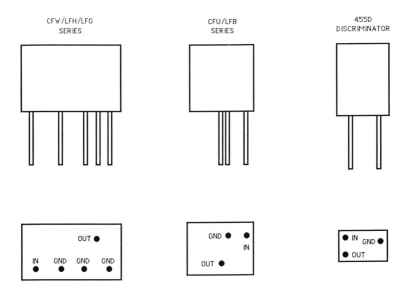

**Figure 5.5** 455 kHz ceramic filters and discriminator (see text and tables for specifications)

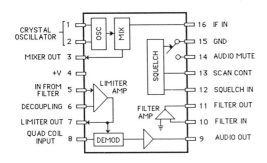

**Figure 5.6** The MC3357 — universally used as an FM IF/demodulator/squelch

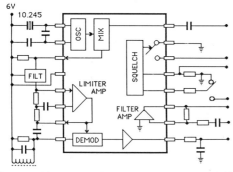

## Integrated circuits

Without any shadow of doubt the most common IC found in scanners is the MC3357 IF/Demodulator/Squelch chip. This IC is a classic design and is found in most scanners that have FM. Figure 5.6 shows the pin-outs and internal functions and is included here to allow anyone servicing this area of a scanner to recognise the various stages.

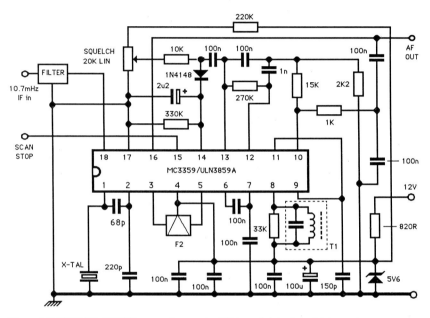

**Figure 5.7** 10.7 MHz/455 kHz second converter/IF/demodulator/squelch/scan stop

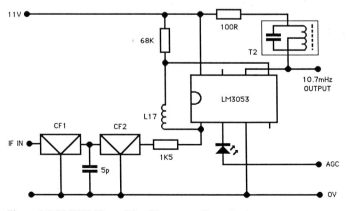

**Figure 5.8** LM3053 IF amplifier (Bearcat configuration)

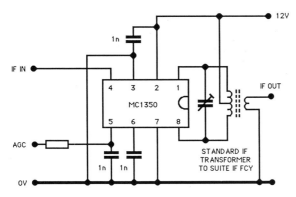

**Figure 5.9** MC1350 IF amplifier with AGC

Do note though that failure of the IC itself is highly unlikely unless of course the scanner has been subject to an abnormally high input voltage.

The IC is now being superceded by the MC3359 which is basically the same IC but with some improvements such as direct matching to ceramic filters. It is likely that new scanner designs will incorporate this device.

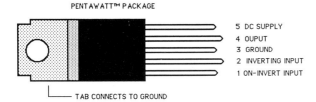

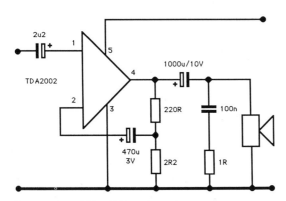

**Fig 5.10** Typical TDA2002 configuration

## Other circuits

Another classic IC is the TDA2002 8 watt audio amplifier which is found in a range of scanners and Figure 5.10 shows the pin-outs. I have never known one of these devices to fail but of course excessive voltage or similar misstreatment could cause problems.

The only other ICs that are common to a variety of scanners are voltage regulators and some IF gain-block circuits which are covered in the chapter on accessories.

## Transistors

In view of the thousands of different types of transistors available it is perhaps surprising that the types commonly found in scanners seem to be restricted to a fairly small number. The list included here covers the more common types and shows American and European equivalents for the various Japanese types.

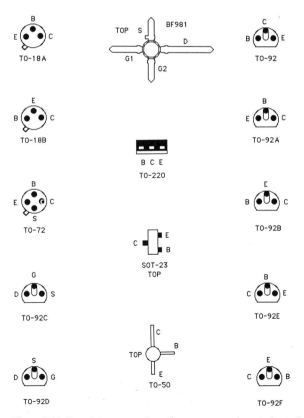

**Figure 5.11** Transistor connections (bases except where indicated)

## Transistor equivalents

| Device | Type | Base | Equivalents |
|---|---|---|---|
| MPS H17A | NPN UHF Silicon | TO92B | BF357/BF337(TO92A) |
| MPS 3393 | NPN Silicon | TO92 | 2N3393(TO92), BC383/ BC548(TO92A) . |
| MPS 3640 | PNP Silicon | TO92E | 2N36499(TO92A) |
| 2N5179 | NPN VHF Silicon | TO72 | 2N5053/2N5054(TO72) BF357/Bf377(TO92A) |
| 2SA642 | PNP Silicon | TO92 | BC178(TO18A), BC213(TO92A), 2N2906/2N2907(TO18A) |
| 2SA733 | PNP Silicon | | BC177(TO18A), BC213(TO92A), 2N2906/2N2907(TO18A) |
| 2SC536 | NPN Silicon | TO92 | BC107(TO18A), 2N2220/21/22(TO18A) |
| 2SC945 | NPN Silicon | TO92 | As 2SC536 |
| 2SC1070 | NPN UHF Silicon | TO92A | BF357(TO92A), BF362/ BF363(TO50) BF377(TO92A) |
| 2SC1623 | NPN 40 V Silicon | Sot23 | BCW71/BCW72/ BCX70(all Sot23) |
| 2SC1674 | NPN 40 V Silicon | | BF199/BF244/BF311(all TO92B) |
| 2SC1675 | NPN Silicon | TO92 | BF241/BF255(TO92B), BF455(TO18B) |
| 2SC1730 | NPN UHF Silicon | TO92 | BF180/BF183(TO72), BF377(TO92B) |
| 2SD227 | NPN Silicon. 3A | TO92 | BC338(TO92A), BC378(TO18A), 2N2220/1/2(TO18A) |
| 2SK68 | N-FET | | BF244(TO92C), BF245(TO92D), 2N382(TO72C) |
| 92 PE 77A | PNP Power | | TIP30(TO220), 2N6708, BD240(TO220) |

## Long distance scanning (DX)

I put long distance scanning in the same category as satellite reception; when you tire of listening to the local traffic you can get your scanner to show what a versatile piece of equipment it really is.

For the most part of course the scanner owner has little option but to listen to local communications because by and large at VHF and UHF we are limited to a theoretical line of sight range. There are however exceptions to the rule. Effects such as Sporadic-E and Tropospherical ducting can mean reception of VHF and UHF signals from hundreds if not thousands of miles away.

### Skywave
Below 150 MHz any 'freak' conditions and long distance reception will be mostly due to signals bouncing off the Ionosphere and back to Earth. This is known as the Skywave and during some periods its effect on the lower frequencies (less than 50 MHz) can be quite dramatic. At the peak of the eleven year sunspot cycles it is occasionally possible to receive transmissions from the other side of the world. The last peak was during 1980 and in the two years before and after that year there were regular 'lifts'. In Europe the first clue to a lift was the reception of strong Citizens Band signals from the USA and simultaneously, the American operators were also able to hear strong signals from Europe. Tuning between 30 and 35 MHz often produced strong reception of mobile communications from the USA. Although opinion varies amongst radio enthusiasts on when the best reception occurs, my own experience during the last peak was that late morning to afternoon and late evening to midnight or later were the best times. Although I have seen claims in some technical journals

that the best reception occurs during the winter, my own experience last time was that the summer produced a greater number of lifts.

## USA reception

So that readers may have some kind of indication of what they are listening to, a list is included of some of the stations that operate in the band 30–37 MHz. The list has been specially compiled to only include stations in those states which can be heard in Europe during sunspot cycle peaks.

One further clue to an impending lift is the reception of some of the 10 metre band FM repeater stations in the USA. These lifts are entirely random, by the way. You may get regular reception for several months on a daily basis and then suddenly nothing with stations appearing again a few days, weeks or even months later. To some extent the unpredictable nature of reception adds to the thrill of hearing communication traffic thousands of miles away.

European listeners will be interested to know that in the USA there is a far more liberal view of listening-in to communications as a hobby and many stations will actually acknowledge a signal report from you. It will seem astounding to some Europeans that some American military stations actually keep a stock of specially printed QSL cards to send on receiving a signal report.

## Tropospherical ducting

Long distance communication via Tropospherical ducting is not quite as dramatic as Skywave propagation but does provide useful lifts occasionally on the UHF bands and even the Microwaves as well. The effect is not connected with sunspot cycles but is due to a meeting of warm and cold air streams in the Troposphere at a height of about 2 kM above the earth's surface. The Dielectric effect created where the streams meet provides a good conductor for signals. Some enthusiasts believe that fog somehow provides a conductive path for signals but this is not so. The truth of the matter is that the meeting of cool and hot air streams often produces fog and so when lifts occur during foggy weather this is due to Tropospherical Ducting.

The effect occurs mostly during the summer with a lesser number of lifts during the autumn and spring and only occasional openings during the winter. The first clues of an impending 'Tropo' lift is the presence of high barometric pressure over a large area. The best reception often occurs just as the high pressure starts to collapse.

One of the vagaries of 'Tropo' is that the effect does not consistently cover all the VHF and UHF bands. I have heard strong signals from distant 23CM amateur beacons hundreds of miles away but at the same time not been able to hear 70CM or 2 metre signals at far less distance.

Another clue that some kind of Tropo lift is on is when wavey patterns start to appear on UHF television channels or when a second station occasionally breaks over the station you are trying to watch. Check the bands and you should find at least one of them active. Amateur bands provide a useful guide because there are so many of them spread across the spectrum that they will give a good indication of which frequencies are being affected. Unlike commercial or government communication, the amateur bands are always active if only with beacons, or even the regular identification transmissions in morse from repeater stations which are transmitted every few minutes even if the repeater is not being used.

**FM radio broadcasts**
The introduction of wide band FM on some of the more recently manufactured scanners has opened up a new aspect to DX-ing and that is the reception of broadcast FM radio stations. Throughout the world there are already thousands of enthusiasts who use ordinary broadcast receivers for this type of reception and one of the advantages of this well established hobby is that nearly all broadcast stations will acknowledge reception reports with a proper QSL card. If you intend to start collecting cards then you will need to get hold of a proper guide to broadcast stations which will not only list them by frequency but will also give an address for reception reports. Without a doubt the finest publication is the World Radio TV Handbook. The 'WRTH' is published annually and has now been going for 40 years and is probably the most comprehensive guide to broadcast radio and television stations produced anywhere. It runs to more than 600 pages and is published by Billboard Publications and can be obtained through most book shops.

**Frequencies**
The main FM broadcast bands will be found between 87.5 and 108 MHz although in Britain a section of that band between 97.6 and 108 Mhz is also allocated for Land Mobile use. Some countries do not have the entire 87.5 to 108 MHz span allocated for broadcasting and may use only a segment of that band.

In some Eastern Bloc countries a range of different frequencies are used and these are typically between 66 and 74 MHz and 76 to 87.5 MHz (The allocations chart for Region 1 gives a more specific listing). Some of the transmitters operating at the lower end of these bands can be heard over considerable distances during lifts and at times I have heard broadcasts from more than 1000 kM distance.

The other variation of note occurs in Japan where the main band is allocated between 80 and 89 MHz.

Any signal reports sent to these stations should include not only a standard SIO (SINPO reports have now been dropped) report but also some details of the contents of the programme heard as proof that you really did hear the station's transmission. Broadcasters are also often interested to know what other distant stations you heard at the same time. Engineers often find these reports quite useful and show their appreciation not only by sending a QSL card in return but also other items such as station pennants, badges, posters, etc.

## SIO reporting

The report you send to a station should show the logging time in Hours UTC (formerly GMT) and the SIO listing now in regular use is given below.

| Meaning | 1 | 2 | 3 | 4 | 5 |
|---|---|---|---|---|---|
| S  Signal Strength | Barely Heard | Poor | Fair | Good | Excellent |
| I  Interference | Extreme | Heavy | Moderate | Slight | None |
| O  Overall | Unusable | Poor | Fair | Good | Excellent |

## DX aerials

The Discone is far from ideal for DX-ing. Signals will be weak and the more gain that is available at the antenna, the better. For broadcast FM radio reception a commercially made multi-element Yagi is the ideal choice and this should be mounted on a rotator. If you can fit a masthead pre-amplifier then this is even better. There will no doubt be occasions when some DX is heard on the Discone but during these conditions it is a fair bet that you are missing even more distant stations by not having a better antenna system. Although most FM broadcasts use horizontal polarisation there are some vertical and slant polarised transmissions also.

For general DX-ing the best choice is probably a Log Periodic (see Chapter on Antennas). Although this is an expensive item, specially if you add a rotator and broadband amplifier, it is the best all round choice if you intend to regularly listen for distant stations.

There is no reason of course why you cannot use a range of antennas such as high gain Yagis stack mounted on a heavy rotator. The swapping of antenna connections at the scanner can be a bit tedious but best results will always be obtained with an antenna designed for a specific band.

European scanner owners who want to hear stations in the 30–37 MHz band shown in the listing will find that some high gain Citizens Band antennas can be effectively used. My own antenna, A GPE-27, has a quoted range of up to 35 MHz when the tuning tip is fully collapsed and during the last Sunspot Cycle this antenna pulled-in many stations from the USA. All these transmissions are vertically polarised. Pre-amplifiers are recommended even at these low frequencies and for best results a tuneable amplifier which can be peaked-up is the best choice and a suitable design is shown elsewhere.

## General tips

If you intend to listen-out regularly for distant stations then it is essential that you keep some kind of log book. There is nothing more frustrating when DX-ing than not really knowing what you are doing and unless you start to keep some kind of record of what you hear, when you hear it and conditions at the time, you will not be able to keep track of the patterns that become established. The direction from which DX is coming, the weather (pressure especially), the time of day, the time of year and similar information can all provide important clues for future use. When signs of a lift occur, a look back across your log book may save you hours of fruitless searching on dead bands. You can see what happened under similar conditions last time and know where to start hunting.

The log book does not need to be anything elaborate. An old exercise book will do fine but you should jot down as much information as possible. Do not treat it like an amateur radio log book where just basic information is noted but use it more like a diary by recording not just factual information on distant stations received but also various conditions that prevailed at the time and your overall impressions. It is surprising how quickly our memory of events fades and there will come a time when you will be glad you jotted down so much detail.

## TV reception

Although there are a few hobbyists that bother to just listen-out for Television sound (you can also hear the buzz of the vision signal as well of course), these signals can again provide useful clues on which bands are open. In particular the transmissions at about 45 MHz can travel thousands of kilometres under certain lift conditions. For scanner users who want to listen for these signals a list is included of some of the more common systems in operation around the world.

## Television systems

| System | Lines | Channel width | Vision b/width | Vision/sound separation | Vestigal sideband | Modulation Vision | Sound |
|--------|-------|---------------|----------------|-------------------------|-------------------|-------------------|-------|
| A | 405 | 5 | 3 | −3.5 | 0.75 | POS | AM |
| B | 625 | 7 | 5 | +5.5 | 0.75 | NEG | FM |
| C | 625 | 7 | 5 | +5.5 | 0.75 | POS | AM |
| D | 625 | 8 | 6 | +6.5 | 0.75 | NEG | FM |
| G | 625 | 8 | 5 | +5.5 | 0.75 | NEG | FM |
| H | 625 | 8 | 5 | +5.5 | 1.25 | NEG | FM |
| I | 625 | 8 | 5.5 | +6 | 1.25 | NEG | FM |
| K | 625 | 8 | 6 | +6.5 | 0.75 | NEG | FM |
| K+ | 625 | 8 | 6 | +6.5 | 1.25 | NEG | FM |
| L | 625 | 8 | 6 | +6.5 | 1.25 | POS | AM |
| M | 525 | 8 | 4.2 | +4.5 | 0.75 | NEG | FM |
| N | 625 | 8 | 4.2 | +4.5 | 0.75 | NEG | FM |

All frequencies are in MegaHertz.

## International television channels

| Channel | Frequency MHz | Channel | Frequency MHz |
|---------|---------------|---------|---------------|

Australia — System 'B' — 625 lines

| Channel | Frequency MHz | Channel | Frequency MHz |
|---------|---------------|---------|---------------|
| 0 | 46.25/51.75 | 6 | 175.25/180.75 |
| 1 | 57.25/62.75 | 7 | 182.25/187.75 |
| 2 | 64.25/69.75 | 8 | 189.25/194.75 |
| 3 | 86.25/91.75 | 9 | 196.25/201.75 |
| 4 | 95.24/100.75 | 10 | 209.25/214.75 |
| 5 | 102.25/107.75 | 11 | 216.25/221.75 |
| 5A | 102.25/107.75 | | |

Peoples Republic of China — System 'D' — 625 lines

| Channel | Frequency MHz | Channel | Frequency MHz |
|---------|---------------|---------|---------------|
| C1 | 49.75/56.25 | C6 | 168.25/174.75 |
| C2 | 57.75/64.25 | C7 | 176.25/182.75 |
| C3 | 65.75/72.25 | C8 | 184.25/190.75 |
| C4 | 77.25/91.75 | C9 | 192.25/198.75 |
| C5 | 85.25/91.75 | C10 | 200.25/206.75 |
| | | C11 | 208.25/214.75 |
| | | C12 | 216.25/222.75 |

## International television channels *continued*

| Channel | Frequency MHz | Channel | Frequency MHz |
|---------|---------------|---------|---------------|

**Europe (excluding France, Italy, Monaco, United Kingdom and OIRT members — System 'B' — 625 lines**

| Channel | Frequency MHz | Channel | Frequency MHz |
|---------|---------------|---------|---------------|
| E–2 | 48.25/53.75 | E–7 | 189.25/194.75 |
| E–2A | 49.75/54.25 | E–8 | 196.25/201.75 |
| E–3 | 55.25/60.75 | E–9 | 203.25/208.75 |
| E–4 | 62.25/67.75 | E–10 | 210.25/215.75 |
| E–5 | 175.25/180.75 | E–11 | 217.25/222.75 |
| E–6 | 182.25/187.75 | E–12 | 224.25/229.75 |

**France & Monaco — System 'L' – 625 lines**

| Channel | Frequency MHz | Channel | Frequency MHz |
|---------|---------------|---------|---------------|
| 2 | 49.25/55.75 | 7 | 192.00/198.50 |
| 3 | 54.00/50.50 | 8 | 200.00/206.50 |
| 4 | 57.25/63.75 | 9 | 208.00/214.50 |
| 5 | 176.00/182.50 | 10 | 216.00/222.50 |
| 6 | 184.00/190.50 | | |

**French Colonies & Protectorates — System 'K+' – 625 lines**

| Channel | Frequency MHz | Channel | Frequency MHz |
|---------|---------------|---------|---------------|
| K–4 | 175.25/181.75 | K–7 | 207.25/213.75 |
| K–5 | 183.25/189.75 | K–8 | 207.25/213.75 |
| K–6 | 191.25/197.75 | K–9 | 215.25/221.75 |

**Italy — System 'B' — 625 lines**

| Channel | Frequency MHz | Channel | Frequency MHz |
|---------|---------------|---------|---------------|
| A | 53.75/59.25 | F | 191.25/197.75 |
| B | 62.25/67.75 | G | 201.25/206.75 |
| C | 82.25/87.75 | H | 201.25/206.75 |
| D | 171.25/180.75 | H1 | 217.25/222.75 |
| E | 183.75/189.25 | | |

**Republic of Ireland — System 'I' — 625 lines**

| Channel | Frequency MHz | Channel | Frequency MHz |
|---------|---------------|---------|---------------|
| A | 45.75/51.75 | F | 191.25/205.25 |
| B | 53.75/59.75 | G | 199.25/205.25 |
| C | 61.75/67.75 | H | 207.25/213.25 |
| D | 175.25/181.25 | I | 215.25/221.25 |
| E | 183.25/189.25 | J | 223.25/229.25 |

**International television channels** *continued*

| Channel | Frequency MHz | Channel | Frequency MHz |
|---------|---------------|---------|---------------|
| Japan — System 'M' — 525 lines | | J–7 | 189.25/193.75 |
| J–1 | 91.25/95.75 | J–8 | 193.25/197.75 |
| J–2 | 97.25/101.75 | J–9 | 199.25/203.75 |
| J–3 | 103.25/107.75 | J–10 | 205.25/209.75 |
| J–4 | 171.25/175.75 | J–11 | 211.25/215.75 |
| J–5 | 177.25/181.75 | J–12 | 217.25/221.75 |
| J–6 | 183.25/187.75 | | |
| | | | |
| Morocco — System 'B' — 625 lines | | | |
| M4 | 175.25/168.75 | M8 | 195.25/200.75 |
| M5 | 171.25/176.75 | M9 | 203.25/208.75 |
| M6 | 179.25184.75 | M10 | 211.25/216.75 |
| M7 | 187.25/192.75 | | |
| | | | |
| New Zealand — System 'B' — 625 lines | | | |
| 1 | 45.25/50.75 | 6 | 189.25/194.75 |
| 2 | 55.25/60.75 | 7 | 196.25/201.75 |
| 3 | 62.25/27.75 | 8 | 203.25/208.75 |
| 4 | 175.25/180.75 | 9 | 210.25/215.75 |
| 5 | 182.25/187.75 | | |
| | | | |
| Republic of South Africa — System 'I' — 625 lines | | | |
| 4 | 175.25/181.25 | 9 | 215.25/221.25 |
| 5 | 183.25/189.25 | 10 | 223.25/229.25 |
| 6 | 191.25/197.25 | 11 | 231.25/237.25 |
| 7 | 199.25/205.25 | 13 | 247.43/253.43 |
| 8 | 207.25/213.25 | | |
| | | | |
| United States of America — System 'M' — 525 lines | | | |
| A–2 | 55.25/59.75 | A–7 | 175.25/179.75 |
| A–3 | 61.25/65.75 | A–8 | 181.25/185.75 |
| A–4 | 67.25/71.75 | A–9 | 187.25/191.75 |
| A–5 | 77.25/81.75 | A–10 | 193.25/197.75 |
| A–6 | 83.25/87.75 | A–11 | 199.25/203.75 |
| | | A–12 | 204.25/209.75 |
| | | A–13 | 211.25/215.75 |

## International television channels *continued*

| Channel | Frequency MHz | | Channel | Frequency MHz |
|---------|---------------|---|---------|---------------|
| USSR and O.I.R.T. Members — System 'D' — 625 lines | | | | |
| R1 | 49.75/56.25 | | R6 | 175.25/181.75 |
| R2 | 59.25/65.75 | | R7 | 183.25/189.75 |
| R3 | 77.25/83.75 | | R8 | 191.25/197.75 |
| R4 | 85.25/91.75 | | R9 | 199.25/205.75 |
| R5 | 93.25/99.75 | | R10 | 207.53/213.75 |
| | | | R11 | 215.25/221.75 |
| | | | R12 | 223.25/229.75 |

## US–30

| Base | Mobile | Service | Users |
|------|--------|---------|-------|
| 30.010 | | SPACE | NASA Allocation |
| 30.020 | | SPACE | NOAA Allocation |
| 30.030 | | SPACE | Geological Survey Allocation |
| 30.040 | | SPACE | Satellite Ident |
| 30.050 | | SPY | Secret Service 4 digit group broadcasts |
| 30.060 | | INT/COMM | Dept of the Interior/Dept of Commerce |
| 30.070 | | INT/COMM | Dept of the Interior/Dept of Commerce |
| 30.080 | | INT/COMM | Dept of the Interior/Dept of Commerce |
| 30.090 | | INT/COMM | Dept of the Interior/Dept of Commerce |
| 30.10 | | PSS | Parks |
| 30.10 | | MIL | Army |
| 30.11 | | MIL | Army |
| 30.12 | | MIL | Army |
| 30.17 to 30.24 | | INT/COMM | Dept of the Interior/Dept of Commerce |
| 30.25 | | SPY | Secret Service 4 Digit group broadcasts |
| 30.26 | | PARKS | National Parks Service |

**US–30** *continued*

| Base | Mobile | Service | Users |
|------|--------|---------|-------|
| 30.29 | | MIL | Army |
| 30.30 | | MIL | Army |
| 30.31 | | MIL | Army |
| 30.33 | | CGD | Coast Guard |
| 30.36 | | CGDR | Coast Guard Reserve |
| 30.38 | | CGDR | Coast Guard Reserve |
| 30.41 | | CGD | Coast Guard Reserve |
| 30.42 | | SPY | Secret Service 4 digit group broadcasts |
| 30.43 | | CGD | Coast Guard |
| 30.47 | | SPY | Secret Service 4 digit group broadcasts |
| 30.50 | | MIL | Army |
| 30.51 | | MIL | Army |
| 30.54 | | MIL | Navy MARS Military affiliated radio system |
| 30.565 | | IND | Industrial equipment, Press relays, Telephone repairs, Utilities |
| 30.58 | | IND | Special Industrial |
| 30.60 | | IND | Special Industrial |
| 30.62 | | IND | Special Industrial |
| 30.64 | | IND | Special Industrial |
| 30.66 | | URBAN | Urban transport and Property Agencies |
| 30.66 | | IND | Petroleum Companies |
| 30.66 | | URBAN | Buses |
| 30.68 | | PSS | Forestry Allocation |
| 30.70 | | IND | Petroleum Companies |
| 30.72 | | PSS | Forestry |
| 30.74 | | URBAN | Transport/Property Agents |
| 30.74 | | IND | Petroleum Companies |
| 30.74 | | URBAN | Buses (Supervisors) |
| 30.76 | | BMR | Business users |
| 30.76 | | BMR | Bob Jones University (Greenville South Carolina) |
| 30.78 | | IND | Petroleum Companies |
| 30.80 | | BMR | Business users |
| 30.80 | | BMR | Wildwater Expeditions (West Virginia) |

**US–30** *continued*

| Base | Mobile | Service | Users |
|------|--------|---------|-------|
| 30.80 | | BMR | Milwaukee War Memorial (Wisconsin) |
| 30.82 | | URBAN | Transport/Property Agencies |
| 30.82 | | IND | Petroleum Companies |
| 30.82 | | IND | Petroleum Companies |
| 30.82 | | URBAN | Transport/Property Agencies |
| 30.82 | | URBAN | Pennsylvania Port Authority (transit) |
| 30.84 | | BMR/UNIV | Business/Universities (mobile-to-mobile) |
| 30.84 | | UNIV | University of Idaho (Moscow) |
| 30.84 | | UNIV | University of Indiana (Bloomington) |
| 30.84 | | BMR | Business users |
| 30.84 | | UNIV | State University NY Athletics |
| 30.84 | | UNIV | Oregon State University (Corvallis) |
| 30.84 | | UNIV | Pennsylvania State University (Statewide) |
| 30.84 | | BMR | Business users (2 Watt Max) |
| 30.86 | | PSS | Forestry |
| 30.86 | | Urban | Transport/Property Agencies |
| 30.86 | | URBAN | Manchester Parks/Recreation dept (New Hampshire) |
| 30.86 | | URBAN | S. Carolina Dept of Health and Environment |
| 30.88 | | BMR | Business users |
| 30.88 | | BMR | International Pavilion (Leesberg Virginia) |
| 30.90 | | PSS/URBAN | Forestry & Transport/Property agencies |
| 30.90 | | URBAN | South Carolina Dept of Health and Environment |
| 30.90 | | URBAN | Pennsylvania Port Authority (Transit) |
| 30.90 | | PSS | Kentucky Dept of Forestry/Natural Resources |
| 30.94 | | PSS | Kentucky Dept of Forestry/Natural Resources |
| 30.96 | | BMR | Business users |

## US–30 *continued*

| Base | Mobile | Service | Users |
|------|--------|---------|-------|
| 30.98 | | PSS/URBAN | Forestry & Transport/Property agencies |
| 30.98 | | STATE | Kentucky Dept of Forestry/Natural resources |

## US–31 and 32

| Frequency | Allocation | Users |
|-----------|------------|-------|
| 31.00 *SPECIAL* | MIL | US Army wire integration network (possible use in West Germany as well) |
| 31.00 | BMR | Business Users |
| 31.00 | BMR | Four Seasons Lodge (Lake Ozark Missouri) |
| 31.00 | BMR | Do Mor Refuge (Ohio) |
| 31.00 | BMR | Ohio State University Bowling Green |
| 31.00 | BMR | Texas Christian University (Fort Worth) |
| 31.00 | BMR | Rare Animal Survival park (Ocala Florida) |
| 31.02 | PSS/URBAN | Forestry & Transport/Property Agencies |
| 31.02 | URBAN | South Florida Water Management |
| 31.02 F–1 | PSS | South Carolina Dept of Wildlife Enforcement |
| 31.02 | PSS | Wheeling Park Commission (West Virginia) |
| 31.04 | BMR | Business Users |
| 31.04 | BMR | Big Bass Lake Inc. (Pennsylvania) |
| 31.06 | PSS/URBAN | Forestry & Transport Property Agencies |
| 31.06 | URBAN | Buses (Security) |
| 31.06 F–2 | PSS | South Caroline Dept of Wildlife Enforcement |

**US–31 and 32** *continued*

| Frequency | Allocation | Users |
|-----------|------------|-------|
| 31.08 | URBAN | Transport/Property Agencies |
| 31.10 | PSS/URBAN | Forestry & Transport/Property Agencies |
| 31.10 | PSS | Missouri Parks Dept |
| 31.12 | URBAN | Transport/Property Agencies |
| 31.14 | PSS/URBAN | Forestry & Transport/Property Agencies |
| 31.14 | URBAN | Boston Bus repair crews (Massachusetts) |
| 31.14 | URBAN | Maryland University |
| 31.14 | URBAN | San Francisco Buses |
| 31.16 | BMR/UNIV | Business Users & Universities |
| 31.16 | UNIV | Pennsylvania State University (Statewide) |
| 31.16 | BMR | Penn Hills Lodge (Analomink Pennsylvania) |
| 31.16 | BMR | Ajax Air Tram Pittsburgh Apt (Pennsylvania) |
| 31.16 | BMR | Horsehoe Bay Country Club (Marble Falls) |
| 31.18 | PSS | Forestry Statewide |
| 31.18 F–3 | PSS | South Carolina Dept of Wildlife Enforcement |
| 31.20 | BMR | Business Users |
| 31.20 | BMR | Washington/Baltimore Int. Airport |
| 31.20 | BMR | Oak Hill Country Club (Rochester New York) |
| 31.20 | BMR | Outer Banks Lts (North Carolina) |
| 31.20 | BMR | Pennsylvania State University (Statewide) |
| 31.20 | BMR | Wintergreen Property Co (Virginia) |
| 31.22 | PSS | Forestry |
| 31.24 | BMR | Business Users |
| 31.24 | BMR | Wintergreen Property Co (Virginia) |
| 31.24 | BMR | Massachusetts Maritime Academy |
| 31.24 | BMR | Yale University (New Haven) |
| 31.24 | BMR | Maryland University |
| 31.24 | BMR | Hofstra University (Hempstead New York) |

## US–31 and 32 *continued*

| Frequency | Allocation | Users |
|-----------|------------|-------|
| 31.24 | BMR | Appalachian State University (Boone North Carolina) |
| 31.24 | BMR | Davidson College (Davidson North Carolina) |
| 31.24 | BMR | Grit Publishing Corp (Williamsport Pennsylvania) |
| 31.26 | PSS | Forestry |
| 31.26 | PSS | Montana Forestry Commission |
| 31.30 | PSS | Forestry |
| 31.30 | PSS | Missouri Parks Dept |
| 31.32 | IND | Special Industrial |
| 31.34 | PSS | Forestry |
| 31.34 | PSS | Maryland Dept of natural Resources (Int) |
| 31.34 | PSS | North Carolina Forest Service |
| 31.34 | PSS | Ohio Dept of Environment |
| 31.36 | IND | Special Industrial |
| 31.38 | PSS | Forestry |
| 31.40 | IND | Special Industrial |
| 31.42 | PSS | Forestry |
| 31.42 | PSS | North Carolina Forest Service |
| 31.44 | IND | Special Industrial |
| 31.46 | PSS | Forestry |
| 31.46 | PSS | North Carolina Forest Service |
| 31.46 | PSS | Massachusetts Dept of Environment (car-to-car) |
| 31.46 | PSS | Maryland Dept of Water/Natural resources |
| 31.46 | PSS | Ohio Dept of Environment |
| 31.48 | IND | Special Industrial |
| 31.50 | PSS | Forestry |
| 31.50 | PSS | Massachusetts Dept of Environment |
| 31.52 | IND | Special Industrial |
| 31.54 | PSS | Forestry |
| 31.54 | PSS | North Carolina Forest Service |
| 31.54 | PSS | Rhode Island Parks police |
| 31.56 | IND | Special Industrial |
| 31.58 | PSS | Forestry |

**US–31 and 32** *continued*

| Frequency | Allocation | Users |
|-----------|------------|-------|
| 31.58 | PSS | Rhode Island Parks police |
| 31.58 | PSS | Maryland Game Wardens |
| 31.58 | PSS | West Virginia Dept of Natural Resources |
| 31.60 | IND | Special Industrial |
| 31.62 | PSS | Forestry |
| 31.62 | PSS | West Virginia Dept of Natural Resources |
| 31.62 | PSS | Rhode Island Forest Fire Suppression |
| 31.64 | IND | Special Industrial |
| 31.66 | PSS | Conservation |
| 31.66 | PSS | Kentucky Dept of Land Reclamation |
| 31.68 | IND | Special Industrial |
| 31.70 | PSS | Conservation |
| 31.70 | PSS | West Virginia Dept of Natural Resources |
| 31.72 | IND | Special Industrial |
| 31.74 | PSS | Forestry |
| 31.74 | PSS | Rhode Island Forest Fire Suppression |
| 31.74 | PSS | Kentucky Dept of Forestry |
| 31.76 | IND | Special Industrial |
| 31.78 | PSS | Forestry/Conservation |
| 31.78 | PSS | Kentucky Dept of Forestry/Natural Resources |
| 31.78 | PSS | Hampton Beach Park (New Hampshire) |
| 31.78 | PSS | Du Page Forest Preservation (Illinois) |
| 31.78 | PSS | South Carolina Forestry Commission (admin) |
| 31.80 | IND | Special Industrial |
| 31.82 | PSS | Forestry/Conservation |
| 31.82 | PSS | Du Page Forest Preservation (Illinois) |
| 31.82 | PSS | West Virginia Dept of Natural Resources |

## US–31 and 32 *continued*

| Frequency | Allocation | Users |
|-----------|------------|-------|
| 31.84 | IND | Special Industrial |
| 31.86 | PSS | Forestry/Conservation |
| 31.86 | PSS | West Virginia Dept of Natural Resources |
| 31.86 | PSS | Maryland Game Wardens |
| 31.86 | PSS | Du Page Forest Preservation (Illinois) |
| 31.86 | PSS | Illinois Park/Forestry |
| 31.88 | IND | Special Industrial |
| 31.90 | PSS | Forestry/Conservation |
| 31.90 | PSS | Kentucky Dept of Forestry/Natural Resources |
| 31.90 | PSS AM | New Hampshire Forestry Fire Towers |
| 31.92 | IND | Special Industrial |
| 31.94 | PSS | Forestry/Conservation |
| 31.94 | PSS | West Virginia Dept of Natural Resources |
| 31.96 | IND | Special Industrial |
| 31.98 | PSS | Forestry/Conservation |
| 31.98 | PSS | New York Dept of Environment (Statewide) |
| 31.98 | PSS | West Virginia Dept Natural Resources (Statewide) |
| 32.01 | INT | Dept of the Interior (Nationwide) |
| 32.03 | INT | Dept of the Interior (Nationwide) |
| 32.05 | MIL | Navy |
| 32.06 | MIL | Navy MARS Military Integration Network |
| 32.10 | MIL | Army |
| 32.13 | CGD | Coast Guard |
| 32.19 | CGD | Coast Guard |
| 32.21 | CGD | Coast Guard |
| 32.23 | SPY | Secret Service — Camp David (President) |
| 32.25 | MIL/STATE | Army/Dept of State |
| 32.27 | MIL | Army |
| 32.29 | MIL | Army |
| 32.30 | MIL | Army |

**US–31 and 32** *continued*

| Frequency | Allocation | Users |
|---|---|---|
| 32.32 | MIL | Air Force |
| 32.35 | MIL | Air Force |
| 32.37 | MIL | Air Force |
| 32.39 | PSS | Forestry Dept |
| 32.40 | MIL | Army |
| 32.43 | MIL | Navy |
| 32.49 | MIL | Army |
| 32.50 | MIL | Army |
| 32.51 | MIL | Army |
| 32.55 to 32.59 | PSS | Forestry Dept |
| 32.60 | MIL | National Guard (Georgia) |
| 32.61 | MIL | Forestry Dept |
| 32.63 | PSS | Forestry Dept |
| 32.69 | MIL | Army |
| 32.70 | MIL | Army |
| 32.71 | MIL | Army |
| 32.73 | PSS | National Parks Service |
| 32.75 to 32.83 | PSS/JUST | Forestry Dept & Dept of Justice |
| 32.85 | MIL | Air Force |
| 32.89 | MIL | Army |
| 32.90 | MIL | Army |
| 32.91 | MIL | Army |
| 32.93 to 32.99 | INT | Dept of the Interior |

**US–33**

| MHz | Call | Allocation | Users |
|---|---|---|---|
| 33.02 | | URBAN | Highways/Special Emergency |
| 33.02 | | URBAN | Jefferson County (Alabama) Highway Dept |
| 33.02 | | URBAN | FM Essex County Highways (New Jersey State) |
| 33.02 | | URBAN | University of Wisconsin (Statewide) |
| 33.04 | | URBAN | Special Emergency |

**US–33** *continued*

| MHz | Call | Allocation | Users |
|---|---|---|---|
| 33.04 | | URBAN | Appalachian Mountain Club (New Hampshire) |
| 33.06 | | URBAN | Highways/Special Emergency |
| 33.06 | | URBAN | Washington D.C. Ambulance Dispatch |
| 33.08 | | URBAN | Special Emergency |
| 33.10 | | URBAN | Highways/Special Emergency |
| 33.12 | | IND | Special Industrial (2 Watt Max) |
| 33.14 | | UNIV | Business & Universities (mobile-to-mobile) |
| 33.14 | | UNIV | University of Michigan |
| 33.14 | | UNIV | Falmouth Marine Biology Lab (Cape Cod Massachusetts) |
| 33.14 | | UNIV | New Mexico State University |
| 33.14 | | UNIV | Iowa State University (Ames) |
| 33.14 | | BMR | Minneapolis Golf Club |
| 33.14 | | UNIV | University of Purdue (West Lafeyette — Indiana) |
| 33.14 | | BMR | Mountain Retreat Association (North Carolina) |
| 33.14 | | UNIV | Ohio State University (Columbus) |
| 33.14 | | UNIV | Oregon College of Education (Monmouth) |
| 33.14 | | UNIV | Oregon State University (Corvallis) |
| 33.14 | | UNIV | Pennsylvania State University (Statewide) |
| 33.14 | | UNIV | University of Vermont (Burlington) |
| 33.14 | | UNIV | Sugarbush Valley Sports & Recreation area (Vermont) |
| 33.14 | | UNIV | University of Wisconsin (Statewide) |
| 33.16 | | BMR | Business Users (100 Watt Max) |
| 33.16 | | BMR | Towne Plaza/Billerica (Boston Massachusetts) |
| 33.16 | | BMR | Evergreen Search & Rescue (Washington) |
| 33.18 to 33.36 | | IND | Petroleum Companies |
| 33.38 | | POL | Upper Saddle River Police (Bergen County New York) |

**US–33** *continued*

| MHz | Call | Allocation | Users |
|---|---|---|---|
| 33.40 | | UNIV | Universities (mobile-to-mobile) |
| 33.40 | | UNIV | Louisiana State University (Baton Rouge) |
| 33.40 | | UNIV | Louisiana Technical University (Ruston) |
| 33.40 | | UNIV | Cooper—Hewitt Museum (New York City) |
| 33.40 | | UNIV | University of North Carolina |
| 33.40 | | UNIV | Pennsylvania State University (Statewide) |
| 33.40 | | UNIV | Fairmont State College (West Virginia) |
| 33.40 | | UNIV | University of Wisconsin (Statewide) |
| 33.42 to 33.98 | | FIRE | Fire Services |
| 33.44 | | FIRE | Jefferson/Kenner District Fire (Louisiana) |
| 33.44 | | FIRE | Pottstown Fire (Pennsylvania) |
| 33.44 | | FIRE | Paramus Fire (Bergen County New York) |
| 33.46 | Able | FIRE | Provincetown Fire Dept (Cape Cod Massachusetts) |
| 33.46 | | FIRE | Hampden County Fire Net (Massachusetts) |
| 33.48 | | FIRE | Franklin County Fire Net (Massachusetts) |
| 33.48 | | FIRE | Barnstable Fire Dept (Cape Cod Massachusetts) |
| 33.48 | | FIRE | South Vermont Tri-State Mutual Aid |
| 33.48 | | FIRE | Iselin Fire Dept (Middlesex County New Jersey) |
| 33.50 | | POL | Dover Police (Boston Massachusetts) |
| 33.52 | King | FIRE | Brewster Fire Dept (Cape Code Massachusetts) |
| 33.52 | | FIRE | Hampden County Fire Net (Massachusetts) |

**US–33** *continued*

| MHz | Call | Allocation | Users |
|-----|------|-----------|-------|
| 33.52 | | FIRE | Jefferson Fireground (Louisiana) |
| 33.52 | | FIRE | Fire Dept car-to-car |
| 33.54 | | FIRE | Franklin County Fire Net (Massachusetts) |
| 33.54 | | FIRE | South West New Hampshire Fire (Mutual Aid) |
| 33.54 | | FIRE | Vermont Tri-State Mutual Aid Fire Depts |
| 33.56 | | POL | Framingham Police (Boston Massachusetts) |
| 33.56 | | MUNI | University of Connecticut |
| 33.56 | | FIRE | Edison Fire Dept (Middlesex County New Jersey) |
| 33.60 | | FIRE | Jefferson/Marerro District Fire (Lousiania) |
| 33.60 | Henry | FIRE | Sandwich Fire Dept (Cape Cod Massachusetts) |
| 33.60 | | FIRE | Fire Dept Press Information Channel |
| 33.60 | F–3 | POL | Montgomery County Police & Fire (Pennsylvania) |
| 33.62 | | FIRE | South Worcester Fire Net (Massachusetts) |
| 33.64 | | FIRE | Jefferson/Harahan District Fire (Louisiana) |
| 33.64 | | FIRE | South Central New Hampshire Fire |
| 33.66 | Mike | FIRE | Orleans Fire Dept |
| 33.66 | | FIRE | Merrimack Valley Fire Net (Massachusetts) |
| 33.66 | Charlie | FIRE | Wellfleet Fire Dept (Cape Cod Massachusetts) |
| 33.66 | Baker | FIRE | Truro Fire Dept (Cape Cod Massachusetts) |
| 33.66 | F–2 | FIRE | Montgomery County (Pennsylvania) |
| 33.68 | | FIRE | Jefferson/Baratavia District Fire (Lousiana) |
| 33.68 | | FIRE | Manchester Fire Dept (New Hampshire) |

**US–33** *continued*

| MHz | Call | Allocation | Users |
|-----|------|------------|-------|
| 33.70 | | FIRE | W Barnstable Fire Dept (Cape Cod Massachusetts) |
| 33.70 | | FIRE | North Worchester Fire Net (Massachusetts) |
| 33.70 | | FIRE | Fire Dept Dispatch |
| 33.70 | | FIRE | Jefferson/Harahan/Kenner District Fire (Louisiana) |
| 33.70 | | FIRE | Jefferson Fire Dispatch (Louisiana) |
| 33.70 | F–1 | FIRE | Montgomery County (Pennsylvania) |
| 33.70 | | FIRE | Pottstown Fire (Pennsylvania) |
| 33.72 | | FIRE | Tangipahoa Parish Fire (Louisiana) |
| 33.72 | | FIRE | Cleveland Fire — Greater Alarms (Ohio) |
| 33.76 | Union | FIRE | Martha's Vineyard Fire Dept (Cape Cod Massachusetts) |
| 33.76 | | FIRE | Jefferson/Avondale District Fire (Louisiana) |
| 33.76 | | FIRE | Conshohocken Fire (Pennsylvania) |
| 33.76 | F–2 | FIRE | Allegheny South Hills Dispatch (Pennsylvania) |
| 33.78 | Oscar | FIRE | Falmouth Fire Dept (Cape Cod Massachusetts) |
| 33.78 | | FIRE | South West New Hampshire Fire (Mutual Aid) |
| 33.78 | F–1 | FIRE | New Castle County Fire Net (Pennsylvania) |
| 33.80 | F–3 | FIRE | Allegheny East Dispatch (Pennsylvania) |
| 33.82 | | FIRE | Iselin, Edison, New Brunswick, South Plainfield (all Middlesex County New Jersey) |
| 33.82 | | FIRE | Jefferson/Gould Fire (Louisiana) |
| 33.82 | | AMB | Middlesex County Fire/Ambulance Dispatch (New Jersey) |
| 33.84 | | FIRE | Osterville Fire Dept (Cape Cod Massachusetts) |
| 33.84 | | FIRE | Marstons Mills Fire Dept (Cape Cod Massachusetts) |

**US–33** *continued*

| MHz | Call | Allocation | Users |
|-----|------|------------|-------|
| 33.84 | | FIRE | Lower Merion Fire (Pennsylvania) |
| 33.86 | | FIRE | Somerville Fire (Boston Massachusetts) |
| 33.86 | | FIRE | Cotuit Fire Dept (Cape Cod Massachusetts) |
| 33.86 | | FIRE | Worcester Fire-Admin (Boston Massachusetts) |
| 33.86 | | FIRE | Tangipahoa Parish Fire (Louisiana) |
| 33.86 | | FIRE | Fire Dept Mutual Aid Channel |
| 33.86 | | FIRE | Bergen County Fire Net (New York) |
| 33.86 | | FIRE | Franklin County Fire Net (Columbus Ohio) |
| 33.86 | Master | FIRE | Allegheny County (Pennsylvania) |
| 33.86 | | FIRE | Allendale, Garfield, Elmwood Park, Fair Lawn, Saddle Brook, Saddle River, Ramsey & Rochelle Park (all are NY/NJ Metro Area) |
| 33.88 | | FIRE | Wareham Fire Dept (Cape Cod Massachusetts) |
| 33.88 | | FIRE | Jefferson/Westwego District Fire (Louisiana) |
| 33.90 | | FIRE | Plymouth County Fire Net (Massachusetts) |
| 33.90 | | FIRE | Fire Dept Dispatch |
| 33.90 | | FIRE | New Hampshire Lakes Region Fire |
| 33.90 | | FIRE | South Central New Hampshire Fire |
| 33.90 | | FIRE | Cleveland Fire (Ohio) |
| 33.92 | | FIRE | Wareham Fire Dept (Cape Cod Massachusetts) |
| 33.92 | | FIRE | Jefferson/Live Oak Manor District Fire (Louisiana) |
| 33.92 | | FIRE | New Brunswick & South Plainfield Fire Depts (New Jersey) |
| 33.92 | F–4 | FIRE | Allegheny N Hills Dispatch (Pennsylvania) |
| 33.94 | Easy | FIRE | Hyannis Fire Dept (Cape Cod Massachusetts) |
| 33.94 | | FIRE | Fire Dept Dispatch |
| 33.94 | F–2 | FIRE | New Castle County Fireground (Pennsylvania) |

**US–33** *continued*

| Base | Mobile | Service | Users |
|------|--------|---------|-------|
| 33.96 | | FIRE | Jefferson/Harvey District Fire (Louisiana) |
| 33.96 | | FIRE | New Hampshire Lakes District Fire |
| 33.96 | | FIRE | South Plainfield Fire (New Jersey) |
| 33.98 | | FIRE | South Middlesex County Fire Net (Massachusetts) |

## US–34

| Frequency | Allocation | User |
|-----------|------------|------|
| 34.01 | CGD | Coast Guard |
| 34.02 | NOAA | National Weather Service |
| 34.03 | FED | Department of Energy |
| 34.05 | CGD | Coast Guard |
| 34.09 | MIL | Army |
| 34.10 | MIL | Army |
| 34.11 | MIL | Army |
| 34.15 | MIL | Air National Guard (Brady Field Connecticut) |
| 34.17 | MIL | Air National Guard/Air Force |
| 34.19 | MIL | Air Force |
| 34.21 | MIL | Air Force |
| 34.23 | MIL | |
| 34.25 | PSS | Forestry Departments |
| 34.29 | MIL | Army |
| 34.30 | MIL | Army/Navy MARS Military Integration Network |
| 34.50 | MIL | Army National Guard (Connecticut Statewide) |
| 34.75 | MIL | Air National Guard (Brady Field Connecticut) |
| 34.79 | PSS | Statue of Liberty Monument Dept (New York) |
| 34.81 | PSS | US Fish & Wildlife Service |
| 34.95 | MIL | Marines |
| 34.98 | | National Oceanographic Survey Teams |

## US–35

| MHz | Allocation | Users |
|-----|-----------|-------|
| 35.02 | BMR | Business Users (2 Watt Max) |
| 35.02 | BMR | New Britain Red Sox (Connecticut) |
| 35.02 | BMR | Florida Cypress Gardens |
| 35.02 | BMR | Purdu University (Indiana) |
| 35.02 | BMR | Louisiana State University |
| 35.02 | PSS | Special Emergency |
| 35.02 | BMR | Jared Coffin House (Nantucket Massachusetts) |
| 35.02 | BMR | University of Michigan |
| 35.02 | BMR | Pennsylvania State University |
| 35.02 | BMR | Rutgers University (New Jersey) |
| 35.02 | BMR | Timeless Towns (Gettysburg Pennsylvania) |
| 35.02 | BMR | University of Vermont |
| 35.04 | BMR | Itinerant Business Users |
| 35.04 | BMR | Ramapo Arabians Sports (New Jersey) |
| 35.04 | BMR | Heart of Dixie Shows |
| 35.06 | BMR | Business (110 Watt Max) |
| 35.06 | BMR | Riverside Park (Agawarm Massachusetts) |
| 35.06 | BMR | Easy Bay Lodge (Osterville Massachusetts) |
| 35.06 | BMR | Columbia University (New York City) |
| 35.06 | BMR | Niagara University (New York) |
| 35.06 | BMR | Okemo Mountain (Ludlow Vermont) |
| 35.08 | BMR | Business (110 Watt Max) |
| 35.08 | BMR | Lafeyette Conference Centre (Pennsylvania) |
| 35.08 | BMR | Shawnee Inn (Shawnee on Deleware Pennsylvania) |
| 35.08 | BMR | Harrison Conference Centre (Glen Cove North) |
| 35.08 | BMR | Bonhomme Richard Co (Williamsburg Virginia) |
| 35.10–35.18 | BMR | Business (110 Watt Max) |
| 35.10 | BMR | Science Park Inc (Pennsylvania) |

**US–35** *continued*

| MHz | Allocation | Users |
|---|---|---|
| 35.10 | BMR | Lake Placid Resort Club (New York) |
| 35.12 | BMR | Union Theological Seminary (Virginia) |
| 35.12 | BMR | Air Charters of Tidewater (Charlottsville) |
| 35.14 | BMR | Playland Amusement Park (Cape Coral Florida) |
| 35.14 | BMR | M.V. Mount Washington (Lake Winnipesauk) |
| 35.14 | BMR | Paul Smiths College (New York) |
| 35.14 | BMR | University of Vermont (Burlington) |
| 35.16 | UTIL | Telephone Company maintenance |
| 35.18 | BMR | Maggie Valley Country Club (North Carolina) |
| 35.26 | PHONE | Mobile Telephone Channel ZO |
| 35.30 | PHONE | Mobile Telephone Channel ZF |
| 35.34 | PHONE | Mobile Telephone Channel ZH |
| 35.38 | PHONE | Mobile Telephone Channel ZM |
| 35.42 | PHONE | Mobile Telephone Channel ZA |
| 35.46 | PHONE | Mobile Telephone Channel ZY |
| 35.50 | PHONE | Mobile Telephone Channel ZR |
| 35.54 | PHONE | Mobile Telephone Channel ZB |
| 35.62 | PHONE | Mobile Telephone Channel ZW |
| 35.64 | PSS | Special Emergency Paging |
| 35.66 | PHONE | Mobile Telephone Channel ZL |
| 35.68 | PSS | Special Emergency Paging |
| 35.70–35.72 | BMR | Business Use |
| 35.70 | BMR | Newtown Square Shopping Centre (Newtown Pennsylvania) |
| 35.72 | BMR | Bird-in-Hand Motor Inns (Pennsylvania) |
| 35.74–36.00 | IND | Industrial (Various) |
| 35.88 | BMR | Indiana University |
| 35.90 | BMR | Holiday Inn (Atlantic City New Jersey) |
| 35.90 | BMR | New York University |
| 35.90 | BMR | Associated Press (New York City) |
| 35.92 | BMR | Dublin Diner (Dublin Pennsylvania) |

**US–35** *continued*

| MHz | Allocation | Users |
| --- | --- | --- |
| 35.92 | BMR | Case Western Reserve Univ (Cleveland Ohio) |
| 35.92 | BMR | Merion Golf Club (Ardmore Pennsylvania) |
| 35.94 | BMR | Bowling Green State University (Ohio) |
| 35.94 | BMR | Crystal Plaza (Livingston New Jersey) |
| 35.94 | BMR | Bird-in-Hand Restaurants (Pennsylvania) |
| 35.94 | BMR | Gilliland Racing (Itinerant) |
| 35.94 | BMR | The Mercury (News) (Pottstown Pennsylvania) |
| 35.96 | BMR | Orlando Wrestling Stadium (Florida) |

**US–36 and 37**

| Frequency | Allocation | Users |
| --- | --- | --- |
| 36.15 | MIL | National Guard Florida |
| 36.30 | MIL | National Guard Florida |
| 36.50 | MIL | National Guard Florida |
| 36.55 | MIL | National Guard Florida |
| 36.55 | MIL | Ft Myer Fire (DC) |
| 36.60 | MIL | Ft McNair Military Police (DC) |
| 36.99 | MIL | Ft Myer Fire (DC) |
| 37.02–37.42 | POL | Police Channels |
| 37.02 | POL | Mobiles only |
| 37.06 | POL | Mount Pleasant (Westchester New York) |
| 37.06 | POL | Harris County (Texas) Constables Pct 4 |
| 37.08 | POL | Ramsay, Saddle River, Upper Saddle River, Waldick & Wyckoff Police (NY/NJ Metro) |

**US–36 and 37** *continued*

| Frequency | | Allocation | Users |
|---|---|---|---|
| 37.08 | | POL | Allendale (Bergen County New York) |
| 37.08 | | POL | Ho-Ho-Kus (Bergen County New York) |
| 37.08 | | POL | Mahwah (Bergen County New York) |
| 37.10 | | POL | Mt Pleasant (Westchester New York) |
| 37.10 | | POL | North Tarrytown (Westchester New York) |
| 37.10 | | POL | Ossining (Westchester New York) |
| 37.10 | | POL | Briarcliffe Manor (Westechester New York) |
| 37.10 | | POL | Mahwah (Bergen County New York) |
| 37.10 | | POL | Croton-on-Hudson (Westchester New York) |
| 37.10 | | POL | Rochelle Park Police & Fire, Ramsey Police, (NY/NJ Metro) |
| 37.10 | | POL | Milburn Police (Essex County New Jersey) |
| 37.10 | F2 | STATE | Air Pollution Control Dept (Ohio) |
| 37.10 | | POL | Bethany (Oklahoma) |
| 37.10 | | FIRE | Millington Fire Dept (Tennessee) |
| 37.10 | | POL | Glenn Heights Police (Dallas/Fort Worth) |
| 37.10 | | POL | Harris County (Texas) Constables Car-to-Car Supervisors |
| 37.12 | | URBAN | Dade County Public Safety inter-agency |
| 37.12 | | POL | Milburn Police (Essex County New Jersey) |
| 37.12 | | POL | Tarrants County Sheriffs Repeater (Tennessee) |
| 37.14 | | POL | Rochelle Park Police (NY/NJ Metro) |
| 37.18 | | POL | Police/CD paging system Dade County (Florida) |
| 37.18 | F1 | STATE | Ohio Air Pollution Control Dept |
| 37.18 | | POL | Millington Police (Tennessee) |

**US–36 and 37** *continued*

| Frequency | Allocation | Users |
|-----------|------------|-------|
| 37.18 | POL | Glenn Heights & Hutchings Police, Seagonville & Wilmer Fire Dept (all Dallas/Fort Worth area) |
| 37.20 | | Worcester County House of Correction (Mobiles) |
| 37.24 | POL | West Milford Police (Passaic County New Jersey) |
| 37.24 | POL | Tarrants County Sheriffs Repeater (Tennessee) |
| 37.26 | POL | Leonia Police & Rochelle Park Fire Dept (Bergen County New York) |
| 37.26 | POL | Tennessee & Oklahoma Sherriffs |
| 37.26 | POL | Seagonville Police (Texas) |
| 37.28 | POL | Forest Park Police (Ohio) |
| 37.30 | POL | Spencer Police (Ohio) |
| 37.30 | POL | Pequannock, Pompton Lakes, Ringwood, Wanaque & West Milford Police (all Passaic County New Jersey) |
| 37.32 | POL | Moonachie (Bergen County New York) |
| 37.32 | POL | Pompton Lakes Police (Passaic County New Jersey) |
| 37.36 | | Worcester County House of Correction (Maine) |
| 37.38 | POL | Mahwah (Bergen County New York) |
| 37.38 | POL | Ho-Ho-Kus Police (Bergen County New York) |
| 37.38 | POL | Bergen County Alert/Sheriff/Dispatch (N) |
| 37.38 | POL | Moonachie, Saddle River, South Hackensack, Teterboro & Waldick Police (all Bergen County New York) |
| 37.40 | POL | Bergen County Sheriff Car-to-Car (New York) |
| 37.50 | | Water Supply/Operations Police (New York) |

**US–36 and 37** *continued*

| Frequency | Allocation | Users |
|-----------|-----------|-------|
| 37.50 | UTIL | Three Mile Island Nuclear Plant |
| 37.52 | UTIL | Three Mile Island Nuclear Plant |
| 37.54 | UTIL | Three Mile Island Nuclear Plant |
| 37.56 | UTIL | Three Mile Island Nuclear Plant |
| 37.82 | URBAN | Suffolk County Water Supply (New York) |
| 37.83 | STATE | Fish & Wildlife Service (Swanton Texas) |
| 37.90 | | Fairface County Civil Defence (Virginia) |
| 37.94 | | Palisades Interstate Parkway (New York) |
| 37.98 | URBAN | Suffolk County Highways Dept (New York) |

## International 10 Metre and 6 Metre Beacon Stations (Amateur)

| Frequency/MHz | Callsign | Location |
|---------------|----------|----------|
| 28.1750 | VE3TEN | Ottowa |
| 28.2025 | ZS5YHF | Durban RSA |
| 28.2050 | DLOIGI | Mount Predgistuhl |
| 28.2070 | WD4HES | Florida USA |
| 28.2100 | ZD1G1 | Gough Island |
| 28.2100 | 3B8MS | Mauritius |
| 28.2150 | GB3SX | Crowborough UK |
| 28.2170 | VE2TEN | Chicoutimi |
| 28.2200 | 5B4CY | Zyyi |
| 28.2220 | HG2BHA | Tapolca |
| 28.2280 | EAZ6AU | Spain |
| 28.2500 | VE8AA | Lake Contwoyoto |
| 28.2300 | ZL2MHF | Mount Climie |
| 28.2350 | VP9BA | Bermuda |
| 28.2370 | LA5TEN | Oslo Denmark |
| 28.2370 | ZS3HL | Tsumeb RSA |
| 28.2400 | OA4CK | Lima Peru |

## International 10 Metre and 6 Metre Beacon Stations (Amateur)
*continued*

| Frequency/MHz | Callsign | Location |
| --- | --- | --- |
| 28.2425 | ZS1CTB | Capetown RSA |
| 28.2450 | A9XC | Bahrain |
| 28.2500 | Z21ANB | Bulawayo |
| 28.2520 | YE7TEN | Vancouver VC |
| 28.2570 | DKOTE | Konstanz |
| 28.2600 | VK5WI | Adelaide |
| 28.2620 | VK2WI | Sydney |
| 28.2640 | VK6RWA | Perth |
| 28.2660 | VK6RTW | Western Australia |
| 28.2700 | ZS6PW | RSA |
| 28.2720 | TU2ABJ | Abidjan |
| 28.2720 | 9L1FTN | Freetown |
| 28.2750 | VE3TEN | Ottawa |
| 28.2770 | DFOABB | Schleswig Holstein |
| 28.2800 | VV5AVV | Caracas |
| 28.2840 | KA1YEB | Henriette NY |
| 28.2850 | VP8ADE | Queen Adelaide Island |
| 28.2870 | H44SI | Soloman Islands |
| 28.2870 | W80MV | Tuckasegee NC |
| 28.2900 | VS6HK | Mount Matilde |
| 28.2920 | JA2 | Mount Asama |
| 28.2930 | VU2BCN | New Delhi |
| 28.2950 | VU2BCN | Bangalore |
| 28.2960 | W3VD | Laurel MD |
| 28.3000 | PY2AMI | Sao Paulo Brazil |
| 28.3020 | ZS1STB | Still Bay |
| 28.3120 | ZS6DN | RSA |
| 28.8880 | W6IRT | Hollywood |
| 28.8940 | WD9GOE | USA |
| 28.9220 | DLONF | Nuremburg |
| 29.2660 | Z22JY | Harare Zimbabwe |
| 50.005 | ZSSIX | Cape Province |
| 50.005 | H44HIR | Soloman Islands |
| 50.010 | ZS1STB | North Transvaal RSA |
| 50.010 | JA2IGY | Mie Japan |
| 50.010 | ZS6STB | Yereeniging RSA |
| 50.015 | SZ2DH | Athens Greece |
| 50.020 | GB3IX | UK |

**International 10 Metre and 6 Metre Beacon Stations (Amateur)**
*continued*

| Frequency/MHz | Callsign | Location |
| --- | --- | --- |
| 50.025 | 6Y5RC | Jamaica |
| 50.025 | ZS6IX | RSA |
| 50.030 | ZS6PW | RSA |
| 50.035 | ZB2VHF | RSA |
| 50.039 | FY7THF | French Guiana |
| 50.041 | WA8KGG | Ohio USA |
| 50.045 | OX3VHF | Greenland |
| 50.050 | GB3NHQ | North London |
| 50.060 | GB3RMK | UK |
| 50.060 | ZS6DN/B | Pretoria RSA |
| 50.062 | PY2AA | Sau Paulo Brazil |
| 50.062 | W3VD | Laurel USA |
| 50.070 | 4U1ITU | Geneva |
| 50.070 | W2CAP/B | Cape Cod Mass |
| 50.075 | VS6HK | Hong Kong |
| 50.080 | 9H1SIX | Proposed |
| 50.088 | VE1SIX | New Brunswick |
| 50.099 | KH6EQI | Pearl Harbour |
| 50.110 | ZS6LN | RSA |
| 50.500 | 5B4CY | Zyyi |
| 50.925 | ZS5VHF | Durban |
| 50.945 | ZS1SIX | Captetown RSA |
| 52.200 | VK8YF | Darwin |
| 52.250 | ZL2VHM | Pahiatua Track |
| 52.300 | VK6RTV | Perth |
| 52.320 | VK6RTT | Carnarvon |
| 52.330 | VK3RGG | Geelong |
| 52.350 | VK6RTU | Kalgorrlie |
| 52.510 | ZL2MHF | Mount Climie |

# 7 International spectrum

## International frequency allocations

Delegates from all countries are entitled to be represented at the International Telecommunications Union, ITU, where agreement is reached on who will transmit on what frequency. For the purposes of global allocation the world is actually split into three separate regions (see map). Region 1 consists of Europe, Africa and China. Region 2 comprises North and South America and region 3 the Pacific, Australasia and Asia (except China). There is a further sub-division with what is called the 'Tropical Zone' but by and large this has little effect on VHF/UHF planning and notes are included in the allocations lists where there are exceptions.

Despite the overall regional allocation, many countries, subject to agreement with their neighbours, may use a given band for slightly different purposes. Where this is the case, notes are included in the lists. There are also instances where countries may have different specific allocations for a broad category. For instance, 'Mobile' in one country may mean Public Mobile Radio (itinerant or commercial) but in the same region, the same frequencies in another country may be allocated for government mobile radio only. It is clearly beyond the scope of one book to give a complete breakdown for each individual country. However, from the enclosed lists, the scanner owner should soon be able to get a good idea of the kind of services in any given band in his own location.

Although many of the frequencies listed for some regions will not be of great interest to scanner owners in other regions, it should be noted that a complete list of all three regions is a useful reference source. During periods of high propagation, such as those experienced during sunspot cycles, some of the lower frequencies, particularly those below 50 MHz, can often be received world-wide. As an example, 50 MHz beacons from all over the world have been heard in Britain, and during a sunspot cycle, for two consecutive summers

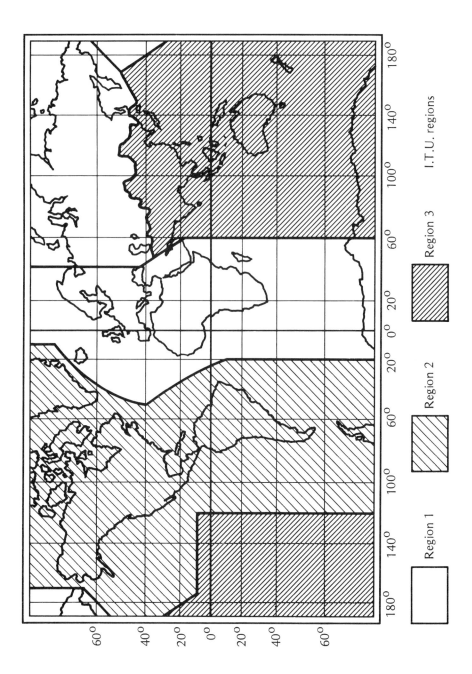

mobile radio operators in the USA, at frequencies between 30 and 40 MHz were heard at my home on the Island of Guernsey off the coast of France, at strengths of up to and over S9.

An additional reason for having a complete list is to check on space operations also. Allocations for satellite operation in your own region may be different to other countries.

Using the allocation list is quite simple. Each band is separated from the next by a rule and within the rules are notes about regional variations.

## Definitions

*Aeronautical mobile*   Communications between air and ground or aircraft and another aircraft.

*Aeronautical navigation*   The use of radio signals for homing, direction finding, distance measuring, determining altitude, etc.

*Aeronautical mobile satellite service*   Communication between an aircraft and satellite or the use of satellite tracking facilities for the location of aircraft, homing beacons, etc.

*Amateur service*   Hobbyist use of communications for self-training.

*Broadcasting*   The transmission of sound radio or television pictures for reception by the public for entertainment purposes.

*Deep space exploration*   The study of space at distances of greater than the distance between the earth and the moon.

*Duplex*   The use of two radio frequencies so that communications are possible (both transmit and receive) simultaneously.

*Earth exploration satellite*   The use of on-board sensors on a satellite to gather information about the earth.

*Fixed service*   Communications between two fixed points (as opposed to moving stations, i.e. mobile).

*Industrial, scientific and medical*   The use of radio transmissions for non-communication in instruments or machinery. Typically includes everything from the use of radio waves to heal tissue to the use of waves to heat up certain types of industrial glue.

*Inter-satellite service*   Communications or telemetry between orbitting satellites.

*Land mobile (mobile) service*   Communication between a moving station and a base station or between two mobile stations.

*Mobile satellite service*   Communication between a mobile station and satellite.

*Maritime mobile service*   Communication between ship and shore or ship-to-ship and on-board-ship communications.

*Maritime mobile satellite service*   Links between a ship and satellite for communication or location purposes.

*Meteorological aids*   The use of radio to send data from weather sensors to a ground station.

*Meterological satellite*    Space satellite which sends data from on-board sensors to a ground station.

*Radio astronomy*    The reception of radio signals from Cosmic origins. These services do not include the transmission of any signals by the Radio Astronomy Station.

*Radiolocation*    The determining of the position of a transmitter for positioning purposes.

*Space operation service*    The communication for the operation of spacecraft including tracking and command telemetry.

*Standard frequency and time signal*    Precise emission of frequency and exact time for scientific and calibration purposes.

*Telecommand*    Transmission of a signal to control equipment at a remote location (even used to switch on such things as street lights).

*Telemetry*    The use of radio to record measurements or data from a remote location.

## ITU Region 1

| Frequency (MHz) | Allocated services |
| --- | --- |
| 25.005–25.010 | Standard frequency and time signal, space research |
| 25.010–25.070 | Fixed and mobile (not aeronautical) |
| 25.070–25.210 | Maritime mobile |
| 25.210–25.550 | Fixed and mobile (not aeronautical) |
| 25.550–25.670 | Radio astronomy |
| 25.670–26.100 | Broadcasting |
| 26.100–26.175 | Maritime mobile |
| 26.175–27.500 | Fixed and mobile (not aeronautical) |
| 27.500–28.00 | Meteorological aids, fixed and mobile (CB) |

## ITU Region 1 *continued*

| Frequency (MHz) | Allocated services |
| --- | --- |
| 28.000–29.700 | Amateur (including satellites) |
| 29.700–30.005 | Fixed and mobile |
| 30.005–30.010 | Space research, satellite ident, fixed and mobile |
| 30.010–37.500 | Fixed mobile |
| 37.500–38.250 | Fixed and mobile, radio astronomy |
| 38.250–39.986 | Fixed and mobile |
| ** 40.050 ** | Military distress frequency |
| 39.986–40.020 | Fixed and mobile, space research |
| 40.020–40.980 | Fixed and mobile, industrial, scientific and medical |
| 40.980–41.015 | Fixed and mobile, space research |
| 41.015–44.000 | Fixed and mobile |
| 44.000–47.000 | Fixed and mobile (aeronavigation in parts Africa) |
| 47.000–68.000 | Broadcasting with variations as listed |
| 47.000–48.500 | Fixed and land mobile on secondary basis in Kenya |
| 56.500–58.000 | Czechoslovakia, Hungary, Mongolia and USSR |
| 47.000–68.000 | Land mobile in Albania, Austria, Belgium, |

**ITU Region 1** *continued*

| *Frequency (MHz)* | *Allocated services* |
| --- | --- |
| | Bulgaria, Denmark, FRG, Finland, France, Gabon, Greece, Israel, Italy, Lebanon, Liechtenstein, Luxembourg, Mali, Malta, Morocco, Nigeria, Norway, Netherlands, Poland, Senegal, Sweden, Switzerland, Tunisia, Turkey, United Kingdom, Yugoslavia, FRG, Roumania (47–58 MHz) |
| 47.000–68.000 | Fixed and mobile (not aeronautical) in Angola, Camaroon, Congo, Chad, Madagascar, Mozambique, Somalia, Sudan, Tanzania and Yemen |
| 50.000–54.000 | Amateur (primary basis) in Botswana, Burundi, Lesotho, Malawi, Namibia, Rwanda, Republic of South Africa, Swaziland, Zaire, Zambia and Zimbabwe |
| 54.000–58.000 | Fixed and mobile (not aeronautical) in Botswana, Burundi, Lesotho, Malawi, Mali, Namibia, Rwanda, Republic of South Africa, Swaziland, Zaire, Zambia and Zimbabwe |
| 68.000–74.800 | Fixed and mobile (not aeronautical) with variations as listed below. |
| 68.000–73.000 | Broadcasting (FM) in Bulgaria, Hungary, Poland, Roumania, Czechoslovakia and USSR |
| 73.000–74.000 | Broadcasting (FM) in Bulgaria, Hungary, Mongolia, Czechoslovakia and USSR |
| 74.800–75.200 | Aeronavigation (Fan Markers on 75.000 MHz) |
| 75.200–87.500 | Fixed and mobile (not aeronautical) with variations as listed below |
| 76.000–87.500 | Aeronavigation in Mongolia and USSR |
| 76.000–87.500 | Broadcasting (FM) in Bulgaria, Czechoslovakia, Hungary, Poland and Roumania |
| 81.000–87.500 | Broadcasting (FM) in Albania |

## ITU Region 1 *continued*

| Frequency (MHz) | Allocated services |
| --- | --- |
| 87.500–100.000 | Broadcasting (FM) with variations as listed |
| 87.500–88.000 | Land mobile in France, FRG, Ireland, Italy, Leichtenstein, Monaco, Spain, United Kingdom, Switzerland and Yemen |
| 97.600–108.000 | Land mobile in United Kingdom to be discontinued after 1989 |
| 100.000–108.000 | Broadcasting |
| 108.000–117.975 | Aeronautical navigation |
| 117.975–136.000 | Aeronautical mobile. Worldwide use, channelised |
| ** 121.500 ** | Aeronautical distress frequency |
| 136.000–137.000 | Fixed and mobile |
| 137.000–138.000 | Space operations including meteorology and aeronautical mobile in Austria, Bulgaria, Egypt, Greece, Hungary, Lebanon, Mongolia, Poland, Czechoslovakia, GDR, Roumania, USSR, Yugoslavia and Finland |
| 138.000–143.600 | Aeronautical mobile with variations as listed |
| 138.000–143.600 | Space research (secondary) in Austria, Czechoslovakia, France, FRG, Israel, Italy, Liechtenstein, Luxembourg, Sweden, Switzerland, United Kingdom and Belgium |
| 138.000–144.000 | Maritime and land mobile (primary) in Austria, Bahrain, Belgium, Denmark, Finland, Greece, Ireland, FRG, Saudi Arabia, United Arab Emirates, Spain, |

**ITU Region 1** *continued*

| Frequency (MHz) | Allocated services |
|---|---|
| 138.000–144.000 | Israel, Kenya, Kuwait, Liechtenstein, Luxembourg, Mali, Malta, Norway, Netherlands, Qatar, United Kingdom, Somalia, Sweden, Switzerland, Tanzania, Tunisia, Turkey and Yugoslavia<br>Fixed and mobile (primary) in Angola, Botswana, Burundi, Camaroon, Central African Republic, Congo, Gabon, Gambia, Ghana, Guinea, Iraq, Lesotho, Liberia, Libya, Malawi, Mozambique, Namibia, Nigeria, Oman, Rwanda, Sierra Leone, South Africa, Swaziland, Tongo, Chad, Zambia, Zaire, Zimbabwe and Jordan |
| 138.000–144.000 | Fixed (primary) in Ethiopia, Finland, Kenya, Malta, Somalia, Sudan, Tanzania, Yemen and Yugoslavia |
| 143.600–143.650 | Aeronautical mobile and space research with variations as listed above |
| 143.650–144.000 | Aeronautical mobile with variations as listed above |
| 144.000–146.000 | Amateur (2 metre) |
| 146.000–149.900 | Fixed and mobile (not aeronautical) and space operation |
| 149.900–150.050 | Satellite navigation |
| 150.050–153.080 | Mobile and radio astronomy with aeronautical mobile in Sweden and Switzerland |
| 153.000–154.000 | Fixed and mobile (not aeronautical) and meteorology |

## ITU Region 1 *continued*

| Frequency (MHz) | Allocated services |
| --- | --- |
| ** 156.8000 ** | Maritime distress frequency |
| 156.7625–156.8375 | Maritime mobile |
| 156.8375–174.0000 | Fixed and mobile (not aeronautical) |
| 174.000–223.000 | Broadcasting with variations as listed<br>Land mobile in Austria, FDR, Belgium, Denmark, Finland, France, Italy, Liechtenstein, Monaco, Norway, Netherlands, Sweden, United Kingdom and Yemen<br>Fixed and mobile in Congo, Ethiopia, Gambia, Guinea, Kenya, Libya, Malawi, Mali, Uganda, Senegal, Sierra Leone, Somalia, Tanzania and Zimbabwe |
| 216.000–225.000 | Aeronavigation in Somalia |
| 216.000–235.000 | Radiolocation (secondary) in Oman, Turkey and United Kingdom |
| 223.000–230.000 | Broadcasting with variations as listed (above and below)<br>Land mobile in Austria, Belgium, Denmark, FDR, Finland, France, Israel, Italy, Liechtenstein, Luxembourg, Monaco, Norway, Netherlands, Portugal, Spain, Sweden, Switzerland, United Kingdom and Yemen.<br>Fixed service in Spain and Portugal. |
| 223.000–235.000 | Aeronavigation in Bahrain, Israel, Jordan, Oman, Qatar, Saudi Arabia, Syria and United Arab Emirates |
| 223.000–235.000 | Aeronavigation in Spain, Sweden and Portugal until 1st January 1990 |

## ITU Region 1 *continued*

| Frequency (MHz) | Allocated services |
| --- | --- |
| 230.000–235.000 | Fixed and mobile with variations as listed above and below |
| 230.000–238.000 | Aeronavigation in Nigeria and Yugoslavia Broadcasting in Botswana, Lesotho, Namibia, South Africa, Swaziland and Zambia |
| 235.000–267.000 | Fixed and mobile with variations as listed |
| ** 243.000 ** | Frequency (SARBE lifejacket and liferaft beacons, etc). Satellite location of beacons |
| 235.000–322.000 | Mobile satellite service (secondary) |
| 267.000–272.000 | Fixed, mobile and space (space to earth) |
| 399.900–400.050 | Satellite radionavigation |
| 400.000–400.150 | Satellite standard frequency and time signal (400.100 MHz) |
| 400.150–401.000 | Meteorological aids meteorological satellites (space to earth) and space operation (space to earth) |
| 402.000–403.000 | As above plus mobile (not aeronautical) |
| 403.000–406.000 | Meteorological aids, fixed and mobile (not aeronautical) |
| 406.000–406.100 | Mobile satellite (earth to space) |
| 406.100–410.000 | Radio astronomy, fixed and mobile (not aeronautical) |

**ITU Region 1** *continued*

| Frequency (MHz) | Allocated services |
| --- | --- |
| 410.000–420.000 | Fixed and mobile (not aeronautical) |
| 420.000–430.000 | Radiolocation, fixed and mobile (not aeronautical) with variations as listed |
| 420.000–460.000 | Aeronavigation (radio altimeters) in GDR, China, India, United Kingdom and USSR |
| 430.000–440.000 | Amateur and radiolocation with variations as listed above and below |
| 430.000–432.000 | Fixed and mobile in Denmark, Norway, Sweden, Finland, Yugoslavia and Libya |
| 438.000–440.000 | As above |
| 430.000–440.000 | Additional fixed service in Afghanistan, Algeria, Bahrain, Egypt, Saudi Arabia, United Arab Emirates, Ethiopia, Greece, Iran, Iraq, Israel, Italy, Jordan, Kenya, Kuwait, Lebanon, Libya, Liechtenstein, Malta, Nigeria, Oman, Qatar, Syria, Somalia, Switzerland and Tanzania |
| 430.000–435.000 | Mobile (except aeronautical) in countries listed above |
| 438.000–440.000 | As above |
| 430.000–440.000 | Fixed service (primary) in Angola, Bulgaria, Camaroon, The Congo, Gabon, Hungary, Mali, Mongolia, Niger, Poland, GDR, Roumania, Rwanda, Chad, Czechoslovakia and USSR |
| 433.050–434.790 | Industrial scientific and medical except in the countries listed in the two sections above |
| 438.000–440.000 | Fixed and mobile (except aeronautical) in Austria |
| 440.000–450.000 | Fixed, mobile and radiolocation with variation as listed |
| 449.750–450.250 | Space operation and research (earth to space) |

**ITU Region 1** *continued*

| Frequency (MHz) | Allocated services |
| --- | --- |
| 450.000–460.000 | Fixed and mobile with variations as listed above and below<br>Maritime on-board communications on 457.525, 457.550, 457.575, 467.555 and 467.575 |
| 460.000–470.000 | Fixed, mobile and meteorological-satellite (space to earth) |
| 470.000–790.000 | Broadcasting (television), fixed and mobile with variations as listed |
| 470.000–582.000 | Fixed service in Burundi, Camaroon, The Congo, Ethiopia, Israel, Kenya, Libya, Senegal, Sudan, Syria and Yemen |
| 582.000–590.000 | Aeronautical navigation (closes Dec 1987) in United Kingdom |
| 598.000–606.000 | Aeronautical navigation (closes Dec 1994) in United Kingdom |
| 582.000–606.000 | Aeronautical navigation in Oman, France and Italy (closes Jan 1990) |
| 590.000–598.000 | Aeronautical navigation in Denmark and Kuwait (closes Jan 1995) and United Kingdom |
| 606.000–614.000 | Radio astronomy in African broadcast region |
| 620.000–790.000 | Broadcast by television satellite (FM only) |
| 645.000–682.000 | Aeronautical navigation in Bulgaria, Czechoslovakia, Hungary, Mongolia, Roumania and USSR |
| 890.000–942.000 | Fixed, mobile (not aeronautical) and broadcasting with variations as listed below |
| 862.000–890.000 | Broadcasting limited to African broadcast region only and excluding Algeria, Egypt, Libya and Morocco |

## ITU Region 1 *continued*

| Frequency (MHz) | Allocated services |
|---|---|
| 862.000–960.000 | Aeronautical navigation in Bulgaria, Hungary, Czechoslovakia, Mongolia, Poland, GDR and USSR |
| 942.000–960.000 | Fixed and mobile (not aeronautical) with variations as listed above |
| 960.000–1215.00 | Aeronautical navigation. The band is used world-wide for developments to navigation |
| 1215.00–1240.00 | Radiolocation and radionavigation-satellite with variations as listed |
| 1215.00–1300.00 | Fixed and mobile in Afghanistan, Angola, Arabia, Bahrain, Cameroon, China, United Arab Emirates, Saudi Arabia, Ethiopia, Iran, Iraq, Israel, Jordan, Kuwait, Lebanon, Libya, Malawi, Morocco, Mozambique, Nigeria, Oman, Qatar, Syria, Somalia, Sudan, Chad and Yemen |
| 1215.00–1300.00 | Radionavigation in Algeria, Austria, Bahrain, Belgium, Benin, Burundi, Cameroon, China, Denmark, United Arab Emirates, DRG, France, Greece, Iran, Iraq, Kenya, Liechtenstein, Luxembourg, Mali, Mauritania, Norway, Oman, Netherlands, Portugal, Qatar, Senegal, Sudan, Somalia, Sweden, Switzerland, Tanzania, Turkey and Yugoslavia |
| 1240.00–1260.00 | Radiolocation and radionavigation satellite with variations listed above |
| 1260.00–1300.00 | Radiolocation and amateur (23 cm band) with variations as listed above |
| 1300.00–1350.00 | Aeronautical navigation and radiolocation |

## ITU Region 1 *continued*

| Frequency (MHz) | Allocated services |
| --- | --- |
| 1350.00–1400.00 | Fixed, mobile and radiolocation with variations as listed below |
| 1350.00–1400.00 | Radionavigation in Bulgaria, Hungary, Mongolia, Poland, GDR, Roumania, Czechoslovakia and USSR |
| 1370.00–1400.00 | Space research (passive) |
| 1400.00–1429.00 | Earth exploration satellite (passive), radio astronomy and space research (passive). There is international agreement not to transmit in this band. Some countries have programmes to monitor the band 1400–1727 MHz for transmissions of extra-terrestrial origin |
| 1429.00–1525.00 | Fixed and mobile (not aeronautical) with variation as listed above |
| 1525.00–1530.00 | Space operation (space to earth) fixed, earth exploration satellite and mobile (not aeronautical) |
| 1530.00–1535.00 | Space operation (space to earth), maritime mobile satellite, earth exploration satellite, fixed and mobile (not aeronautical) |
| 1535.00–1544.00 | Maritime mobile satellite (space to earth) with variations as listed below |
| 1540.00–1645.50 | Fixed in Afghanistan, Bahrain, The Congo, Saudi Arabia, Egypt, United Arab Emirates, Ethiopia, Iran, Iraq, Israel, Jordan, Kuwait, Lebanon, Malta, Morocco, Niger, Oman, Qatar, Syria, Somalia, Sudan, Chad, Yemen and Zambia |
| 1646.50–1660.00 | As above |

## ITU Region 1 *continued*

| Frequency (MHz) | Allocated services |
|---|---|
| 1544.00–1545.00 | Mobile satellite (space to earth). Variations as listed above and below |
| ** 1544.00–1545.00 ** | Restricted to distress and safety |
| ** 1645.50–1646.50 ** | Restricted to distress and safety |
| 1545.00–1559.00 | Aeronautical mobile satellite (space to earth). Variations as listed above and below |
| 1550.00–1645.50 | Fixed in FDR, Austria, Bulgaria, Camaroon, Mali, Hungary, Libya, Mongolia, Nigeria, Poland, GDR, Roumania, Senegal, Czechoslovakia and USSR |
| 1559.00–1610.00 | Aeronautical navigation and radionavigation satellite |
| 1610.00–1626.50 | Aeronautical navigation. Reserved world wide for development of navigational aids |
| 1626.50–1645.50 | Maritime mobile satellite (earth to space). Variations as listed above |
| 1645.50–1646.50 | Mobile satellite (earth to space). Variations as listed above |
| 1646.50–1660.00 | Aeronautical mobile satellite |
| 1660.00–1660.50 | Aeronautical mobile satellite (earth to space) and radio astronomy |
| 1660.50–1668.40 | Radio astronomy, space research (passive), fixed and mobile (not aeronautical). The sub-band 1660.50–1668.40 is used for the study of hydroxyl spectral lines by astronomers |

## ITU Region 1 *continued*

| Frequency (MHz) | Allocated services |
|---|---|
| 1668.40–1700.00 | Meteorological aids and satellite (space to earth) fixed and mobile (not aeronautical) |
| 1700.00–1710.00 | Meteorological satellite (space to earth), fixed and mobile (not aeronautical) |
| 1710.00–2290.00 | Fixed and mobile with variations as listed |
| 1718.00–1722.20 | Radio astronomy for spectral line observation. |
| 1770.00–1790.00 | Meteorological satellite in Bulgaria, Hungary, Mali, Mongolia, Poland, GDR, Roumania, Czechoslovakia and USSR |
| 2025.00–2110.00 | Earth to space and space to space (inter-satellite) transmissions |
| 2110.00–2120.00 | Earth to space (deep space research) |
| 2200.00–2290.00 | Space to earth, space to space (inter-satellite) and space exploration satellite |

## ITU Region 2

| Frequency (MHz) | Allocated services |
|---|---|
| 25.005–25.010 | Standard frequency and time signal, space research |
| 25.010–25.070 | Fixed and mobile (not aeronautical) |
| 25.070–25.210 | Maritime mobile |
| 25.210–25.550 | Fixed and mobile (not aeronautical) |
| 25.550–25.670 | Radio astronomy |

**ITU Region 2** *continued*

| Frequency (MHz) | Allocated services |
|---|---|
| 25.670–26.100 | Broadcasting |
| 26.100–26.175 | Maritime mobile |
| 26.175–27.500 | Fixed and mobile (not aeronautical) |
| 27.500–28.000 | Meteorological aids, fixed and mobile (C.B.) |
| 28.000–29.700 | Amateur (including satellites) |
| 29.700–30.005 | Fixed and mobile |
| 30.005–30.010 | Space research, satellite ident, fixed and mobile |
| 30.010–37.500 | Fixed and mobile |
| 37.500–38.250 | Fixed and mobile, radio astronomy |
| 38.250–39.986 | Fixed and mobile |
| ** 40.050 ** | Military distress frequency |
| 39.986–40.020 | Fixed and mobile, space research |
| 40.020–40.980 | Fixed and mobile, industrial, scientific and medical |
| 40.980–41.015 | Fixed and mobile, space research |
| 41.015–44.000 | Fixed and mobile |

**ITU Region 2** *continued*

| Frequency (MHz) | Allocated services |
|---|---|
| 44.000–47.000<br>44.000–47.000 | Fixed, mobile with variations as listed<br>Broadcasting (primary) in New Zealand and Australia |
| 47.000–50.000 | Fixed, mobile and broadcasting |
| 50.000–54.000 | Amateur (6 metre) |
| 54.000–72.000 | Broadcasting (television), fixed and mobile |
| 72.000–73.000 | Fixed and mobile |
| 73.000–74.600 | Radio astronomy with variations as listed. Fixed and mobile (secondary) in Colombia, Costa Rica, Cuba, El Salvador, Ecuador, Guatamala, Guyana, Honduras and Nicaragua |
| 74.800–75.200 | Aeronavigation (fan markers on 75.000 MHz) |
| 75.200–76.000 | Fixed and mobile |
| 76.000–88.000 | Broadcasting, fixed and mobile. In French overseas departments (Region 2), Guyana, Jamaica, Mexico, Paraguay and USA the fixed and mobile allocation is primary |
| 88.000–108.000 | Broadcasting (FM radio) |
| 108.000–117.975 | Aeronautical navigation |
| 117.975–136.000 | Aeronautical mobile (internationally used, channelised band) |

## ITU Region 2 *continued*

| Frequency (MHz) | Allocated services |
|---|---|
| ** 121.500 ** | Aeronautical distress frequency |
| 136.000–137.000 | Fixed and mobile, space operation service, meteorological satellite (space to earth) |
| 137.000–138.000 | Space operations including meteorology (several NOAA, MET, meteor sats, etc. see satellite listings). Additionally allocated to fixed and mobile on a secondary basis |
| 138.000–144.000 | Fixed, mobile, radiolocation and space research (space to earth) |
| 144.000–148.000 | Amateur (2 metre) including satellite operation |
| 148.000–149.900 | Fixed and mobile and space operation |
| 149-900–150.050 | Satellite navigation |
| 150.050–174.000 | Fixed and mobile. Main international maritime sub-bands (channelised — see marine section) fall within this segment. 156.525 is reserved for digital Selcall and 156.825 is allocated for direct printing telegraphy for distress and safety purposes |
| ** 156.800 ** | Maritime distress frequency |
| 174.000–216.000 | Broadcasting (television) with fixed and mobile on secondary basis |
| 216.000–220.000 | Fixed, maritime mobile and radiolocation |

**ITU Region 2** *continued*

| Frequency (MHz) | Allocated services |
| --- | --- |
| 220.000–225.000 | Amateur, fixed, mobile and radiolocation |
| 225.000–235.000 | Fixed and mobile |
| 235.000–267.000 | Fixed and mobile with the variation listed below (distress and satellite service) |
| ** 243.000 ** | Distress frequency (SARBE lifejacket and liferaft beacons, etc). Satellite location of beacons |
| 235.000–322.000 | Mobile satellite service (secondary) |
| 267.000–272.000 | Fixed, mobile and space (space to earth) |
| 272.000–273.000 | Space operation (space to earth), fixed and mobile |
| 273.000–322.000 | Fixed and mobile |
| 322.000–328.600 | Fixed, mobile and radio astronomy |
| 328.600–335.400 | Aeronautical navigation (mostly instrument landing system — ILS — glidepath) |
| 335.400–399.900 | Fixed and mobile |
| 399.900–400.050 | Satellite radionavagition |
| 400.000–400.150 | Satellite standard frequency and time signal (400.100 MHz) |

## ITU Region 2 *continued*

| Frequency (MHz) | Allocated services |
| --- | --- |
| 400.150–401.000 | Meteorological aids, meteorological satellites (space to earth) and space operation (space to earth) |
| 402.000–403.000 | As above plus mobile (not aeronautical) |
| 403.000–406.000 | Meteorological aids, fixed and mobile (not aeronautical) with the variation listed below. |
| 405.500–406.000 | Mobile (not aeronautical) satellite service (earth to space) in Canada |
| 406.000–406.100<br>406.100–410.000 | Mobile satellite (earth to space). Variation as listed below<br>Mobile (not aeronautical) satellite service (earth to space) in Canada |
| 406.100–410.000 | Radio astronomy, fixed and mobile (not aeronautical). Variation as listed above (Canada) |
| 410.000–420.000 | Fixed and mobile (not aeronautical) |
| 420.000–440.000 | Radiolocation, fixed and mobile (not aeronautical), amateur (70 cm band) |
| 440.000–450.000 | Fixed, mobile and radiolocation with variation as listed |
| 449.750–450.250 | Space operation and research (earth to space) |

**ITU Region 2** *continued*

| *Frequency (MHz)* | *Allocated services* |
| --- | --- |
| 450.000–460.000 | Fixed and mobile including maritime on-board communications (see marine section) |
| 460.000–470.000 | Fixed, mobile and meteorological-satellite (space to earth) |
| 470.000–512.000 | Broadcasting (television) with fixed and mobile on secondary basis except as listed below |
| 470.000–512.000 | Fixed and mobile (primary) in Chile, Colombia, Ecuador, Guyana, Mexico, Jamaica, USA and Venezuala |
| 512.000–608.000 | Broadcasting (television). Variation as listed below |
| 512.000–608.000 | Additional fixed and mobile allocation in USA, Costa Rica, El Salvador, Ecuador, Guatamala, Guyana, Honduras, Jamaica and Venezuala. |
| 608.000–614.000 | Radio astronomy, mobile (not aeronautical) satellite service (earth to space) |
| 614.000–806.000 | Broadcasting (television) with fixed and mobile on secondary basis except as listed below. Fixed and mobile (primary) in Chile, Colombia, Ecuador, Guyana, Jamaica and USA Fixed (primary) in Costa Rica, El Salvador and Honduras |
| 620.000–790.000 | Direct broadcasting by television satellite (FM only) |

## ITU Region 2 *continued*

| Frequency (MHz) | Allocated services |
| --- | --- |
| 806.000–890.000 | Fixed, mobile, broadcasting (television) and mobile (not aeronautical) satellite service |
| 890.000–902.000 | Fixed, mobile (not aeronautical) and radiolocation |
| 902.000–928.000 | Fixed, mobile (not aeronautical), amateur and radiolocation |
| 928.000–942.000 | Fixed, mobile (not aeronautical) and radiolocation |
| 942.000–960.000 | Fixed and mobile |
| 960.000–1215.00 | Aeronautical navigation. The band is used world-wide for developments to navigation |
| 1215.00–1240.00 | Radiolocation and radionavigation-satellite |
| 1240.00–1260.00 | Radiolocation, radionavigation satellite (space to earth) and amateur (23 cm band) |
| 1260.00–1300.00 | Radiolocation and amateur (23 cm band) |
| 1300.00–1350.00 | Aeronautical navigation and radiolocation. Some radio astronomy (spectral line observation) |
| 1350.00–1400.00 | Radiolocation with the variation listed below. |
| 1370.00–1400.00 | Passive space research and earth exploration satellites |

**ITU Region 2** *continued*

| Frequency (MHz) | Allocated services |
| --- | --- |
| 1400.00–1429.00 | Earth exploration satellite (passive), radio astronomy and space research (passive). There is international agreement not to transmit in this band. Some countries have programmes to monitor the band 1400–1727 MHz for transmissions for extra-terrestrial origin |
| 1429–1525.00 | Fixed and mobile (not aeronautical) with variation as listed above |
| 1525.00–1530.00 | Space operation (space to earth), fixed, earth exploration Satellite fixed and mobile (not aeronautical) |
| 1530.00–1535.00 | Space operation (space to earth), maritime mobile satellite, earth exploration satellite, fixed and mobile |
| 1544.00–1545.00<br>** 1544.00–1545.00 **<br>** 1645.00–1646.50 ** | Mobile satellite (space to earth). Variations as listed below<br>Restricted to distress and safety<br>Restricted to distress and safety |
| 1545.00–1559.00 | Aeronautical mobile satellite (space to earth) |
| 1559.00–1610.00 | Aeronautical navigation and radionavigation satellite |
| 1610.00–1626.50 | Aeronautical navigation. Reserved world wide for development of navigational aids |
| 1626.50–1645.50 | Maritime mobile satellite (earth to space) |

## ITU Region 2 *continued*

| Frequency (MHz) | Allocated services |
| --- | --- |
| 1645.50–1646.50 | Mobile satellite (earth to space) |
| 1646.50–1660.00 | Aeronautical mobile satellite |
| 1660.00–1660.50 | Aeronautical mobile satellite (earth to space) and radio astronomy |
| 1660.50–1668.40 | Radio astronomy, space research (passive), fixed and mobile (not aeronautical). The sub-band 1660.50–1668.40 is used for the study of hydroxyl spectral lines by astronomers |
| 1668.40–1670.00 | Radio astronomy, space research (passive), fixed and mobile (not aeronautical) |
| 1670.00–1690.00 | Meteorological aids, meteorological satellites (space to earth), fixed and mobile (not aeronautical) |
| 1690.00–1700.00 | Meteorological aids and meteorological satellites (space to earth). Variations as listed below |
| 1690.00–1700.00 | Fixed and mobile (not aeronautical) in Costa Rica and Cuba |
| 1700.00–1710.00 | Meteorological satellite (space to earth) fixed and mobile (not aeronautical) |
| 1710.00–2290.00 | Fixed and mobile with variations as listed |
| 1718.80–1722.20 | Radio astronomy for spectral line observation |
| 2025.00–2110.00 | Earth to space and space to space (inter-satellite) transmissions |

## ITU **Region 2** *continued*

| Frequency (MHz) | Allocated services |
| --- | --- |
| 2110.00–2120.00<br>2200.00–2290.00 | Earth to space (deep space research)<br>Space to earth, space to space (inter-satellite) and earth exploration satellite |

## ITU **Region 3**

| Frequency (MHz) | Allocated services |
| --- | --- |
| 25.005–25.010 | Standard frequency and time signal, space research |
| 25.010–25.070 | Fixed and mobile (not aeronautical) |
| 25.070–25.210 | Maritime mobile |
| 25.210–25.550 | Fixed and mobile (not aeronautical) |
| 25.550–25.670 | Radio astronomy |
| 25.670–26.100 | Broadcasting |
| 26.100–26.175 | Maritime mobile |
| 26.175–27.500 | Fixed and mobile (not aeronautical) |
| 27.500–28.000 | Meteorological aids, fixed and mobile (C.B.) |
| 28.000–29.700 | Amateur (including satellites) |
| 29.700–30.005 | Fixed and mobile |

## ITU Region 3 *continued*

| Frequency (MHz) | Allocated services |
| --- | --- |
| 30.005–30.010 | Space research, satellite ident, fixed and mobile |
| 30.010–37.500 | Fixed and mobile |
| 37.500–38.250 | Fixed and mobile, radio astronomy |
| 38.250–39.986 | Fixed and mobile |
| ** 40.050 ** | Military distress frequency |
| 39.986–40.020 | Fixed and mobile, space research |
| 40.020–40.980 | Fixed and mobile, industrial, scientific and medical |
| 40.980–41.015<br>41.000–44.000 | Fixed and mobile, space research with variation as listed below<br>Radiolocation (secondary) in Japan |
| 41.015–44.000 | Fixed and mobile with variation as listed above |
| 44.000–47.000<br>44.000–47.000 | Fixed and mobile with variation as listed below<br>Broadcasting (primary) in Australia and New Zealand |
| 47.000–50.000 | Fixed, mobile and broadcasting |
| 50.000–54.000 | Amateur (6 metre) |
| 54.000–68.000 | Broadcasting (television), fixed and mobile |

**ITU Region 3** *continued*

| Frequency (MHz) | Allocated services |
|---|---|
| 68.000–74.800 | Fixed and mobile with the variation listed below |
| 66.000–74.000 | Broadcasting (primary) in Australia, South and North Korea, The Philippines and Western Somoa |
| 74.800–75.200 | Aeronavigation (fan markers on 75.000 MHz) |
| 75.200–76.000 | Fixed and mobile |
| 75.400–87.000 | Fixed and mobile with variations as listed below |
| 75.400–87.000 | Broadcasting (primary) in Western Samoa |
| 76.000–87.000 | Broadcasting (primary) in North and South Korea, Philippines and Japan |
| 79.750–80.250 | Radio astronomy in all region 3 except for South Korea, India, Japan, Malaysia, Thailand, Singapore and The Philippines |
| 85.000–87.000 | Broadcasting (primary) in Australia |
| 87.000–100.00 | Fixed, mobile and broadcasting |
| 100.00–108.000 | Broadcasting (FM Radio) |
| 108.000–117.975 | Aeronautical navigation |
| 117.975–136.000 | Aeronautical mobile (internationally used, channelised band) |
| ** 121.500 ** | Aeronautical distress frequency |
| 136.000–137.000 | Fixed and mobile, space operation service, meteorological satellite (space to earth) |

**ITU Region 3** *continued*

| Frequency (MHz) | Allocated services |
| --- | --- |
| 137.000–138.000 | Space operations including meteorology (several NOAA, MET, Meteor sats, etc, see satellite listings). Additionally allocated to fixed and mobile on a secondary basis with variation listed below |
| 137.000–144.000 | Broadcasting (primary) in Australia |
| 138.000–144.000 | Fixed, mobile and space research (space to earth) with the variation listed above (Australia) |
| 144.000–148.000 | Fixed, mobile and amateur (2 metre) including satellite operation |
| 148.000–149.900 | Fixed and mobile and space operation |
| 149.900–150.050 | Satellite navigation |
| 150.050–174.000 | Fixed and mobile. Main international maritime sub-bands (channelised — see marine section) fall within this segment. 156.525 is reserved for digital Selcall and 156.825 is allocated for direct printing telegraphy for distress and safety purposes. Variations as listed below |
| 150.050–153.000 | Radio astronomy (primary) in Australia and India |
| 167.000–174.000 | Broadcasting (primary) in Afghanistan, China and Pakistan |
| 170.000–174.000 | Broadcasting (primary) in Japan |
| ** 156.800 ** | Maritime distress frequency |
| 174.000–223.000 | Broadcasting (television), fixed and mobile with variations listed below |

## ITU Region 3 *continued*

| Frequency (MHz) | Allocated services |
|---|---|
| 200.000–216.000 | Aeronautical navigation in Bangladesh, India, Pakistan and The Philippines |
| 204.000–208.000 | Aeronautical navigation in Australia and Papua New Guinea |
| 222.000–223.000 | Aeronautical navigation in Australia and Papua New Guinea and Japan with radiolocation in Japan as well |
| 223.000–230.000 | Fixed, mobile, broadcasting, aeronautical navigation and radiolocation |
| 230.000–235.000 | Fixed, mobile and aeronautical navigation |
| 235.000–267.000 | Fixed and mobile with the variation listed below (distress and satellite service) |
| ** 243.000 ** | Distress frequency (SARBE lifejacket and liferaft beacons, etc). Satellite location of beacons |
| 267.000–272.000 | Fixed, mobile and space (space to earth) |
| 272.000–273.000 | Space operation (space to earth), fixed and mobile |
| 273.000–322.000 | Fixed and mobile |
| 322.000–328.600 | Fixed, mobile and radio astronomy |
| 328.600–335.400 | Aeronautical navigation (mostly instrument landing system — ILS — Glidepath) |
| 335.400–399.900 | Fixed and mobile |

**ITU Region 3** *continued*

| Frequency (MHz) | Allocated services |
| --- | --- |
| 399.900–400.050 | Satellite radionavigation |
| 400.000–400.150 | Satellite standard frequency and time signal (400.100 MHz) |
| 400.150–401.000 | Meteorological aids, meteorological satellites (space to earth) and space operation (space to earth) with variations listed below |
| 400.500–401.000 | Fixed and mobile (primary) in Indonesia, Malaysia, Pakistan, The Philippines, Singapore, Sri Lanka and Thailand |
| 401.000–402.000 | Meteorological aids, space operation (space to earth), earth exploration satellites, fixed, meteorological satellites, mobile (not aeronautical) |
| 402.000–403.000 | Meteorological aids, earth exploration satellites (earth to space), fixed, mobile (not aeronautical) and meteorological satellites |
| 403.000–406.000 | Meteorological aids, fixed and mobile (not aeronautical) with the variation listed below |
| 406.000–406.100 | Mobile satellite (earth to space). Variation as listed below |
| 406.100–410.000 | Radio astronomy, fixed and mobile (not aeronautical) |
| 410.000–420.000 | Fixed and mobile (not aeronautical) |

**ITU Region 3** *continued*

| Frequency (MHz) | Allocated services |
|---|---|
| 420.000–440.000 | Radiolocation, fixed and mobile (not aeronautical), amateur (70 cm band) |
| 440.000–450.000 | Fixed, mobile and radiolocation with variation as listed |
| 449.750–450.250 | Space operation and research (earth to space) |
| 450.000–460.000 | Fixed and mobile including maritime on-board communications (see marine section) |
| 460.000–470.000 | Fixed, mobile and meteorological-satellite (space to earth) |
| 470.000–585.000 | Broadcasting (television) with fixed and mobile variation as listed below |
| 549.750–550.250 | Space operation (space to earth) in India |
| 585.000–610.000 | Fixed, mobile, broadcasting and radionavigation with the variation listed below |
| 608.000–614.000 | Radio astronomy (primary) in India |
| 610.000–890.000 | Fixed, mobile, mobile (not aeronautical) satellite service (earth to space) and broadcasting with variations listed above and below |
| 610.000–620.000 | Amateur (secondary) in New Zealand |
| 890.000–942.000 | Fixed, mobile, broadcasting and radiolocation |

## ITU Region 3 *continued*

| Frequency (MHz) | Allocated services |
| --- | --- |
| 942.000–960.000 | Fixed, mobile, broadcasting and mobile satellite service (not aeronautical). |
| 960.000–1215.00 | Aeronautical navigation. The band is used world-wide for developments to navigation |
| 1215.00–1240.00 | Radiolocation and radionavigation-satellite with variations listed below |
| 1215.00 1300.00 | Fixed and mobile (primary) in Bangladesh, China, India, Indonesia, Japan, Nepal, Pakistan, Sri Lanka, The Philippines, Thailand and Togo |
| 1240.00–1260.00 | Radiolocation, Radionavigation satellite (space to earth) and amateur (23 cm band) with variation listed above |
| 1260.00–1300.00 | Radiolocation, and amateur (23 cm band) with variation listed previously |
| 1300.00–1350.00 | Aeronautical navigation and radiolocation. Some radio astronomy (spectral line observation) and variation listed below |
| 1300.00–1350.00 | Fixed and mobile (primary) in Indonesia |
| 1350.00–1400.00 | Radiolocation with the variation listed below |
| 1370.00–1400.00 | Passive space research and earth exploration satellites |
| 1400.00–1429.00 | Earth exploration satellite (passive), radio astronomy and space research (passive). There is international agreement not to transmit in this band. Some countries |

## ITU Region 3 *continued*

| Frequency (MHz) | Allocated services |
|---|---|
| | have programmes to monitor the band 1400–1727 MHz for transmissions of extra-terrestrial origin |
| 1429.00–1525.00 | Fixed and mobile (not aeronautical) with variation as listed above |
| 1525.00–1530.00 | Space operation (space to earth), fixed, earth exploration satellite, fixed and mobile (not aeronautical) with variations listed below |
| 1435.00–1535.00 | Aeronautical mobile telemetry in Australia and Papua New Guinea |
| 1530.00–1535.00 | Space operation (space to earth), maritime mobile satellite, earth exploration satellite, fixed and mobile with the variation listed above |
| 1535.00–1544.00 | Maritime mobile satellite (space to earth) with variations listed below |
| 1646.50–1660.00 | Fixed service (secondary) in Bangladesh, Sri Lanka and Thailand |
| 1544.00—1545.00 | Mobile satellite (space to earth). Variations as listed above and below |
| ** 1544.00–1545.00 ** | Restricted to distress and safety |
| ** 1645.50–1646.50 ** | Restricted to distress and safety |
| 1545.00–1559.00 | Aeronautical mobile satellite (space to earth) with variation previously listed |
| 1559.00–1610.00 | Aeronautical navigation and radionavigation satellite with variation previously listed |

## ITU Region 3 *continued*

| Frequency (MHz) | Allocated services |
| --- | --- |
| 1610.00–1626.50 | Aeronautical navigation. Reserved world wide for development of navigational aids |
| 1626.50–1645.50 | Maritime mobile satellite (earth to space) |
| 1645.50–1646.50 | Mobile satellite (earth to space) |
| 1646–1660 | Aeronautical mobile satellite |
| 1660.00–1660.50 | Aeronautical mobile satellite (earth to space) and radio astronomy |
| 1660.50–1668 40 | Radio astronomy, space research (passive), fixed and mobile (not aeronautical). The sub-band 1660.50–1668.40 is used for the study of hydroxyl spectral lines by astronomers variations as listed below |
| 1660.50–1668.40 | Fixed and mobile (not aeronautical) in Indonesia, India, Malaysia, Pakistan, Singapore, Sri Lanka and Thailand |
| 1660.50–1668.40 | Meteorological aids (secondary) in Bangladesh, India, Indonesia, Pakistan, Sri Lanka and Thailand |
| 1668.40–1670.00 | Radio astronomy, space research (passive), fixed and mobile (not aeronautical) and meteorological aids |
| 1670.00–1690.00 | Meteorological aids, meteorological satellites (space to earth), fixed and mobile (not aeronautical) |
| 1690.00–1700.00 | Meteorological aids and meteorological satellites (space to earth). Variations as listed below |

**ITU Region 3** *continued*

| *Frequency (MHz)* | *Allocated services* |
| --- | --- |
| 1690.00–1700.00 | Fixed and mobile (not aeronautical) in Australia, India, Malaysia, Pakistan, Sri Lanka, Singapore, Thailand and Indonesia |
| 1700.00–1710.00 | Meteorological satellite (space to earth) fixed and mobile (not aeronautical) with the variations listed below |
| 1700.00–1710.00 | Space research (space to earth) in Indonesia, India, Japan and Thailand |
| 1710.00–2290.00 | Fixed and mobile with variations as listed |
| 1718.80–1722.20 | Radio astronomy for spectral line observation |
| 2025.00–2110.00 | Earth to space and space to space (inter-satellite) transmissions |
| 2110.00–2120.00 | Earth to Space (deep space research) |
| 2200.00–2290.00 | Space to earth, space to space (inter-satellite) and earth exploration satellite |

## Marine bands

The marine VHF bands fall into two categories: international and USA. The band between 156 and 162 MHz is channelised and a complete list is shown for both sets of allocations. The frequency pairings are almost identical and most synthesised marine band transceivers sold these days have a switch which allows the transceiver to be switched between the two systems. The emergency frequency, 156.800 MHz is common to both systems and is used not only for distress purposes but also for initial calls to the required station. This way all ships keep a listening watch on the frequency. Some modern transceivers incorporate a 'Dual-Watch' facility which makes the receiver scan between two channels, 16 and whatever alternative channel is tuned-in

The allocations shown for both the international and USA system include a variety of uses including ship-to-ship, ship-to-shore (port operations) and Public Correspondence channels. The latter are semi or full Duplex systems which allow the shore station to connect the ship's radiophone with a public telephone system (land-line). This facility is often referred to as a 'Link Call'.

The only other 'channelised' marine allocation is at UHF where a limited number of channels are allocated for on-board communication.

## Marine radiotelephone channels — International

| Channel | Ship TX | Coast TX | Service |
|---------|---------|----------|---------|
| 0 | 156.000 | | Coastguard/lifeboat |
| 1 | 156.050 | 160.650 | Port operations/public correspondence |
| 2 | 156.100 | 160.700 | Port operations/public correspondence |
| 3 | 156.150 | 160.750 | Port operations/public correspondence |
| 4 | 156.200 | 160.800 | Port operations/public correspondence |
| 5 | 156.250 | 160.850 | Port operations/public correspondence |
| 6 | 156.300 | | Intership |
| 7 | 156.350 | 160.950 | Port operations/public correspondence |
| 8 | 156.400 | | Intership |
| 9 | 156.450 | | Intership |
| 10 | 156.500 | | Intership |
| 11 | 156.550 | | Port operations |
| 12 | 156.600 | | Port operations |
| 13 | 156.650 | | Port operations |
| 14 | 156.700 | | Port operations |
| 15 | 156.750 | | Port operations |
| 16 | 156.800 | | Distress and calling (international and US) |
| 17 | 156.850 | | Port operations |
| 18 | 156.900 | 161.500 | Port operations |
| 19 | 156.950 | 161.550 | Port operations |
| 20 | 157.000 | 161.600 | Port operations |
| 21 | 157.050 | 161.650 | Port operations |
| 22 | 157.100 | 161.700 | Port operations |
| 23 | 157.150 | 161.750 | Public correspondence |
| 24 | 157.200 | 161.800 | Public correspondence |
| 25 | 157.250 | 161.850 | Public correspondence |
| 26 | 157.300 | 161.900 | Public correspondence |

## Marine radiotelephone channels — International *continued*

| Channel | Ship TX | Coast TX | Service |
|---------|---------|----------|---------|
| 27 | 157.350 | 161.950 | Public correspondence |
| 28 | 157.400 | 161.200 | Public correspondence |
| 60 | 156.025 | 160.625 | Public correspondence |
| 61 | 156.075 | 160.675 | Public correspondence |
| 62 | 156.125 | 160.725 | Public correspondence |
| 63 | 156.175 | 160.775 | Public correspondence |
| 64 | 156.225 | 160.825 | Public correspondence |
| 65 | 156.275 | 160.875 | Public correspondence |
| 66 | 156.325 | 160.925 | Public correspondence |
| 67 | 156.375 | | Intership/small yacht safety/ coastguard |
| 68 | 156.425 | | |
| 69 | 156.475 | | Intership |
| 70 | 156.525 | | Digital selective calling/distress |
| 71 | 156.575 | | Port operations |
| 72 | 156.625 | | Intership |
| 73 | 156.675 | | Intership |
| 74 | 156.725 | | Port operations |
| 77 | 156.875 | | Intership |
| 78 | 156.925 | 161.525 | Port operations |
| 79 | 156.975 | 161.575 | Port operations |
| 80 | 157.025 | 161.625 | Port operations |
| 81 | 157.075 | 161.675 | Port operations |
| 82 | 157.125 | 161.725 | Port operations |
| 83 | 157.175 | 161.775 | Port operations |
| 84 | 157.225 | 161.825 | Port operations |
| 85 | 157.275 | 161.875 | Port operations |
| 86 | 157.325 | 161.925 | Public correspondence |
| 87 | 157.375 | 161.975 | Public correspondence |
| 88 | 157.425 | 162.025 | Public correspondence |
| M | 157.850 | | Marinas |

## Marine radiotelephone channels — USA

| Channel | Ship TX | Coast TX | Service |
|---------|---------|----------|---------|
| 6 | 156.300 | | Intership safety |
| 7 | 156.350 | | Commercial |

## Marine radiotelephone channels — USA *continued*

| Channel | Ship TX | Coast TX | Service |
|---------|---------|----------|---------|
| 8 | 156.400 | | Commercial |
| 9 | 156.450 | | Commercial/marinas/yacht clubs |
| 10 | 156.500 | | Commercial |
| 11 | 156.550 | | Commercial |
| 12 | 156.600 | | Port operations/US coastguard |
| 13 | 156.650 | | Navigational/bridge-to-bridge |
| 14 | 156.700 | | Port operations/US coastguard |
| 15 | 156.750 | | Environmental/hydrographic |
| 16 | 156.800 | | Distress/calling |
| 17 | 156.850 | | State use only |
| 18 | 156.900 | | Commercial |
| 19 | 156.950 | | Commercial |
| 20 | 157.000 | 161.600 | Port operations |
| 21 | 157.050 | | US coastguard only |
| 22 | 157.100 | | US coastguard only |
| 23 | 157.150 | | US coastguard only |
| 24 | 157.200 | 161.800 | Public correspondence |
| 25 | 157.250 | 161.850 | Public correspondence |
| 26 | 157.300 | 161.900 | Public correspondence |
| 27 | 157.350 | 161.950 | Public correspondence |
| 28 | 157.400 | 162.000 | Public correspondence |
| 65 | 157.250 | | Port operations |
| 66 | 156.325 | | Port operations |
| 67 | 156.375 | | Commercial |
| 68 | 156.425 | | Non-commercial |
| 69 | 156.475 | | Non-commercial |
| 70 | 156.525 | | Non-commercial |
| 71 | 156.575 | | Non-commercial |
| 72 | 156.625 | | Non-commercial |
| 77 | 156.675 | | Port operations |
| 78 | 156.925 | | Non-commercial |
| 79 | 156.975 | | Commercial |
| 80 | 157.025 | | Commercial |
| 83 | 157.175 | | US coastguard auxilliary |
| 84 | 157.225 | 161.825 | Public correspondence |
| 85 | 157.275 | 161.875 | Public correspondence |
| 86 | 157.325 | 161.925 | Public correspondence |
| 87 | 157.375 | 161.975 | Public correspondence |

## Marine radiotelephone channels — USA *continued*

| Channel | Ship TX | Coast TX | Service |
|---------|---------|----------|---------|
| 88 | 157.425 | | Commercial |
| | 162.400 | | NOAA weather |
| | 162.425 | | NOAA weather |
| | 162.475 | | NOAA weather |
| | 162.550 | | NOAA weather |

## Marine radiotelephone band — onboard communications (handsets)

There are now two sets of standard frequencies, depending on area, for on-board communication on ships. This communication consists mainly of plain speech using hand-portable transceivers. Typical communications are between bridge and deck during docking, loading, etc. Although two sets of frequencies are quoted, both sets can usually be found being used despite the area. This is no doubt because ships are hardly likely to carry two complete sets of hand-portables just for different areas. However, both sets of frequencies are given here and it should be observed that some on-board communication also takes place in the VHF marine mobile allocation (165–162 MHz).

### International allocation

| CH1 | 457.525 | CH1A | 467.525 |
|-----|---------|------|---------|
| CH2 | 457.550 | CH2B | 467.550 |
| CH3 | 457.575 | CH3B | 467.675 |

### USA, Canada and Philippines allocation

| CH1 | 457.525 | CH1A | 567.750 |
|-----|---------|------|---------|
| CH2 | 457.550 | CH2A | 467.775 |
| CH3 | 457.575 | CH3A | 467.800 |
| CH4 | 457.600 | CH4A | 467.825 |

# 8 Callsigns

## ITU allocated callsigns

The International Telecommunication Union, ITU, based in Geneva, Switzerland, co-ordinated all radio communications, broadcasting, etc. As part of their mandate they also co-ordinate the allocation of callsign prefixes for use by various countries. The only variation on these callsigns is in the aeronautical bands and a separate list of prefixes for that service is listed separately.

The call-sign allocations shown here will be used extensively by amateur stations, ships (indicating their origin) and government, commercial and telecommunication (telegraphic) stations. In some instances, particularly stations in the USA, the prefix will also give an indication of the country or area in which the station is allocated.

For the sake of quick reference and clarity the amateur callsign list is also shown separately. The only variations that will occur on the amateur prefixes are where special stations are in operation but even then the callsign should comply with the main ITU list.

| ITU allocation | Prefix | Country |
| --- | --- | --- |
| A2A–A2Z | A22 | Botswana |
| A3A–A3Z | A35 | Tonga |
| A4A–A4Z | A4X | Oman |
| A5A–A5Z | A51 | Bhutan |
| A6A–A6Z | A6X | United Arab Emirates |
| A7A–A7A | A71 | Qatar |
| A8A–A8Z | | Liberia |
| A9A–A9Z | A9X | Bahrain |

| ITU allocation | Prefix | Country |
|---|---|---|
| AAA–ALZ | | United States of America |
| | AA–AG | USA (see also 'W') |
| | AH0 | Northern Mariana Island |
| | AH1 | Baker Island |
| | AH1 | Howland Island |
| | AH2 | Guam |
| | AH3 | Johnston Island |
| | AH4 | Midway Island |
| | AH5 | Jarvis Island |
| | AH5 | Palmyra Island |
| | AH5K | Kingman Reef |
| | AH6 | Hawaii |
| | AH7 | Kure Island |
| | AH8 | American Samoa |
| | AH9 | Peale Island |
| | AH9 | Wake Island |
| | AI–AK | USA (see also 'W') |
| | AL7 | Alaska |
| AMA–AOZ | | Spain |
| APA–ASZ | AP | Pakistan |
| ATA–AWZ | | India |
| AXA–AXZ | | Australia |
| AYA–AZZ | | Argentine |
| BAA–BZZ | | China |
| | BY | Taiwan |
| C2A–C2Z | C21 | Nauru |
| C3A– | C31 | Andorra |
| C4A–C4Z | | Cyprus |
| C5A–C5Z | C5A | The Gambia |
| | CE9 | Shetland Isles |
| CFA–CKZ | | Canada |
| CLA–CMZ | CM | Cuba |
| CNA–CNZ | CN | Morocco |
| COA–COZ | CO | Cuba |
| CPA–CPZ | CP1 | Bolivia |
| | CP2–7 | Bolivia |
| | CP8–9 | Bolivia |
| CQA–CUZ | | Portugal |
| | CR9 | Macao |
| | CT1,4 | Portugal |
| | CT2 | Azores |

| ITU allocation | Prefix | Country |
|---|---|---|
| | CT3 | Maderia |
| CVA–CXZ | CX | Uruguay |
| CYA–CZZ | | Canada |
| D2A–D3Z | D2 | Angola |
| D4A–D4Z | D4 | Cape Verde |
| D54–D5Z | | Liberia |
| D6A–D6Z | D68 | Comoros |
| D7A–D9Z | | Korea (RK) |
| DAA–DRZ | DA–DL | Germany FRG |
| DSA–DTZ | | Korea (RK) |
| DUA–DZZ | DU | Philippines |
| EAA–EHZ | EA | Spain |
| | EA6 | Canary Islands |
| | EA9 | Ceuta/Melilla |
| | EA1–EJZ | Eire |
| EKA–EKZ | | USSR |
| ELA–ELZ | EL | Liberia |
| EMA–EOZ | | USSR |
| EPA–EQZ | EP | Iran |
| ERA–ESZ | | USSR |
| ETA–ET2 | ET | Ethiopia |
| EUA–EWZ | | Byelorussia USSR |
| EXA–EZZ | EZ | USSR |
| FAA–FZZ | F | France |
| | FB8W | Crozet Island |
| C6A–C6Z | C6 | Bahamas |
| C8A–C9Z | C9 | Mozambique |
| CAA–CEZ | | Chile |
| | CEOA | Easter Island |
| | CEOX | San Felix Island |
| | CEOZ | Juan Fernandez Island |
| | CE1–5 | Chile |
| | CE6–8 | Chile |
| | CE9 | Chilean Antartica |
| | FK8 | New Caledonia |
| | FM7 | Martinique |
| | FO8 | Clipperton Island |
| | FO8 | Marquesas Island |
| | FO8 | Rapa Island |
| | FO8 | Gambier Island |
| | FO8 | Society Island |

| ITU allocation | Prefix | Country |
|---|---|---|
| | FO8 | Tubua Island |
| | FP8 | St Pierre et Miquelon |
| | FR7 | Europa Island |
| | FR7 | Glorieuses Island |
| | FR7 | Reunion Island |
| | FR7 | Tromelin Island |
| | FR7 | Juen de Nova |
| | FS7 | St Martin |
| | FW8 | Wallis & Futuna Islands |
| | FY7 | French Guiana |
| | FY7 | Inini |
| GAA–GZZ | | Great Britain |
| | G– | England |
| | GD | Isle of Man |
| | GI | Northern Ireland |
| | GJ | Jersey |
| | GM | Scotland |
| | GU | Guernsey |
| | GU | Alderney |
| | GU | Sark |
| | GW | Wales |
| | FB8X | Kerguelen Island |
| | FB8Y | Terre Adelie |
| | FB8Z | Amsterdam Island |
| | FB8Z | St Paul Island |
| | FC | Corsica |
| | FG7 | Guadaloupe |
| | FH8 | Mayotte |
| | FH8 | Chesterfield Island |
| | FK9 | Loyalty Island |
| | JT | Mongolia |
| | JWA–JXZ | Norway |
| | JW | Svalbard |
| | JX | Jan Mayen Island |
| JYA–JYZ | JY | Jordan |
| JZA–ZZ | | Indonesia |
| KAA–KZZ | | United States of America |
| | K | USA (see 'W') |
| | KA | Japan (US personnel) |
| | KA | USA (see 'W') |
| | KA1 | Minami Torishima |

| ITU allocation | Prefix | Country |
|---|---|---|
| | KA1 | Ogasawara |
| | KB | USA (see 'W') |
| | KB6 | Baker Island |
| | KB6 | Howland Island |
| | KC | USA (see 'W') |
| | KC4 | Nevassa Island |
| | KC6 | Eastern Caroline Island |
| | KC6 | Western Caroline Island |
| | KD–KG | USA (see 'W') |
| | KG4 | Guantanamo Bay |
| | KG6 | Guam |
| | KH0 | Northern Mariana Island |
| | KH1 | Baker Island |
| | KH1 | Howland Island |
| | KH2 | Guam |
| | KH3 | Johston Island |
| | KH4 | Midway Island |
| H2A–HZZ | | Cyprus |
| H3A–H3Z | | Panama |
| H4A–H4Z | H44 | Solomon Islands |
| H6A–H7Z | | Nicaragua |
| H8A–H9Z | | Panama |
| HAA–HAZ | HA | Hungary |
| HBA–HBZ | | Switzerland |
| | HBO | Liechtenstein |
| HCA–HDZ | HC | Ecuador |
| | HC8 | Galapagos Islands |
| HEA–HEZ | | Switzerland |
| HFA–HFZ | | Poland |
| HGA–HGZ | HG | Hungary |
| HHA–HHZ | HH | Haiti |
| HIA–HIZ | HI | Dominican Republic |
| HJA–HKZ | HK | Colombia |
| | HKO | Baja Nuevo |
| | HKO | Malpelo Island |
| | HKO | Providencia Island |
| | HKO | San Andres Island |
| HLA–HLZ | | Korea (RK) |
| HMA–HMZ | | Korea (RK) |
| HNA–HNZ | | Iraq |
| HOA–HPZ | HP | Panama |

| ITU allocation | Prefix | Country |
|---|---|---|
| HQA–HRZ | HR | Honduras |
| HSA–HSZ | HS | Thailand |
| HTA–HTZ | HT | Nicaragua |
| HUA–HUZ |  | El Salvador |
| HVA–HVZ | HV | Vatican City |
| HWA–HYZ |  | France |
| HZA–HZZ | HZ | Saudi Arabia |
| IAA–IAZ | I | Italy |
|  | ISO | Sardina |
| J2A–J2Z | J28 | Djibouti |
| J3A–J3Z | J3 | Grenada |
| J4A–J4Z |  | Greece |
| J5A–J5Z | J5 | Guinea Bissau |
|  | KH5 | Jarvis Island |
|  | KH5 | Palmyra Island |
|  | KH5K | Kingman Reef |
|  | KH6 | Hawaii |
|  | KH6 | Kure Island |
|  | KH7 | Kure Island |
|  | KH8 | American Samoa |
|  | KH9 | Peale Island |
|  | KH9 | Wilkes Island |
|  | KI,KJ | USA (see 'W') |
|  | KJ6 | Johnston Island |
|  | KK | USA (see 'W') |
|  | KL7 | Alaska |
|  | KM–KO | USA (see 'W') |
|  | KP1 | Navassa Island |
|  | KP2 | Virgin Island |
|  | KP3 | Roncador Key |
|  | KP3 | Serrana Bank |
|  | KP4 | Desecheo Island |
|  | KP4 | Puerto Rico |
|  | KP6 | Jarvis Island |
|  | KP6 | Palmyra Island |
|  | KQ–KS | USA (see 'W') |
|  | KV4 | Virgin Islands |
|  | KW | USA (see 'W') |
|  | KW6 | Wake Island |
|  | KX | USA (see 'W') |
|  | KX6 | Marshall Islands |

| ITU allocation | Prefix | Country |
|---|---|---|
| | KY,KZ | USA (see 'W') |
| L2A–L9Z | | Argentina |
| LAA–LNZ | LA,LB | Norway |
| LOA–LWZ | LUA–U | Argentina |
| | LUV–X | Argentina |
| | LUY | Argentina |
| | LUZ | Argentine Antartica |
| LXA–LXZ | LX | Luxembourg |
| LYA–LYZ | | USSR |
| J6A–J6Z | J6 | St Lucia |
| J7A–J7Z | J73 | Dominica |
| J8A–J8Z | J88 | St Vincent |
| JAA–JSZ | JA | Japan |
| | JD | Minami Torishima |
| | JD | Ogasswara |
| | JE–JR | Japan |
| JTA–JVZ | JT | Mongolia |
| LZA–LZZ | LZ | Bulgaria |
| MAA–MZZ | | Great Britain |
| NAA–NZZ | | United States of America |
| | N | USA (see 'W') |
| | NA–NG | USA (see 'W') |
| | NH0 | Northern Mariana Island |
| | NH1 | Baker Island |
| | NH1 | Howland Island |
| | NH2 | Guam |
| | NH3 | Johnston Island |
| | NH4 | Midway Island |
| | NH5 | Jarvis Island |
| | NH5 | Palmyra Island |
| | NH5K | Kingman Reef |
| | NH6 | Hawaii |
| | NH7 | Kure Island |
| | NH8 | American Samoa |
| | NH9 | Peale Island |
| | NH9 | Wake Island |
| | NH9 | Wilkes Island |
| | NI–NK | USA (see 'W') |
| | NL7 | Alaska |
| | NM–NO | USA (see 'W') |
| | NP1 | Navassa Island |

| ITU allocation | Prefix | Country |
|---|---|---|
| | NP2 | Virgin Island |
| | NP3 | Roncador Key |
| | NP3 | Serrana Bank |
| | NP4 | Desecheo Island |
| | NP4 | Puerto Rico |
| | NP6 | Jarvis Island |
| | NP6 | Palmyra Island |
| | NQ–NZ | USA (see 'W') |
| OAA–OCZ | OA | Peru |
| ODA–ODZ | OD5 | Lebanon |
| OEA–OEZ | OE | Austria |
| OFA–OJZ | OH | Finland |
| | OHO | Aaland Island |
| | OJO | Market Reef |
| OKA–OMZ | OK,OL | Czechoslovakia |
| ONA–OTZ | ON | Belgium |
| | OR4 | Belgian Antartica |
| OAU–OZZ | OZ | Denmark |
| | OX | Greenland |
| | OY | Faroe Islands |
| P2A–P2Z | P29 | Papua New Guinea |
| P3A–P3Z | | Cyprus |
| P4A–P4Z | | Netherlands Antilles |
| P5A–P9Z | | Korea (DPRK) |
| PAA–PIZ | PA–PI | Netherlands |
| PJA–PJZ | | Netherlands Antilles |
| | PJ2 | Curacao |
| | PJ3 | Aruba |
| | PJ4 | Bonin |
| | PJ5 | St Eustatius |
| | PJ6 | Saba |
| | PJ7,8 | St Maarten |
| PKA–POZ | | Indonesia |
| PPA–PYZ | PP1,2 | Brazil |
| | PP5 | Brazil |
| | PR6–8 | Brazil |
| | PR7,8 | Brazil |
| | PS7 | Brazil |
| | PT2,7,9 | Brazil |
| | PU8 | Brazil |
| | PV8 | Brazil |

| ITU allocation | Prefix | Country |
|---|---|---|
| | PW8 | Brazil |
| | PYO | Fernando de Noronha |
| | PYO | St Paul Island |
| | PYO | St Peter Island |
| | PYO | Trinidade Island |
| | PYO | Martin Vaz Island |
| | PY1–9 | Brazil |
| PZA–PZZ | PZ | Suriname |
| RAA–RZZ | | USSR |
| S2A–S3Z | S2 | Bangladesh |
| S6A–S6Z | | Singapore |
| S7A–S7Z | | Seychelles |
| S9A–S9Z | S92 | Sao Tome Principe |
| SAA–SMZ | SK,SM | Sweden |
| SNA–SRZ | SP | Poland |
| SSA–SSM | | Egypt |
| SSN–STZ | ST | Sudan |
| SAU–SUZ | SU | Egypt |
| SVA–SZZ | SV | Greece |
| | SV9 | Crete |
| | SV5 | Rhodes |
| | SY | Mount Athos |
| T2A–T2Z | T2 | Tuvalu |
| T3A–T3Z | T30 | Kiribati |
| | T31 | Northern Line Island |
| | T31 | Line Island |
| | T32 | Phoenix Island |
| T4A–T4Z | | Cuba |
| T5A–T5Z | T5 | Somalia |
| T6A–T6Z | | Afghanistan |
| TAA–TCZ | TA | Turkey |
| TDA–TDZ | | Guatemala |
| TEA–TEZ | | Costa Rica |
| TFA–TFZ | TF | Iceland |
| TGA–TGZ | TG | Guatamala |
| THA–THZ | | France |
| TIA–TIZ | TI | Costa Rica |
| | T19 | Cocos Islands |
| TJA–TJZ | TJ | Camaroon |
| TKA–TKZ | | France |
| TLA–TLZ | TL8 | Central African Republic |

| ITU allocation | Prefix | Country |
|---|---|---|
| TMA–TMZ | | France |
| TNA–TNZ | TN8 | Congo |
| TOA–TQZ | | France |
| TRA–TRZ | TR8 | Gabon |
| TSA–TSZ | | Tunisia |
| TTA–TTZ | TT8 | Chad |
| TUA–TUZ | TU | Ivory Coast |
| TVA–TXZ | | France |
| TYA–TYZ | TY | Benin |
| TZA–TZZ | TZ | Mali |
| UAA–UQZ | | USSR |
| | UA0–9 | RSFSR |
| | UB5 | Ukraine |
| | UC2 | Byelorussia |
| | UD6 | Azerbaijan |
| | UF6 | Georgia |
| | UG6 | Armenia |
| | UH8 | Turkmen |
| | UI8 | Uzbek |
| | UJ8 | Tadzhik |
| | UL7 | Kazakh |
| | UM8 | Kirghiz |
| | UN1 | RSFSR |
| | UO5 | Moldavia |
| | UP2 | Lithuania |
| | UQ2 | Latvia |
| URA–UTZ | UT5 | Ukraine |
| | UR2 | Estonia |
| UUA–UZZ | | USSR |
| | UV,UW | RSFSR |
| | UY5 | Ukraine |
| | UZ | RSFSR |
| V2A–V2Z | V2A | Antigua |
| V3A–V3Z | V3A | Belize |
| VAA–VGZ | VE1–8 | Canada |
| VHA–VNZ | | Australia |
| | VKO | Heard Island |
| | VKO | Macquarie Island |
| | VK1–8 | Australia |
| | VK9N | Norfolk Island |
| | VK9X | Christmas Island |

| ITU allocation | Prefix | Country |
|---|---|---|
|  | VK9Y | Cocos Keeling Island |
|  | VK9Z | Willis Island |
| VOA–VOZ | VO | Canada |
| VPA–VPZ |  | Great Britain |
|  | VP2 | Leeward Islands |
|  | VP2 | Windward Islands |
|  | VP5 | Caicos Islands |
|  | VP5 | Turks Islands |
|  | VP8 | Falkland Islands |
|  | VP8 | South Georgia |
|  | VP8 | South Orkney Island |
|  | VP8 | South Sandwich Island |
|  | VP8 | South Shetland Island |
|  | VP9 | Bermuda |
|  | VQ9 | Chagos Islands |
|  | VR6 | Pitcairn Island |
|  | VS5 | Brunei |
|  | VS6 | Hong Kong |
| VTA–VTZ | VU | India |
|  | VU | Andaman Island |
|  | VU | Laccadive Island |
|  | VU | Nicobar Island |
| VXA–VYZ | VY1 | Canada |
|  | VX9 | Sable Island |
|  | VYO | St Paul Island |
| VZA–VZZ |  | Australia |
| WAA–WZZ | W0–W9 | United States of America |
|  | WA–WG | United States of America |
|  | WH0 | North Mariana Island |
|  | WH1 | Baker Island |
|  | WH1 | Howland Island |
|  | WH2 | Guam |
|  | WH3 | Johnston Island |
|  | WH4 | Midway Island |
|  | WH5 | Jarvis Island |
|  | WH5 | Palmyra Island |
|  | WH5K | Kingman Reef |
|  | WH6 | Hawaii |
|  | WH7 | Kure Island |
|  | WH8 | American Samoa |
|  | WH9 | Peale Island |

| ITU allocation | Prefix | Country |
|---|---|---|
| | WH9 | Wake Island |
| | WH9 | Wilkes Island |
| | WI–WK | United States of America |
| | WL7 | Alaska |
| | WM–WO | United States of America |
| | WP1 | Navassa Island |
| | WP2 | Virgin Islands |
| | WP3 | Roncador Key |
| | WP3 | Serrana Bank |
| | WP4 | Desecheo Island |
| | WP4 | Puerto Rico |
| | WQ–WZ | United States of America |
| XAA–XIZ | XE | Mexico |
| | XF4 | Revilla Gigedo Island |
| XJA–XOZ | | Canada |
| XPA–XPZ | | Denmark |
| XQA–XRZ | | Chile |
| XSA–XSZ | | China |
| XTA–XTZ | XT | Volta |
| XUA–XUZ | XU | Kampuchea |
| XVA–XVX | | Vietnam |
| XWA–XWZ | | Laos |
| XXA–XXZ | | Portugal |
| XYA–XZZ | XZ | Burma |
| Y2A–Y9Z | | Germany (GDR) |
| YAA–YAZ | YA | Afghanistan |
| YBA–YHZ | YB–YD | Indonesia |
| YIA–YIZ | YI | Iraq |
| YJA–YJZ | YJ | Vanuatu |
| YKA–YKZ | YK | Syria |
| YLA–YLZ | | Latvia |
| YMA–YMZ | | Turkey |
| YNA–YNZ | YN | Nicaragua |
| YOA–YRZ | YO | Romania |
| YSA–YSZ | YS | El Salvador |
| YTA–YUZ | YU | Yugoslavia |
| VYA–VYZ | YV | Venezuela |
| | YYO | Aves Island |
| YZA–YZZ | | Yugoslavia |
| Z2A–Z2Z | | Zimbabwe |
| ZAA–ZAZ | ZA | Albania |

| ITU allocation | Prefix | Country |
| --- | --- | --- |
| ZBA–ZJZ |      | Great Britain |
|         | ZB2  | Gibraltar |
|         | ZC4  | Cyprus (UK Bases) |
|         | ZD7  | St Helena |
|         | ZD8  | Ascension Island |
|         | ZD9  | Gough Island |
|         | ZD9  | Tristan da Cunha |
|         | ZF   | Cayman Islands |
| ZKA–ZMZ | ZL   | New Zealand |
|         | ZK1  | Manihiki Island |
|         | ZK1  | Cook Island |
|         | ZK2  | Niue Island |
|         | ZL1/K | Kermadec Island |
|         | ZK2  | Niue Island |
|         | ZL4/A | Auckland Island |
|         | ZL4/A | Campbell Island |
|         | ZL5  | New Zealand Antartic |
|         | ZM7  | Tokelau Island |
| ZNA–ZOZ |      | Great Britain |
| ZPA–ZPZ | ZP   | Paraguay |
| ZQA–ZQZ |      | Great Britain |
| ZRA–ZUZ | ZR,ZS | South Africa |
|         | ZS2  | Marion Island |
|         | ZS3  | SW Africa (Namibia) |
| ZVA–ZZZ |      | Brazil |
| 2AA–2ZZ |      | Great Britain |
| 3AA–3AZ | 3A   | Monaco |
| 3BA–3BZ | 3B   | Mauritius |
| 3CA–3CZ | 3C   | Equitorial Guinea |
|         | 3CO  | Pagalu Island |
| 3DA–3DM | 3D6  | Swaziland |
| 3DN–3DZ | 3D2  | Fiji |
| 3EA–3FZ |      | Panama |
| 3GA–3GZ |      | Chile |
| 3HA–3HZ |      | China |
| 3VA–3VZ | 3V8  | Tunisia |
| 3WA–3WZ |      | Vietnam |
| 3XA–3XZ | 3X   | Guinea |
| 3YA–3YZ |      | Norway |
|         | 3Y   | Bouvet Island |
| 3ZA–3ZZ |      | Poland |

| ITU allocation | Prefix | Country |
|---|---|---|
| 4AA–4CZ | | Mexico |
| 4DA–4IZ | | Philippines |
| 4JA–4LZ | | USSR |
| | 4K1 | Antartica (USSR Bases) |
| 4MA–4MZ | | Venezuela |
| 4NA–4OZ | | Yugoslavia |
| 4PA–4SZ | 4S7 | Sri Lanka |
| 4TA–4TZ | | Peru |
| 4UA–4UZ | 4U1 | United Nations |
| 4VA–4VZ | | Haiti |
| 4WA–4WZ | 4W | Yemen (YAR) |
| 4XA–4XZ | 4X4 | Israel |
| 4YA–4YZ | | ICAO |
| 4ZA–4ZZ | 4Z4 | Israel |
| 5AA–5AZ | 5A | Libya |
| 5BA–5BZ | 5B4 | Cyprus |
| 5CA–5GZ | | Morocco |
| 5HA–5IZ | 5H | Tanzania |
| 5JA–5KZ | | Colombia |
| 5LA–5MZ | | Liberia |
| 5NA–5OZ | 5N | Nigeria |
| 5PA–5QZ | | Denmark |
| 5RA–5SZ | 5R8 | Madagascar |
| 5TA–5TZ | 5T5 | Mauritania |
| 5UA–5UZ | 5U7 | Niger |
| 5VA–5VZ | 5V7 | Togo |
| 5WA–5WZ | 5W1 | Western Samoa |
| 5XA–5XZ | 5X5 | Uganda |
| 5YA–5ZZ | 5Z4 | Kenya |
| 6AA–6BZ | | Egypt |
| 6CA–6CZ | | Syria |
| 6DA–6JZ | | Mexico |
| 6KA–6NZ | | Korea (RK) |
| 6OA–6OZ | | Somalia |
| 6PA–6SZ | | Pakistan |
| 6TA–6UZ | | Sudan |
| 6VA–6WZ | 6W8 | Senegal |
| 6XA–6XZ | | Madagascar |
| 6YA–6YZ | 6Y5 | Jamaica |
| 6ZA–6ZZ | | Liberia |
| 7AA–7IZ | | Indonesia |

| ITU allocation | Prefix | Country |
|---|---|---|
| 7JA–7NZ | | Japan |
| 7OA–7OZ | 7O | Yemen (PDR) |
| | 7O | Socotra Island |
| 7PA–7PZ | 7P8 | Lesotho |
| 7QA–7QA | 7Q7 | Malawi |
| 7RA–7RZ | | Algeria |
| 7SA–7SZ | | Sweden |
| 7TA–7YX | 7X | Algeria |
| 7ZA–7ZZ | | Saudi Arabia |
| 8AA–8IZ | | Indonesia |
| 8JA–8NZ | | Japan |
| | 8J1 | Japanese Antartica |
| 8OA–8OZ | | Botswana |
| 8PA–8PZ | 8P6 | Barbados |
| 8QA–8QZ | 8Q | Maldives |
| 8RA–8RZ | 8R | Guyana |
| 8SA–8SZ | | Sweden |
| 8TA–8YZ | | India |
| 8ZA–8ZZ | | Saudi Arabia |
| | 8Z4 | Neutral Zone |
| 9AA–9AZ | 9A | San Marino |
| 9BA–9DZ | | Iran |
| 9EA–9FZ | | Ethiopia |
| 9GA–9GZ | 9G1 | Ghana |
| 9HA–9HZ | 9H | Malta |
| 9IA–9JZ | 9J | Zambia |
| 9KA–9KZ | 9K2 | Kuwait |
| 9LA–9LZ | 9L | Sierra Leone |
| 9MA–9MZ | | Malaysia |
| | 9M2 | West Malaysia |
| | 9M6 | Sabah |
| | 9M8 | Sarawak |
| 9NA–9NZ | 9N | Nepal |
| 9OA–9TZ | 9Q5 | Zaire |
| 9UA–9UZ | 9U5 | Burundi |
| 9VA–9VZ | 9V | Singapore |
| 9WA–9WZ | | Malaysia |
| 9XA–9XZ | 9X5 | Rwanda |
| 9YA–9ZZ | 9Y4 | Trinidad and Tobago |

## Amateur radio prefixes

| Prefix | Country |
| --- | --- |
| A2 | Botswana |
| A35 | Tonga |
| A4X | Oman |
| A51 | Bhutan |
| A6X | United Arab Emirates |
| A71 | Qatar |
| A92 | Bahrain |
| AA–AL | See USA table |
| AP | Pakistan |
| BL | Tibet |
| BV | Formosa (Taiwan) |
| BY | China |
| C5 | Gambia |
| C6 | Bahamas |
| C9 | Mozambique |
| C21 | Nauru |
| C31 | Andorra |
| CE | Chile |
| CE9 | Antartica (Chile) |
| CE0A | Easter Island |
| CE0X | SanFelix Island |
| CE0Z | Juan Fernandez Island |
| CM | Cuba |
| CN | Morocco |
| CO | Cuba |
| CP | Bolivia |
| CR9 | Macau |
| CT1,4 | Portugal |
| CT2 | Azores |
| CT3 | Madeira |
| CX | Uruguay |
| D2 | Angola |
| D4 | Cape Verde Islands |
| D68 | State of the Comoros |
| DA,DB, DC, DF, DJ, DK, DL | West Germany |
| DU, DX | Philippines |
| EA | Spain |
| EA6 | Balearic Islands |

## Amateur radio prefixes *continued*

| Prefix | Country |
|---|---|
| EA8 | Canary Islands |
| EA9 | Spanish North Africa (Ceuta, Melilla) |
| EI, EJ | Eire |
| EL | Liberia |
| EP | Iran |
| EZ | USSR (novice) |
| F | France |
| FB8W | Crozet Islands |
| FB8X | Kerguelen Islands |
| FB8Y | Terre Adelie |
| FB8Z | Amsterdam Island, St Paul Island |
| FC | Corsica |
| FG | Guadeloupe |
| FH8 | Mayotte Island |
| FK | New Caledonia |
| FM | Martinique |
| FO | French Oceania (eg Tahiti), Clipperton Island |
| FP | St Pierre and Miquelon Islands |
| FR | Reunion Island, etc |
| FS7 | St Martin |
| FW | Wallis and Futuna Island |
| FY | French Guiana, Inini |
| G | England |
| GB | United Kingdom (Exhibitions and Special Purposes) |
| GD | Isle of Man |
| GI | Northern Ireland |
| GJ | Jersey |
| GM | Scotland |
| GU | Guernsey, Alderney, Sark |
| GW | Wales |
| H44 | Solomon Islands |
| HA, HG | Hungary |
| HB4, 9 | Switzerland |
| HE, HB0 | Liechtenstein |
| HC | Ecuador |
| HC8 | Galapagos Islands |
| HH | Haiti |
| HI | Dominican Republic |

## Amateur radio prefixes *continued*

| Prefix | Country |
| --- | --- |
| HK | Colombia |
| HK0 | San Andres, Providencia, etc |
| HL, HM | Korea |
| HP, HO | Panama |
| HR | Honduras |
| HS | Thailand |
| HT | Nicaragua |
| HV | Vatican City |
| HZ | Saudi Arabia |
| I, IA, IB, IC, ID, IE, IF, IG, IH, IL, IP, IZ | Italy |
| IS, IM | Sardinia |
| IT | Sicily |
| J28 | Djibouti |
| J3 | Grenada |
| J5 | Guinea-Bissau |
| J6 | St Lucia |
| J73 | Dominica |
| J88 | St Vincent |
| JA, JE, JF, JG, JH, JI, JJ, JR | Japan |
| JD | Bonin and Volcano Islands (Minami Island, Ogasawara Island) |
| JT | Mongolia |
| JW | Svalbard |
| JX | Jan Mayen |
| JY | Jordan |
| K | USA (for Districts see under 'W') |
| KA–KZ | See USA table |
| KB6 | Baker, Howland Islands |
| KC4 | Navassa Islands, Antarctica |
| KC6 | Caroline Island |
| KG4 | Guantanamo Bay |
| KG6 | Mariana Islands, Marcus Islands, Guam |
| KH6 | Hawaiian Islands |
| KJ6 | Johnston Island |
| KL7 | Alaska |

## Amateur radio prefixes *continued*

| Prefix | Country |
|---|---|
| KM6 | Midway Island |
| KP6 | Palmyra Group, Jarvis Island |
| KS6 | American Samoa |
| KV4 | Virgin Island |
| KW6 | Wake Island |
| KX6 | Marshall Island |
| LA | Norway |
| LU | Argentina |
| LX | Luxembourg |
| LZ | Bulgaria |
| M1 | San Marino |
| N | USA (for districts see under 'W') |
| NA–NZ | See USA table |
| OA | Peru |
| OD | Lebanon |
| OE | Austria |
| OF, OH | Finland |
| OH0 | Aaland Island |
| OH0M, OJ0 | Market Reef |
| OK, OL, OM | Czechoslovakia |
| ON | Belgium |
| OR4 | Antarctica (Belgium) |
| OX | Greenland |
| OY | Faeroes |
| OZ | Denmark |
| P29 | Papua New Guinea |
| PA, PE | Holland |
| PI | Holland (Special) |
| PJ | Dutch West Indies |
| PJ5 | St Eustatius |
| PJ6 | Saba |
| PJ7 | St Maarten |
| PP–PY | Brazil |
| PY0 | Fernando de Noronha, Trinidade and Vaz Islands |
| PZ | Suriname |
| RA–RZ | USSR |
| S2 | Bangladesh |
| S79 | Seychelles |
| S92 | Sao Thome, Principe |

## Amateur radio prefixes *continued*

| Prefix | Country |
| --- | --- |
| SL | Sweden (Special) |
| SM, SK | Sweden |
| SP, SQ | Poland |
| ST | Sudan |
| SU | Egypt |
| SV | Greece |
| SV5 | Rhodes |
| SV9 | Crete |
| SY | Mt Athos |
| T2 | Tuvalu |
| T30 | Kiribati |
| T31 | Line Island |
| T32 | Phoenix Island |
| T5 | Somali Republic |
| TA | Turkey |
| TF | Iceland |
| TG | Guatemala |
| TI | Costa Rica |
| TI9 | Cocos Island |
| TJ | Cameroons |
| TL8 | Central African Republic |
| TN8 | Congo Republic (formerly French Congo) |
| TR8 | Gabon Republic |
| TT8 | Tchad Republic |
| TU2 | Ivory Coast |
| TY | Benin |
| TZ | Mali Republic |
| UA, UV, UW, RA 1,3,4,6 | European Russian SFSR |
| UA2 | Kaliningradsk |
| UA9, 0, UW9, UZ9 | Asiatic RSFSR |
| UB5, UT5, UY5 | Ukraine |
| UC2 | White Russia |
| UD6 | Azerbaijan |
| UF6 | Georgia |
| UG6 | Armenia |
| UH8 | Turkoman |
| UI8 | Uzbek |

## Amateur radio prefixes *continued*

| Prefix | Country |
|--------|---------|
| UJ8 | Tadzhiz |
| UK | Russian club stations |
| UL7 | Kazakh |
| UM8 | Kirghiz |
| UN1 | Finno-Karelia |
| UO5 | Moldavia |
| UP2 | Lithuania |
| UQ2 | Latvia |
| UR2 | Estonia |
| V2 | Antigua, Barbuda |
| V3 | Belize |
| VE, VO | Canada |
| VE1 | Maritime Provinces |
| VE2 | Province of Quebec |
| VE3 | Province of Ontaria |
| VE4 | Province of Manitoba |
| VE5 | Province of Saskatchewan |
| VE6 | Province of Alberta |
| VE7 | Province of British Columbia |
| VY1 | Yukon Territories |
| VE8M–Z | NW Territories |
| VO1 | Newfoundland |
| VO2 | Labrador |
| VK | Australia |
| VK0 | Heard Island, McDonald Island, Macquarie Island |
| VK1 | Canberra |
| VK2 | New South Wales |
| VK3 | Victoria |
| VK4 | Queensland |
| VK5 | South Australia |
| VK6 | Western Australia |
| VK7 | Tasmania |
| VK8 | Northern Territories |
| VK9 | New Guinea, Norfolk Island, Papua, Cocos-Keeling and Admiralty Islands |
| VO | See under VE |
| VP2 | Leeward Islands, Windward Islands |
| VP2E | Anguilla |
| VP2H | Anguilla |

## Amateur radio prefixes *continued*

| Prefix | Country |
| --- | --- |
| VP2K | St Kitts and Nevis |
| VP2M | Montserrat |
| VP2V | British Virgin Isles |
| VP5 | Turks and Caicos Islands |
| VP8 | Falkland Islands, South Georgia, South Orkneys, Shetland Island, Sandwich Island, Grahamland |
| VP9 | Bermuda |
| VQ9 | Chagos Island |
| VR6 | Pitcairn Island |
| VS5 | Brunei |
| VS6 | Hong Kong |
| VU2 | India |
| VU5 | Andaman Island, Laccadive Island |
| W | USA (Note stations can now retain former callsigns when moving districts) (see also KH6, KL7) |
| W1 | Connecticut, Maine, Massachusetts, New Hampshire, Rhode Island, Vermont |
| W2 | New Jersey, New York |
| W3 | Delaware, Maryland, Pennsylvania (including District of Columbia) |
| W4 | Alabama, Florida, Georgia, Kentucky, North Carolina, South Carolina, Tennessee, Virginia |
| W5 | Arkansas, Louisiana, Mississippi, New Mexico, Oklahoma, Texas |
| W6 | California |
| W7 | Arizona, Idaho, Montana, Nevada, Oregon, Utah, Washington, Wyoming |
| W8 | Michigan, Ohio, West Virginia |
| W9 | Illinois, Indiana, Wisconsin |
| W0 | Colorado, Iowa, Kansas, Minnesota, Missouri, Nebraska, North Dakota, South Dakota |
| WA–WZ | See USA table |
| XE, XF | Mexico |
| XE4 | Revilla Gigedo |
| XT2 | Upper Volta |
| XU | Kampuchea (Khmer, Cambodia) |
| XV | Vietnam |
| XW8 | Laos |

## Amateur radio prefixes *continued*

| Prefix | Country |
|---|---|
| XZ | Burma |
| Y | East Germany |
| YA | Afghanistan |
| YB, YC, YD | Indonesia |
| YI | Iraq |
| YJ | Vanuatu |
| YK | Syria |
| YO | Roumania |
| YS | Salvador |
| YU | Yugoslavia |
| YV | Venezuela |
| YV0 | Aves Island |
| Z2 | Zimbabwe |
| ZA | Albania |
| ZB2 | Gibraltar |
| ZC4 | Cyprus (British assigned) |
| ZD7 | St Helena |
| ZD8 | Ascension Island |
| ZD9 | Tristan de Cunha, Gough Island |
| ZF1 | Cayman Isles |
| ZK1 | Cook Island |
| ZK2 | Niue Island |
| ZL, ZM | New Zealand, Chatham Island, Kermadec Island |
| ZL1 | Auckland District |
| ZL2 | Wellington District |
| ZL3 | Canterbury District |
| ZL4 | Otago District |
| ZL5 | New Zealand Antarctica |
| ZM7 | Tokelau Island |
| ZP | Paraguay |
| ZR, ZS | Republic of South Africa, Prince Edward and Marion Islands |
| ZS1 | Cape District |
| ZS2 | Cape Province (excluding ZS1) |
| ZS3 | South West Africa |
| ZS4 | Orange Free State |
| ZS5 | Natal (including Zululand) |
| ZS6 | Transvaal |
| 1S | Spratly Island |

## Amateur radio prefixes *continued*

| Prefix | Country |
| --- | --- |
| 3A2 | Monaco |
| 3B6 | Chagos Island |
| 3B7 | Agalega and St Brandon |
| 3B8 | Mauritius |
| 3B9 | Rodriguezs |
| 3C | Equatorial Guinea |
| 3D2 | Fiji |
| 3D6 | Swaziland |
| 3G3 | Chile |
| 3V8 | Tunisia |
| 3W8 | Vietnam |
| 3X | Republic of Guinea |
| 3Y | Bouvet Island |
| 4M | Venezuela |
| 4S7 | Sri Lanka |
| 4U1ITU | ITU, Geneva |
| 4W | Yemen (AR) |
| 4X, 4Z | Israel |
| 5A | Libya |
| 5B4 | Republic of Cyprus |
| 5H1 | Zanzibar |
| 5H3 | Tanzania (except Zanzibar) |
| 5L | Liberia |
| 5N | Nigeria |
| 5R8 | Malagasy Republic |
| 5T5 | Mauritania |
| 5U7 | Niger Republic |
| 5V | Togo |
| 5W1 | Western Samoa |
| 5X5 | Uganda |
| 5Z4 | Kenya |
| 6D | Mexico |
| 6O | Somali Republic |
| 6W8 | Senegal Republic |
| 6Y | Jamaica |
| 7O | Yemen (PDR) |
| 7P8 | Lesotho |
| 7Q | Malawi |
| 7X | Algeria |

## Amateur radio prefixes *continued*

| Prefix | Country |
|--------|---------|
| 7Z | Saudi Arabia |
| 8F | Indonesia |
| 8J1 | Antarctica (see OR4, VK0, ZL5, VP8) |
| 8P | Barbados |
| 8Q | Maldives |
| 8R | Guyana |
| 8Z4 | Iraq/Saudi Arabia Neutral Zone |
| 9A1 | San Marino |
| 9G1 | Ghana |
| 9H | Malta |
| 9J2 | Zambia |
| 9K2 | Kuwait |
| 9L1 | Sierra Leone |
| 9M2 | Malaysia |
| 9M6 | Sabah |
| 9M8 | Sarawak |
| 9N | Nepal |
| 9Q5 | Zaire |
| 9U5 | Burundi |
| 9V1 | Singapore |
| 9X5 | Rwanda |
| 9Y4 | Trinidad and Tobago |

## ICAO/NATO phonetic alphabet

| | | | |
|---|---|---|---|
| A | Alpha | N | November |
| B | Bravo | O | Oscar |
| C | Charlie | P | Pappa |
| D | Delta | Q | Quebec |
| E | Echo | R | Romeo |
| F | Foxtrot | S | Sierra |
| G | Golf | T | Tango |
| H | Hotel | U | Uniform |
| I | India | V | Victor |
| J | Juliet | W | Whisky |
| K | Kilo | X | X-ray |
| L | Lima | Y | Yankee |
| M | Mike | Z | Zulu |

# Aircraft callsigns

To the uninitiated, listening-in on the air bands can often be a frustrating experience not only because of the high level of jargon used by pilots and ground stations but also by the bewildering number of different callsigns that airlines and operators use.

Callsigns will in fact fall into one of two categories. The first is the prefix which denotes the country of origin, the second is a self-assigned name registered with the telegraphic authorities in the country of registration. One of these options will be used by all civil aircraft. Military aircraft using civilian airways might also use a code name. Typical examples being 'Mac' used by the United States Air Force and 'Ascot' used by the British Royal Air Force Transport Group.

First the country prefix. This first list shows the letters and numbers associated with the registration system for any particular country, but do heed that it is common practice to only give the full callsign on the first contact with a ground station. From then on the last two letters or digits of the callsign are all that are used. These registration prefixes are normally used by light aircraft, those that are privately owned, and the smaller commercial operators, although there are instances where major airlines will use these as well.

If the full callsign consists of letters only, then you can be almost certain that the callsign being used is the standard country prefix followed by the aircraft registration. The vast majority of countries use two, three or four letter groups after the country prefix but there are a few exceptions and the notable ones are:

| | |
|---|---|
| United States of America | N followed by numbers or a mix of numbers and letters |
| USSR | CCCP followed by 5 digit number |
| Japan | JA followed by a 4 digit number |
| Venezuela | YV followed by a 3 digit number then suffixed with a single letter |
| China/Taiwan | B followed by a 3 or 4 digit number |
| Cuba | CU-T followed by a 4 digit number |
| Columbia | HK followed by a 4 digit number suffixed with X |
| Korea | HL followed by a 4 digit number |

The next lists show the self-chosen callsigns and the three letter ICAO designator which is used for such things as timetables, inter agency communications, etc. Typically, the self assigned callsign is followed by a number which in fact denotes the timetable flight number. It is worth bearing in mind that airline timetables are usually available free of charge from airports and travel agencies. The flight number shown in the timetable may well form part of the callsign for the aircraft and so if you are trying to confirm identity, not only will you get a match with the flight number but the timing should also indicate whether or not that flight is overhead your area at that time.

## International aircraft callsign and registration prefixes

| Prefix | Country |
|--------|---------|
| A2– | Botswana |
| A3– | Tonga |
| A5– | Bhutan |
| A6– | United Arab Emirates |
| A7– | Qatar |
| A9– | Bahrain |
| AP | Pakistan |
| B– | China/Taiwan |
| C–F | Canada |
| C–G | Canada |
| C2– | Nauru |
| C3– | Andorra |
| C5– | Gambia |
| C6– | Bahamas |
| C9– | Mozambique |
| CC– | Chile |
| CCCP– | Soviet Union |
| CN– | Morocco |
| CP– | Bolivia |
| CR– | Portuguese Overseas Provinces |
| CS– | Portugal |
| CU– | Cuba |
| CX– | Uruguay |
| D– | German Federal Republic (W) |
| D2– | Angola |
| D4– | Cape Verde islands |
| D6– | Comores Island |
| DDR– | German Democratic Republic (E) |
| DQ– | Fiji |
| EC– | Spain |
| EI–/EJ– | Republic of Ireland |

# International aircraft callsign and registration prefixes *continued*

| Prefix | Country |
| --- | --- |
| EL– | Liberia |
| EP– | Iran |
| ET– | Ethiopia |
| F– | France and French Territories |
| G– | Great Britain |
| H4– | Solomon Islands |
| HA– | Hungarian Peoples Republic |
| HB– | Switzerland and Liechtenstein |
| HC– | Ecuador |
| HH– | Haiti |
| HI– | Dominican Republic |
| HK– | Columbia |
| HL– | South Korea |
| HP– | Panama |
| HR– | Honduras |
| HS– | Thailand |
| HZ– | Saudi Arabia |
| I– | Italy |
| J2– | Djibouti |
| J3– | Grenada |
| J5– | Guinea Bissau |
| J6– | St Lucia |
| J7– | Dominica |
| J8– | St Vincent |
| JA– | Japan |
| JY– | Jordan |
| LN– | Norway |
| LQ–/LV– | Argentina |
| LX– | Luxembourg |
| LZ– | Bulgaria |
| MI– | Marshall Islands |
| N– | United States of America |
| OB– | Peru |
| OD– | Lebanon |
| OE– | Austria |
| OH– | Finland |
| OK– | Czechoslovakia |
| OO– | Belgium |
| OY– | Denmark |

## International aircraft callsign and registration prefixes *continued*

| Prefix | Country |
|---|---|
| P– | North Korea |
| P2– | Papua New Guinea |
| PH– | Netherlands |
| PK– | Indonesia and West Irian |
| PJ– | Netherlands Antilles |
| PP–/PT– | Brazil |
| PZ– | Surinam |
| RDPL– | Lao |
| RP– | Philippines |
| S2– | Bangladesh |
| S7– | Seychelles |
| S9– | Sao Tome |
| SE– | Sweden |
| SP– | Poland |
| ST– | Sudan |
| SU– | Egypt |
| SX– | Greece |
| T2– | Tuvalu |
| T3– | Kiribati |
| T7– | San Marino |
| TC– | Turkey |
| TF– | Iceland |
| TG– | Guatemala |
| TI– | Costa Rica |
| TJ– | Cameroon |
| TL– | Central African Republic |
| TN– | Republic of the Congo |
| TR– | Gabon |
| TS– | Tunisia |
| TT– | Chad |
| TU– | Ivory Coast |
| TY– | Benin |
| TZ– | Mali |
| V2– | Antigua |
| V3– | Belize |
| V8– | Brunei |
| VH– | Australia |
| VN– | Vietnam |
| VP–F | Falkland Islands |

## International aircraft callsign and registration prefixes *continued*

| Prefix | Country |
| --- | --- |
| VP–LKA | St Kitts Nevis |
| VP–LLZ | St Kitts Nevis |
| VP–LMA | Montserrat |
| VP–LUZ | Montserrat |
| VP–LVA | Virgin Islands |
| VP–LZZ | Virgin Islands |
| VQ–T | Turks and Caicos Islands |
| VR–B | Bermuda |
| VR–C | Cayman Islands |
| VR–G | Gibraltar (not currently used. Gibraltar Airways aircraft are registered in Great Britain) |
| VR–H | Hong Kong |
| VT– | India |
| XA–/XB– | Mexico |
| XC– | Mexico |
| XT– | Upper Volta |
| XU– | Kampuchea |
| XY–/XZ– | Burma |
| YA– | Afghanistan |
| YI– | Iraq |
| YJ– | Vanuatu |
| YK– | Syria |
| YN– | Nicaragua |
| YR– | Rumania |
| YS– | El Salvador |
| YU– | Yugoslavia |
| YY– | Venezuela |
| Z– | Zimbabwe |
| ZA– | Albania |
| ZK– | New Zealand |
| ZP– | Paraguay |
| ZS– | Republic of South Africa |
| 3A– | Monaco |
| 3B– | Mauritius |
| 3C– | Equitorial Guinea |
| 3D– | Swaziland |
| 3X– | Guinea |
| 4R– | Sri Lanka |
| 4W– | Yemen Arab Republic |

## International aircraft callsign and registration prefixes *continued*

| Prefix | Country |
| --- | --- |
| 4X– | Israel |
| 4YB– | Jordan/Iraq |
| 5A– | Libya |
| 5B– | Cyprus |
| 5H– | Tanzania |
| 5N– | Nigeria |
| 5R | Madagascar (Malagasy Republic) |
| 5T– | Mauritania |
| 5U– | Niger |
| 5V– | Togo |
| 5W– | Polynesia (Western Samoa) |
| 5X– | Uganda |
| 5Y– | Kenya |
| 6O– | Somalia |
| 6Y–/6W– | Senegal |
| 6Y– | Jamaica |
| 7O– | Democratic Yemen |
| 7P– | Lesotho |
| 7Q– | Malawi |
| 7T– | Algeria |
| 8P– | Barbados |
| 8Q– | Maldives |
| 8R– | Guyana |
| 9G– | Ghana |
| 9H– | Malta |
| 9J– | Zambia |
| 9K– | Kuwait |
| 9L– | Sierra Leone |
| 9M– | Malaysia |
| 9N– | Nepal |
| 9Q– | Zaire |
| 9U– | Burundi |
| 9V– | Singapore |
| 9XR– | Rwanda |
| 9Y– | Trinidad and Tobago |

## International aircraft callsign and registration prefixes *continued*

| Operator/agency | DES | Callsign | Prefix |
|---|---|---|---|
| Adria Airways | IAA | | YU– |
| Aer Lingus | EIN | Shamrock | EI– |
| Aero Charter Midlands | ACC | Aerocharter | G– |
| Aeroflot | AFL | Aeroflot | CCCP– |
| Aerolineas Argentinas | | | LV– |
| Aero Lloyd | AEF | | D– |
| Aeromaritime | | Aeromaritime | F– |
| Aeromexico | | Aeromexico | XA– |
| Aeron International | AEI | | N– |
| Aeroperu | | Aeroperu | OB– |
| Aerotime | AET | Aerotime | G– |
| Aero Transporti Italiani | ATI | | I– |
| Air Afrique | | | TU– |
| Air Algerie | DAH | | 7T– |
| Air Atlantis | TAP | | CS– |
| Air Belgium | ABB | | OO– |
| Air Bridge Carriers | ABR | Airbridge | G– |
| Air BVI | BLB | Air BVI | G– |
| Air Camelot | CME | Air Camelot | G– |
| Air Canada | ACA | | C– |
| Air Charter (Scotland) | | Scotair | G– |
| Air Charter/E.A.S. | ACF | | F– |
| Air Charter and Travel | | Actair | G– |
| Air Coventry | COV | Air Coventry | G– |
| Air Ecosse | ECS | Ecosse Air | G– |
| Air Europa | | | EC– |
| Air Europe | AEL | Air Europe | G– |
| Air Foyle | UPA | Foyle | G– |
| Air France | AFR | Air France | F– |
| Air Furness | AFW | | G– |
| Air Hanson | AHL | Air Hanson | G– |
| Air India | AIC | Air India | VT– |
| Air Inter | | | F– |
| Air Jet | | | F– |
| Air Kilroe | AKL | Kilroe | G– |
| Air Lanka | ALK | | 4R– |
| Air Limousin | | | F– |
| Air Littoral | | | F– |
| Air London | ACG | Air London | G– |

## International aircraft callsign and registration prefixes *continued*

| Operator/agency | DES | Callsign | Prefix |
|---|---|---|---|
| Air Malta | AMC | | 9H– |
| Air Mauritius | MAU | | 3B– |
| Air Navigation and Trading | ANB | Air Nav | G– |
| Air New Zealand | ANZ | | ZK– |
| Air Orkney | ORK | Orkney | G– |
| Air Sardinia International | ARS | | |
| Air Stansted | ASX | | G– |
| Air Sarnia | ASX | Dodo | G– |
| Air Swift | SWF | Airswift | G– |
| Air Tara | | Air Tara | EI– |
| Air 2000 | AMM | | G– |
| Air UK | UKA | Ukay | G– |
| Air Wight | AWL | Air Wight | G– |
| Airgo | | Airgo | G– |
| Airmore Aviation | MAA | National | G– |
| Airship Industries | AIS | Skyship | G– |
| Airstar | GHW | Airstar | G– |
| Airways International Cymru | CYM | Welshair | G– |
| Airwork Limited | HRN | Clansman | G– |
| Airwork Services Training | | Airwork | G– |
| Air Zimbabwe | AZI | | Z– |
| Alan Mann Helicopters | AMH | Mann | G– |
| Albion Aviation | ALA | Albion | G– |
| Alfred McAlpine Aviation | AMA | McAlpine | G– |
| Alia | RJA | Alia | JY– |
| Alisarda | ISS | | I– |
| Alitalia | AZA | Alitalia | I– |
| All Charter Limited | BLA | Allcharter | G– |
| Alton Towers Limited | | Alton | G– |
| Aly Aviation | AAV | Aly Aviation | G– |
| American Airlines | AAL | American | N– |
| American Trans-Air | AMT | Amtram | N– |
| Anglian Air Taxis | MHA | Anglian | G– |
| Anglo Cargo | ANC | Anglo | G– |
| Anywair Travel | | Skybird | G– |
| Aravco | ARV | Aravco | G– |
| Army Air Corps | AAC | Army Air | UK Mil |
| Army Parachute Centre | | Para | UK Mil |
| Atlantic Air Services | AAG | Atlantic | G– |

**International aircraft callsign and registration prefixes** *continued*

| Operator/agency | DES | Callsign | Prefix |
|---|---|---|---|
| ATS Aircharter | AVT | | G– |
| Augusta Airways | | Augusta | VH– |
| Aurigny Air Services | AUR | Ayline | G– |
| Austrian Airlines | AUA | | OE– |
| Automobile Association | | Fanum | G– |
| Aviaco | AYC | Aviaco | EC– |
| Avianca | | | HK– |
| Aviation Beauport | AVB | Beaupair | G– |
| Aviation West | AVW | AV West | G– |
| Aviogenex | AGX | | YU– |
| Avon Air Services | AVZ | Avonair | G– |
| Balair | BBB | Bailair | HB– |
| Balkan Bulgarian Airlines | LAZ | | LZ– |
| Bangladesh Biman | BBC | | S2– |
| Barons (UK) | BNS | Barons | G– |
| BCA Charter | BRC | | G– |
| Bedford Royal Aircraft Estab | RRS | Blackbox | UK Gov |
| Biggin Hill Executive Aviation | BHE | Beeline | G– |
| Birmingham Aerocentre | AUK | Aerocentre | G– |
| Birmingham Aviation | ATX | Airtax | G– |
| Birmingham Executive Airways | BEX | Birmex | G– |
| Bond Helicopters | BND | Bond | G– |
| Boscombe Down (MOD) | BDN | Gauntlet | UK Mil |
| Braethens SAFE | BRA | | LN– |
| Brencham Air Charter | BRE | | G– |
| Bristow Helicopters | BHL | Bristow | G– |
| Brit Air | | | F– |
| Britannia Airways | BAL | Britannia | G– |
| British Aerospace | BAE | | |
| British Aerospace (Bristol) | FIL | Bristol | G– |
| Bristol Aerospace (Dunsfold) | DUN | Hawker | G– |
| British Aerospace (Hatfield) | HFD | Tibbet | G– |
| British Aerospace (Hawarden) | NEW | Newpin | G– |
| British Aerospace (Prestwick) | PWK | Tennant | G– |
| British Aerospace (Scampton) | BBN | Blackburn | G– |
| British Aerospace (Warton) | WTN | Tarnish | G– |
| British Aerospace (Woodford) | WFD | Avro | G– |
| British Air Ferries | BAF | Airferry | G– |
| British Air Ferries Business Jets | | Bafjet | G– |

## International aircraft callsign and registration prefixes *continued*

| Operator/agency | DES | Callsign | Prefix |
|---|---|---|---|
| British Airtours | BKT | Beatours | G– |
| British Airways | BAW | Speedbird | G– |
| British Caledonian Airways | BCA | Caledonian | G– |
| British Caledonian Charter | BCC | Caljet | G– |
| British Caribbean Airways | BCL | | G– |
| British Charter | BCR | Backer | G– |
| British International Helicopters | BIH | Lion | G– |
| British Island Airways | BIS | British Island | G– |
| British Midland Airways | BMA | Midland | G– |
| Brown Air Services | BRW | Brownair | G– |
| Brymon Airways | BRY | Brymon | G– |
| Business Air Travel | BAT | Biztravel | G– |
| Business Aircraft users Assoc | | Bizair | G– |
| Busy Bee | BEE | | LN– |
| CAA Flying Unit | CFU | Minair | UK Gov |
| Cabair Taxis | CBR | Cabair | G– |
| Calair | BCC | Caljet | G– |
| Canadian Pacific | CPC | | C– |
| Cardiff Aviation | LAW | Cambrian | G– |
| Cargolux | CLX | | LX– |
| Casair Aviation Services | CSL | Casair | G– |
| Cathay Pacific Airways | CPX | Cathay | VR–H |
| Cayman Airways | | Cayman | VR– |
| CB Executive Helicopters | CBH | Ceebee | G– |
| Cecil Aviation | CIL | Cecil | G– |
| Cega Aviation | CEG | Cega | G– |
| Ceskoslovenske Aerolini | | | OK– |
| Chad Air Services | | Chad | G– |
| Channel Aviation | GJD | Sarnair | G– |
| Channel Express (cargo) | EXS | Expressair | G– |
| Chartair | | Chartair | G– |
| Cheyne Motors Ltd | | Cheyne | G– |
| Club Air Europe Ltd | CLU | Club | G– |
| Clyde Surveys | CLY | Clyde | G– |
| Compagnie Aerienne du Languadoc | | | F– |
| Conair | OYC | Conair | OY– |
| Condor Flugdienst | CFG | | D– |

**International aircraft callsign and registration prefixes** *continued*

| Operator/agency | DES | Callsign | Prefix |
|---|---|---|---|
| Connectair | CAX | | G– |
| Contactair | | Contactair | D– |
| Continental Airlines | COA | Continental | N– |
| Corse Air | CRL | Corsair | F– |
| County Air Services | CAK | County | G– |
| Cranfield Institute of Technology | CFD | Aeronaut | UK Gov |
| Crest Aviation | PMF | Trehaven | G– |
| Crossair | | Crossair | HB– |
| CSE Aviation | CSE | Wigwam | G– |
| C.T.A. | CTA | | HB– |
| CTA Espania | | Espania | EC– |
| Cubana | | Cubana | CU– |
| Cypress Airways | CYP | | 5B– |
| Danair Services | DAN | Danair | G– |
| Delta Air | | | D– |
| Delta Air Lines | DLA | Delta | N– |
| Delta Air Transport | DAT | | OO– |
| D.L.T. | DLT | | D– |
| Dollar Air Services | DAS | Dollar | G– |
| Dravidian Air Services | DRA | Dravidian | G– |
| Donoghue Aviation | DNX | Donex | G– |
| Eagle Air | EAG | Blue Eagle | G– |
| Eagle Air | | | TF– |
| Easter Air Executive | EAX | Eastex | G– |
| Eastern Airlines | EAL | Eastern | N– |
| East Midland Aviation | EMA | | G– |
| Egyptair | EGY | Egyptair | SU– |
| El Al | ELY | El Al | 4X– |
| Emery Worldwide | EAF | Emery | N– |
| Emirate Airlines | EK | | A6– |
| Empire Test Pilots School | TPS | Tester | UK Mil |
| Ethiopian Airlines | ETH | | ET– |
| Euralair | ERL | | F– |
| Euroair Transport | URO | Euroair | G– |
| Europe Airo Services | EYN | | F– |
| European Air Transport | | | OO– |
| Fairflight | FGT | Fairflight | G– |
| Falcon Jet Centre | FJC | Falcon Jet | G– |

## International aircraft callsign and registration prefixes *continued*

| Operator/agency | DES | Callsign | Prefix |
|---|---|---|---|
| Farnborough Royal Aircraft Establishment | RAE | Nugget | UK Gov |
| Federal Express | FDE | Fedex | N– |
| Ferranti Ltd | | Ferranti | G– |
| Field Aircraft Services | FAS | Fieldair | G– |
| Finnair | FIN | Finnair | OH– |
| Flight Refuelling | FLR | Rushton | G– |
| Flight Safety Ltd | FSL | | G– |
| Flight Services International | FSB | Flint | G– |
| Flying Tiger Line | FTL | Tiger | N– |
| Food Brokers Ltd | FBL | Food | G– |
| Ford Motor Company | FOB | Fordair | G– |
| Foster Yeoman | JFY | Yeoman | G– |
| Fred Olsen Air Transport | FOF | | LN– |
| Gama Aviation | GMA | Gama | G– |
| Garuda Indonesian Airways | GIA | | PK– |
| Gatwick Air Taxis | WSC | Gatwick Air | G– |
| Gatwick Handling | GHL | Handling | G– |
| GB Airways | GBL | Gibair | G– |
| German Cargo | GEC | | D– |
| Germania | | | D– |
| Gill Aviation | GIL | Gillair | G– |
| GKN Group Services | GKN | Guest Keen | G– |
| Gleneagle Helicopters | GLH | Glen | G– |
| Grosvenor Aviation Services | GRV | Grosvenor | G– |
| Guernsey Airlines | GER | Guernsey | G– |
| Hambrair | | Hambrair | G– |
| Hamlin Aviation | HAV | Hamlin | G– |
| Hanse Express | | | D– |
| Hapag-Lloyd | HLF | | D– |
| Harvest Aviation | HAG | Harvest | G– |
| Hatfield Executive Aviation | HEX | Hetair | G– |
| Heavylift Cargo Airlines | HLA | November Papa | G– |
| Helicopter UK Ltd | HUK | Huckle | G– |
| Hispania | HSL | | EC– |
| Holland Aero Lines | HAL | | PH– |
| Hubbardair | HBD | Hubbardair | G– |
| Hunting Surveys | | Hunting | G– |
| Hyde VIP Helicopters | | Hyde | G– |

**International aircraft callsign and registration prefixes** *continued*

| Operator/agency | DES | Callsign | Prefix |
|---|---|---|---|
| Iberia | IBE | Iberian | EC– |
| Icelandair | ICE | | TF– |
| IDS Aircraft | IDS | | G– |
| Instone Airlines | INS | Instone | G– |
| Intavia | FFL | Aircargo | G– |
| Interflight | IFT | Interflight | G– |
| Interflug | IFL | Interflug | DDR– |
| Interland Air Services | | Interland | G– |
| International Aeradio | IAL | Aeradio | G– |
| Iran Air | IRA | | EP– |
| Iraqi Airways | IAW | | YI– |
| Island Aviation and Travel | | Isle Avia | G– |
| Janus Airways | JAN | Janus | G– |
| Japan Air Lines | JAL | | JA– |
| J.C. Bamford Ltd | JCB | Jaycee Bee | G– |
| Jersey European Airways | JEA | Jersey | G– |
| Jointair | ITM | Jointair | G– |
| Jubilee Airways | KCL | Losalt | G– |
| Jugoslovenski Aerotransport | JAT | | YU– |
| Kar-Air | KAR | | OH– |
| Keeler Air Transport Services | KAT | Kats | G– |
| Keenair Services | | Keenair | G– |
| Kenya Airlines | KQA | | 5Y– |
| KLM | KLM | KLM | PH– |
| Kondair | KND | Kondair | G– |
| Korean Air | | | HL– |
| Kraken Air | KRA | Kraken | G– |
| Kuwait Airways | KAC | | 9K– |
| Lauda Air | | | OE– |
| Lec Refrigeration | LEC | Leck | G– |
| Leicester Aero Club | | Fox Club | G– |
| Libyan Arab Airlines | LAA | | 5A– |
| Lineas Aereas Paraguayas (LAP) | LAP | | ZP– |
| Linjeflyg | LIN | | SE– |
| Loganair | LOG | Logan | G– |
| London Flight Centre | LOV | | G– |
| London European | LON | European | G– |
| Lovaux | LVO | Lovo | G– |

## International aircraft callsign and registration prefixes *continued*

| Operator/agency | DES | Callsign | Prefix |
|---|---|---|---|
| LTU | LTU | | D– |
| Lucas Air Transport | AAF | | F– |
| Lufthansa | DLH | Lufthansa | D– |
| Luftransport Sud (LTS) | LU | | D– |
| Luxair | LGL | Luxair | LX– |
| Maersk Air | DMA | | OY– |
| Malev | MAH | | HA– |
| Malinair | MAK | Malin | G– |
| Martinair | MPH | Martinair | PH– |
| Mam Aviation | GEN | | G– |
| Mann Aviation | | Aerostar | G– |
| Manx Airlines | MNX | Manx | G– |
| March Helicopters | MAR | March | G– |
| Marine and Aviation | | | |
| Management International | MMM | Mamair | G– |
| Marshall of Cambridge | | | |
| Engineering | MCE | Marshall | G– |
| Martinair | | | PH– |
| Martin-Baker Ltd | MBE | Martin | G– |
| McAlpine Aviation | MAL | Macline | G– |
| MaAlpine Helicopters | MCH | Macline | G– |
| McDonald Aviation | | McDonald | G– |
| Mediterranean Express | MEE | Mediterranean | G– |
| Memrykord | JPN | Jetplan | G– |
| Meteorological Research Flight | MRF | Metman | UK Gov |
| Metropolitan Police Flying | | | |
| Club | | Metpol | G– |
| Middle East Airlines | MEA | | OD– |
| Milford Docks Air Services | MDS | Midas | G– |
| Minerve | MIN | | F– |
| Ministry of Agriculture, | | | |
| Fisheries and Food | WDG | Watchdog | UK Gov |
| Misr Overseas Airways | MO | | SU– |
| MLP Aviation | BOB | Bobfly | G– |
| Monarch Airlines | MON | Monarch | G– |
| Mountleigh Air Services | MTL | Mountleigh | G– |
| Myson Group | | Myson | G– |
| Netherlines | NET | | PH– |
| Nigerian Airways | NGA | | 5N– |

## International aircraft callsign and registration prefixes *continued*

| Operator/agency | DES | Callsign | Prefix |
| --- | --- | --- | --- |
| Night Flight | NFG | Nightflight | G– |
| NLM | NLM | City | PH– |
| Nordic Air Services | NDC | Nordic | G– |
| Norsk Air | | | LN– |
| Northeast Aviation Services | NAS | | G– |
| Northern Air Taxis | NTL | Northair | G– |
| Northern Executive Aviation | NEX | Neatax | G– |
| Northwest Airlines | NWA | | N– |
| Nurnberger Flugdienst (NFD) | | | |
| Octavia Air | OCT | Octavia | G– |
| Olympic Airways | OAL | Olympic | SX– |
| Optica Industries | OPT | Optica | G– |
| Oriental Pearl Airways | OJA | Pearl | G– |
| Orion Airways | ORN | Orion | G– |
| Pakistan International | PLA | | AP– |
| Pan-American | PAA | Clipper | N– |
| Paramount Airways | PAT | Paramount | G– |
| Partnair | PAR | | LN– |
| Peacock H.E. Ltd | PCK | Peacock | G– |
| People Express | PEX | | N– |
| Peregrine Air Service | PSS | Peregrine | G– |
| Phoenix Aviation | PLP | Puma | G– |
| Pilatus Britten Norman | PBN | Vectis | G– |
| PLM Helicopters | PLM | Plum | G– |
| Pointair | | | F– |
| Police Aviation Services | PLC | Police | G– |
| Polski Linie Lotnicze (LOT) | LOT | | SP– |
| Quantas | QFA | Quantas | VH– |
| Queen's Flights | | Kittyhawk | UK Mil |
| | | Leopard | |
| | | Rainbow | |
| | | Unicorn | |
| Racal Avionics | RCL | Racal | G– |
| RAF 1 Group Air Transport | RRR | Ascot | UK Mil |
| Raven Air | RVR | Raven | G– |
| Rank Organisation | | Rankjet | G– |
| Relief Transport Services | RTS | Relief | G– |
| R.F.G. | | | D– |
| RMC Group Services | RMC | | G– |

## International aircraft callsign and registration prefixes *continued*

| Operator/agency | DES | Callsign | Prefix |
|---|---|---|---|
| Rogers Aviation | RAV | Rogav | G– |
| Rolls Royce Cars | | Roycar | G– |
| Rolls Royce Aero Engines | BTU | Rolls | G– |
| Rolls Royce Military | RRL | Merlin | G– |
| Royal Air Force | RFR | Rafair | UK Mil |
| Royal Air Maroc | RAM | | CN– |
| Royal Brunei Airlines | | | V8– |
| Royal Jordanian Airline | | | JY– |
| Royal Navy | NVY | Navy | UK Mil |
| Ryburn Air | | Ryburn | G– |
| Sabena | SAB | | OO– |
| SAS | SAS | | LN–/OY– |
| SM Exports | SME | Carbon | G– |
| SPT Aircraft | | Southendair | G– |
| Saltair | SLT | Saltair | G– |
| Saudia | SDI | Saudia | HZ– |
| Scanair | VKG | Viking | SE– |
| Scandanavian Airlines System | SAS | SAS | SE– |
| Scholl UK Ltd | | Clog | G– |
| Scottish Express International | SEI | Scottish Express | G– |
| Servisair | SGH | Servisair | G– |
| SFAIR | | | F– |
| Shell Aircraft | SHE | Shell | G– |
| Short Brothers (Belfast) | SBL | Short | G– |
| Simulated Flight Training | SIM | Simflight | G– |
| Singapore Airlines | SIA | | 9V– |
| Skegair | SKA | Skegair | G– |
| Skyfame | | Skyfame | G– |
| Skyguard | SKD | Skyguard | G– |
| Skywork | | Airmove | G– |
| Sloane Aviation | SLN | Sloane | G– |
| Sobelair | SLR | | OO– |
| Solo Flying School | | Solo | G– |
| South African Airways | SAA | Springbok | ZS– |
| South East Air | SEE | Seafly | G– |
| Southern Air Transport | | | N– |
| Southern Joyrides | | Rapeed | G– |
| Spantax | BXS | Spantax | EC– |
| Spooner Aviation | | Spooner | G– |

## International aircraft callsign and registration prefixes *continued*

| Operator/agency | DES | Callsign | Prefix |
|---|---|---|---|
| Star Aviation | STA | Star | G– |
| Stellair | STR | | F– |
| Sterling Airways | SAW | Sterling | OY– |
| Streamline Aviation | STM | Streamline | G– |
| Sudan Airways | SUD | | ST– |
| Sure-Wings | SWG | Surewings | G– |
| Surrey and Kent Flying Club | | Kentair | G– |
| Swedair | | Swedair | SE– |
| Swissair | SWR | Swissair | HB– |
| Syrian Arab Airlines | SYR | | YK– |
| TAP | TAP | | CS– |
| TAT | TAT | | F– |
| Tarom | ROT | Tarom | YR– |
| Telair Ltd | TLR | Telair | G– |
| Thai International Airlines | THA | Thai | HS– |
| Thurston Aviation | THG | Thurston | G– |
| Tiger Fly | MOH | Moth | G– |
| Touchstone Aviation | TOU | | G– |
| Tradewinds Airways | IKA | Tradewinds | G– |
| Trans Arabian Air Transport | | | ST– |
| Transavia | TRH | | PH– |
| Trans Azur Aviation | | | F– |
| Trans Europe Air Charter | TEU | Trans Europe | G– |
| Trans European Airways | TEA | | OO– |
| Trans Mediterranean Airways | TMA | Trans-Med | OD– |
| Transvalair | | | F– |
| Trans World Airlines | TWA | TWA | N– |
| Trent Air Services | TSL | Trent | G– |
| Tropair Air Services | TSV | Tropic | G– |
| Tunis-Air | TAR | | TS– |
| Turbopool | TPL | Aeropool | G– |
| Turk Hava Yollari (THY) | THY | | TC– |
| Tyrolean Airways | | | OE– |
| Uganda Airlines | UGH | | 5X– |
| UK Parachute Centre | | Parachute | G– |
| Uni-Air | | Uni-Air | F– |
| United Biscuit Co | | Yoobee | G– |
| United States Air Force | | Mac | US Mil |
| UTA | | | F– |

## International aircraft callsign and registration prefixes *continued*

| Operator/agency | DES | Callsign | Prefix |
|---|---|---|---|
| Varig | VRG | Varig | PP– |
| Veritair | VRT | Veritair | G– |
| Vernair Transport Services | VFS | Vernair | G– |
| Viasa | VIA | | YV– |
| Vickers Ship Building Group | VSB | Vickers | G– |
| Virgin Atlantic | VIR | Virgin | G– |
| Wardair | WDA | Wardair | C– |
| WDL | | | D– |
| Welsh Airways | WSH | Dragon | G– |
| Wessex Air Charter | WSX | Wessex | G– |
| West London Aero Services | WLA | West London | G– |
| Westair Flying Services | | Cessnair | G– |
| Westland Helicopters | WHE | Westland | G– |
| Woodgate Air Services | WOD | Woodair | G– |
| World Airways | WOA | | N– |
| Worldways Canada | WWC | Worldways | C– |
| Yemen Airways | IYE | | 4W– |
| Yorkshire Flying Services | | Yorkair | G– |
| Zakani Aviation Services | | | SU– |

# Antennas 9

## Discones

Without a doubt the most popular antennas amongst scanner owners are discones. This antenna is vertically polarised, despite its horizontal elements, and a well designed discone can provide some 3 dB gain over a quarter wave. However, there appears to be some controversy over just what dimensions a discone should consist of. Most textbooks claim a frequency coverage in a ratio 1:10, ie if the lowest elements are cut for 100 MHz then the highest frequency of operation will be 1000 MHz.

Many owners of commercially made discones often claim that UHF coverage, even at around 450 MHz is poor. However, some antenna specialists say this is largely because commercially made discones tend to be made mistakenly optimised for lower frequencies. I am reliably informed that for receiving purposes a 1:8 ratio applies but you can also allow a further 20 percent increase in lower frequency coverage (percentage of the lowest frequency theoretically allowed for). My own experiments have largely borne this out and using a discone that is almost half the size of my commercially made one I still get perfectly adequate reception in the 80 MHz band but far better performance right up to 1000 MHz. This particular discone is cut for a theoretical minimum frequency of 130 MHz which means it will still be resonant at 1000 MHz. Using our 20 percent rule we have a theoretical lowest frequency coverage of 104 MHz. In practice the fall off in performance below this frequency is so gradual that even reception of an aeronautical fan-marker beacon (75 MHz) in my area is only marginally worse than with my larger commercial discone.

One other factor that frequently spoils the performance of commercially made discones is the use of PL259 connectors. These plugs and sockets are adequate at VHF but their UHF performance is usually very poor unless high grade industrial types can be obtained. Exceptions to this are some of the later high performance discones such as the one made by Icom which use N-Plugs.

## Practical designs

The discone is not the easiest of antennas to construct. However, if you are prepared to settle for one that mounts in your loft rather than outside the building then construction is relatively simple. Basic ideas are given here but the final design will obviously depend to a large extent on what materials are to hand. The 'disc' and the 'cone' in conventional discones is a compromise skeleton arrangement made up of rods. Obviously if these elements were made of sheet metal the wind resistance would be enormous. In the loft though, there is no such problem and indeed from the construction point of view it is better to make the antenna from a proper disc and cone, the latter making the assembly self supporting. One of the most easily obtained materials is aluminium baking foil. It is not very rigid but this can be overcome by sticking it to large sheets of paper card which is easily obtained, usually from stationery shops. It may be necessary to stick several sheets together.

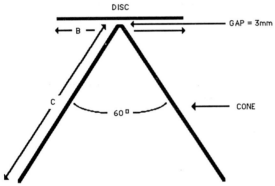

**Figure 9.1** Discone broadband antenna. $C = \frac{1}{4}$ wave at lowest frequency (see text), $B = 70\%$ of $C$

The dimensions for a discone are given in Figure 9.1 and the length of the reflectors, C, can be calculated from the formula: $\frac{1}{4}$ wave = 2952 divided by frequency in megahertz (the result being in inches). Once we have the dimension C we are also able to work out the circumference of the bottom of the cone from the following formula: divide C by 2 and square the result. Then multiply by 22 and divide the number by 7. The reflectors have a 60 degree angle so the diameter of the cone base will be the same as C. We then use the standard formula of circumference = $\pi r^2$ where $\pi$ is assumed to be 22/7. You will need to know this because obviously your cone opened out will have to come to at least this dimension on its lower edge; in practice it is a good idea to allow at least an inch overlap for gluing the two sides together. The card cone should be assembled first and the aluminium foil attached later. Attempts to glue it on first will almost certainly cause it to split or buckle once the card is curved round. The bottom edge of the cone will need to be curved otherwise the cone will be lop-sided when assembled. This will have to be done by trial and error as the degree of curve will vary depending on the dimensions involved. Try cutting the curve with scissors a bit at a time until the result is right.

We have discussed the use of card and aluminium foil but of course there is no reason why metal meshing, often called 'chicken mesh', should not be used, and indeed to some extent it is easier to work with. The cone is roughly made up to shape and the upper and lower edges snipped into alignment with side-cutters. Mesh also has the advantage that the outer braid of the coaxial cable can be soldered direct to it. In the case of card it is probably a good idea to use two solder tags with the braid split so that each section goes to its own tag which is then attached to the cone by small nuts, bolts and washers.

Next comes the disc and again this can simply be aluminium foil or chicken mesh. The diameter should be 70 percent of the radials 'C'. It will need to be insulated from the cone so as to leave a gap of 3 mm but this can easily be achieved with the use of card, plastics or any similar materials that are to hand. The centre core of the coaxial cable must attach securely to the disc at its centre point and again a solder tag, nut bolts and washers will do.

It must be stressed that these connections must be as secure as possible otherwise UHF performance will suffer badly. Ideally good quality low loss coaxial cable should be used even if relatively short cable runs are to be used (standard RG58/U for instance attenuates by about 18 dB per 100 foot at 1000 MHz)

With care in construction, the discone should be fairly stable with an evenly flared cone and disc that is perfectly level. It should stand on its own and a suitable place can be found in the loft to mount it. Keep it well away from electrical cables, metal pipes and tanks. In my own home the inside of the loft is quite high and I have used string attached to the centre of the disc at one end and a nail in the beams at the other end in order to suspend the discone as high as possible. This also has the added advantage that the antenna is now well away from the pipes and electricity cables that run across the joists.

For anyone wanting to use my own dimensions, the 130 MHz theoretical minimum, they are as follows C = 22.7 inches, D = 15.8 inches.

## Outside discones

Discones for external mounting are not so easy to make although not altogether impossible. Again the actual construction will largely

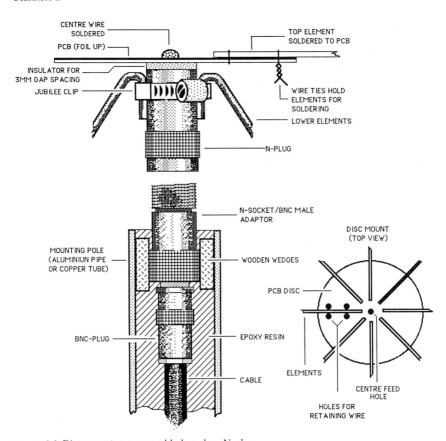

**Figure 9.2** Discone antenna assembly based on N-plug

depend on the materials that can be obtained. Aluminium rod or tubing is not the easiest material to come by and in fact is not that good for home construction projects because it cannot easily be soldered. Thick copper wire or bronze brazing rod is far easier to get hold of. One good source of very thick copper wire is an automobile. A visit to a scrap yard and a look under the hood of an old vehicle may produce a bonanza of material. Many automotive coils such as those used in voltage stabilisers and relays use copper wire as thick as the metal used for making wire clothes-hangers (another useful source depending on the kind of metal used). Bronze brazing rods can often be obtained in lengths of around 2 foot from firms who specialise in welding and metal work. They are available in a range of thicknesses. All these materials will only really be suitable if you intend making a relatively small discone, ie the 130 MHz minimum version described previously.

Mounting all these component parts is the next problem but think along the lines of VHF/UHF plugs and sockets, epoxy resin, jubilee clips, copper water pipes, etc, and you should start to get an idea of how you can assemble them all together. A look at the detailed illustration (Figure 9.2) will show how I assembled my own discone. Note the use of an N-connector rather than a PL-259. Although the latter is physically large enough to mount all the elements it has poor performance at UHF and so was not used. You will need an N-plug, N-socket to BNC-plug (male) adaptor and a BNC-plug. Alternatively, if you are lucky enough to be able to get hold of an N-type line socket then you can forget the adaptor and BNC-plug. It is not possible to use a normal N-socket as this would be too wide to fit into a pipe. The mounting pipe can be either copper or aluminium and construction will be made easier if the pipe is not too long — about a foot longer than dimension 'C' is ideal. The tube or pipe should have an internal diameter just slightly wider than the body of the N-plug adaptor. The feeder cable will have to be made up with its plug and this is then attached to the adaptor. This whole assembly is then passed through the mounting tube and is firmly wedged using small pieces of wood. The threaded portion of the adaptor must be clear of the tube to the extent that the N-plug can be firmly screwed onto it. Tap the wooden wedges to just below the top level of the tube and then apply masking tape or a similar medium so as to seal off the top of the tube around the N-plug. The tube now needs to be inverted (if it can be supported in a bench-vice so much the better) and liquid epoxy resin mixed with hardener poured in. This type of resin is readily available from hardware stores and you will only need enough to seal-in the plug and adaptor assembly at the top of the tube. Once it has set, you can remove the tape and any slight imperfections can be filed off or any small holes filled up with more resin.

The assembly of the actual antenna is next and this is done in several stages. When cutting the lower elements, allow at least 2 inches extra because they will need to be trimmed to size after assembly. First connect a relatively thick wire to the centre pin of the N-plug. This wire should be at least three inches long and once soldered should be covered in a piece of insulated sleeving. Discard all remaining parts of the plug, rings, sleeves, cable retainer, etc, and support the plug so that it is vertical and smear a moderately thick glue around the part of the centre-pin which comes into contact with the plug's insulator ring. This is to seal the plug so that resin does not leak out. Once the glue has set, pour liquid epoxy resin into the body of the plug so that it is flush with the top. This step is essential as considerable pressure will be exerted on the plug body when a clip is used to hold the lower elements in place.

You will now need a piece of unetched printed circuit board cut into a disc of about 3 inches diameter. The easiest way to solder the top elements to this is to drill small holes in the PCB and then initially hold the elements in place with wire. Once they are all soldered these wires can then be trimmed away with side cutters. Alternatively, if you are building a fairly small discone you could actually make the disc entirely from a circular piece of PCB.

Next, the lower elements have to be attached to the plug body and a second pair of hands will be needed at this stage. First, slip the Jubilee clip over the body of the shell and then insert all the elements so that at this stage they are pointing upwards — not down. With a second person holding the elements, carefully space them equally around the plug body. By tightening the Jubilee clip to the point where the elements can only just be moved, this is not too difficult. Once the elements are all aligned and the clip is fully tightened, the elements can now be bent over to the correct degree of flare. Now trim them to the correct length. This method of attaching the lower elements will not in itself stop them from moving in strong winds, so you need to make up a hoop of relatively thick wire (16 SWG is best but slightly thinner wire may do). The hoop must be soldered to the bottom of the lower elements so that it forms a ring that keeps all the elements an equal distance apart. A second hoop could of course be soldered at a point half way up the elements and this will add to the rigidity.

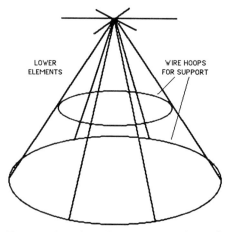

LOWER
ELEMENTS

WIRE HOOPS
FOR SUPPORT

**Figure 9.3** Use of wire hoops to support lower elements

The final step before mounting the antenna is to put the disc in place and you will need some kind of insulators, plastic washers for instance, to build up the gap between the foil side of the PCB and the top of the lower elements to the required 3 mm gap. With these in place the disc assembly and insulators are all glued together and then glued to the top of the plug body (this forms a weather seal and takes pressure from wind force off the single wire attachment). With the top elements correctly aligned against their appropriate lower elements the connector wire is soldered to its hole in the disc PCB and any remaining wire snipped away.

You now have a complete discone built around an N-plug and it is now a good idea to give the assembly a good coating of clear outdoor wood varnish. Pay particular attention to the joint around the disc. This final step will ensure that corrosion of the elements does not spoil the performance; ideally the varnish should be re-coated once a year (it is good practice to 'service' all antennas prior to the winter months). It only remains for the antenna unit to be plugged onto the pole-socket arrangement and this connection sealed with insulating tape to prevent water getting into it.

### Points to watch

At first glance it may appear that many of the steps described above could be skipped, cheaper plugs used, etc. The ultimate performance of this antenna will finally be determined by the amount of care taken to build it and this will make a noticeable difference at UHF. Good solid connections and care over dimensions will provide you with an antenna that will far outperform many commercially made ones with their cheaper PL-259 plugs. The only limitation on this method of construction is that it is not suited to larger discones. Even if all the components described above are bought as new, the antenna will still cost far less than commercially available ones.

## More widebanders

There are a few other wideband antennas commercially available but none of these can really be easily copied by the home constructor. The first is the 'nest of dipoles' which in Britain is marketed under the brand name Radacs and is manufactured by Revco Electronics. It consists of six dipoles all set at slightly offset angles to cancel the self-inductance. It does not have an even response from the lowest frequency to the highest. In practice each set of dipoles is cut to a separate band. It is natural that one should compare the performance of this type of antenna with a discone. I have a Radac and find that for many applications it seems to perform slightly better than some commercial discones. It really boils down to what type of scanning or searching is carried out. If for the majority of time the scanner is used just to hunt through frequencies on certain set bands then I personally believe that the Radac may have the edge in performance. On the other hand if you are the sort of person who spends a lot of time searching for signals across the range 80–1300 MHz then a good discone is probably a better choice.

Amongst the remaining wide band antennas is the log periodic. The

**Photograph 9(a)** Revco's Radac works on the nest-of-dipoles principle

only version I have seen commercially available is Model LT606 made by Hidaka and supplied by South Midland Communications of Britain (I have no doubt similar antennas are also available from specialist antenna suppliers in other countries). This particular antenna has a claimed gain of 7.8 dB and is directional. It boasts a frequency coverage of 50 to 500 MHz and although I have no personal experience of this equipment it would seem to be ideally suited to the keen DXer because it is directional. That means of course that the antenna, which can be used vertically or horizontally, will have to be mounted on a rotator.

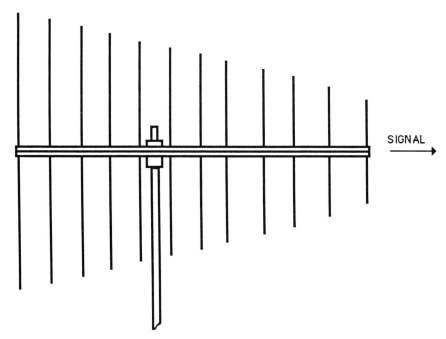

**Figure 9.4** Commercial log periodic with 50–500 MHz claimed bandwidth and 7.8 dB gain

## Self-built antennas

The following antennas are all capable of being copied by anyone with suitable skills and tools but before discussing them in detail here are the all important dimension formulas:

(Metres):   Half wavelength in free air = 150/Frequency in Megahertz

Quarter wavelength in free air = 75/Frequency in Megahertz

(Inches):   Half wavelength in free air = 5904/Frequency in Megahertz

Quarter wavelength in free air = 2952/Frequency in Megahertz

In practice, the actual length is normally reduced by 5 percent relative to a half wave, this being known as the 'correction factor'. Clearly from these figures it easy to work out the various divisions or multiples such as ⅛ths, ¾s, etc.

## Dual banders

Some VHF/UHF antennas will perform well over two chosen bands. Indeed the few mobile antennas that are sold are usually only tuned to two bands. So far it seems the truly wide band mobile antenna with

**Photograph 9(b)** This Revco UHF colinear also works well at ⅓ of the design frequency

discone-like performance has yet to be invented. However, a dual-bander will often perform better than just a straight whip aerial and details of some approaches that can be tried are given here. It should be borne in mind that these details are to give you a start with experimenting and they are not intended as complete projects.

One of the more interesting discoveries I made whilst playing around with antennas was that certain types of mobile UHF colinear also resonate at VHF. For mobile use these antennas obviously have to be end-fed and most manufacturers now use a phasing element that consists of contra-wound coils. Figure 9.6 shows how this is done, but be warned that this design is patented and although you are free to

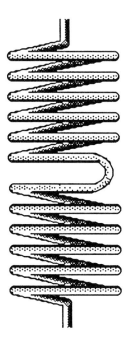

**Figure 9.5** Bi-directional phasing coil for ⅝ over ¼ colinear

copy it for your own use you could be in trouble if you start trying to use the design commercially. Using a 70 cm band ⅝ wave over ¼ wave colinear employing this type of coil I noticed that the antenna was also perfectly usable at 2 metres where the phasing coils appear to be electronically transparent and the antenna behaves like a quarter wave. This is a very interesting effect because of course at UHF the more gain we can get the better and this particular antenna offers a gain of around 5 dB. This antenna had coils which were two turns to each direction on an internal diameter of about ½ an inch.

The next form of dual bander is the 'trapped' vertical. The principle has been employed by amateur operators on the HF bands for many years and most commercially made mobile scanner aerials seem to employ this principle. It consists of a lower section for the highest frequency band required and an upper section, the length of which is combined with that of the lower section to provide an antenna for the lowest band required. The two sections are separated by a parallel tuned coil/capacitor arrangement, known as the trap, which is tuned to the highest frequency; because this presents a high impedance on that band it effectively isolates the top section. However, the story does not end there because below the frequency of the trap, that coil and capacitor act as an inductive reactance which means that the total length of the aerial for the lowest band will in fact be less than a quarter wave.

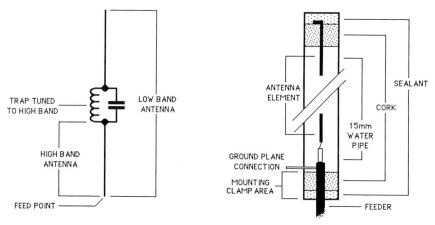

**Figure 9.6**

Next, another effect takes place. At certain frequencies above the resonant frequency of the trap, it acts as series capacitance and the top section will resonate at harmonics of the fundamental. Performance is very much a compromise, even on the two chosen bands, but the principle has been successfully employed by manufacturers such as Radio Shack (Tandy) to produce mobile antennas that offer better performance than the usual whip aerial roughly cut to a quarter wave at 100 MHz.

### Practical experiments

It is impossible to give dimensions because there is no real set formula to work from. At VHF and UHF the coils are unlikely to amount to more than a few turns and the parallel capacitance to more than a few picoFarad. Indeed, the number of turns on the coil will also depend to some extent on the individual capacitor used because at these sort of frequencies the capacitor itself has a certain in-built inductance.

A good starting point though is to determine the lower section first. This should be roughly a quarter wave at the highest frequency band required. We now also have a working point for determining the trap. For instance if we were aiming at a highest frequency of about 150 MHz then 6 turns of wire ($\frac{1}{4}$ inch internal diameter) and about 10 pF capacitance will make a good start (obviously if you own a grid dip oscillator then you can get soon get the arrangement spot on). My own experiments used a crude but effective lash-up: simply a small piece of strip-board providing a stable mount for the coil and a small 20 pF trimmer capacitor with them both connected to an old telescopic antenna. First of all an off-air signal is tuned-in on the highest band required and the trimmer tuned for maximum reception (once it is spot-on, changing the length of the upper section will have little effect). A signal is then found on the chosen lower band and the telescopic adjusted for maximum signal. It is then simply a question of measuring the sections, checking the approximate capacitance from the position of the trimmer vanes and copying this with a fixed value component to a finished design.

The next problem though is how to make a practical aerial for mobile use. Unless you have access to such equipment as a lathe it is best to modify an existing mobile aerial. I actually found the perfect solution in a small, cheap centre-loaded CB aerial. The centre loading section easily unscrewed to reveal a plastic rod over which a coil was wound. This was replaced with my own coil with a small thin capacitor soldered across it. The existing bottom section was accepted as the quarter wave for the highest frequency and the stainless steel top-section whip, which fitted into a small hole with grub-screw adjustment, was re-cut for the dimensions determined earlier.

Having described that method I accept that most readers will not have such an aerial to hand, but it demonstrates the point that many CB antennas can be converted for other uses and they have the great advantage of usually being far cheaper than antennas produced for radiotelephone or amateur use. Most CB shops also stock a range of bases and mounts for vehicles. These nearly all use a standard threaded coupling system making the various parts very adaptable.

## Further experiments
It is also worth experimenting with series coils that do not have a capacitor (in fact most commercial designs do not employ them). A similar trap effect can be achieved and slightly different results will be obtained, particularly at lower frequencies where the combined length of the coil winding and two sections will act as an electrically shortened quarter wave. The resonant points and various impedances that appear on different sections of the antenna are rather complex — if you want to know more, there are several good books dedicated to antenna theory published by the Radio Society of Great Britain and the American Amateur Relay League.

There is of course nothing to stop you using a second trap. Some HF antennas used by amateurs use several in order to cover a number of bands. Although I have never tried this personally, I suspect that at VHF and UHF the theoretical increased performance is likely to be outweighed by the complexity of making such an aerial. If the lower section is for UHF then try just using different low values of capacitor with no coil, 5 pF is a good starting point.

## Monobanders
Although we have looked at wideband antennas and dual banders we should not forget that some scanner owners only monitor one band,

**Photograph 9(c)** Base loaded ⅝ wave on a magnetic mount. Ideal for mobile monoband use

typical examples being the amateurs and people whose interests are limited to the marine or air bands. In most instances, the answer will obviously be to use a simple quarter wave dipole, either for base or mobile use. However it is possible to increase performance with antennas which can offer a degree of gain. One of the best ways to improve reception for mobile use is to use a ⅝th wave base loader. Many designs are available commercially and again I come back to CB antennas because many base loaded antennas designed for 27 MHz use are very easily adapted as ⅝ wave VHF aerials. Figure 9.6 will show that in practice a ⅝ wave antenna is really an electrical ¾ wave with ⅛th of the actual length being used as the loading coil. This antenna provides a good 50 Ohm match to a scanner. The section on which the coil is mounted must be non-metallic or it will affect the inductance.

As an example let us look at a ⅝ wave for 150 MHz. Using the formula given earlier we can determine that the electrical length (coil and element) will be exactly 1.5 metres. The length of the wire used for the coil must be 25 cms and the length of the whip 1.25 metres. Obviously the number of turns that make up the coil will be determined by the base available but the coil should be space wound, not close wound.

## ½ wave over ½ wave

One very useful gain antenna for base use is the ½ wave over ½ wave phased vertical. Useful because it has good performance and is easy to construct. Figure 9.7 will show the basic concept and the 50 Ohm matching point for the feeder. The only difficulty the home constructor is likely to face is making a suitable fixing point. However, an old TV antenna connector block is ideal. These blocks are made to mount on a pole and it is only necessary to bridge the two connector pillars inside the block to ensure continuity across the hairpin section.

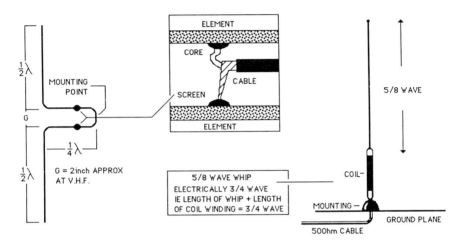

1/2 WAVE OVER 1/2 WAVE PHASED VERTICAL          5/8 WAVE WHIP ANTENNA

**Figure 9.7** Monoband aerials for base and mobile use

The actual feeder of course will not go to this connector block, that is simply used for mounting. The feeder needs to be connected as shown in the diagram and the actual point of connection will have to be found by trial and error — in practice it should be about a third of the way along the quarter wave sections from the fixing point. Once the fixing points have been established they must be sealed against corrosion and this can be done with a variety of sealants available from hardware stores. The actual elements can be made from aluminium rod, copper central heating piping, etc.

## Colinears

A number of Colinear type antennas using the contra-wound phasing coils described earlier have been tried and proved quite successful. One beauty of this type of antenna is it is very simple to make. The actual coils and elements consist of nothing more than a single piece of wire suspended inside a plastic 15 mm water pipe. It is best to dispense with plugs and sockets and simply solder the centre core of the feeder directly onto the base of the antenna wire. The top of the wire can be threaded through a cork so that when vertical it hangs inside the pipe. Obviously the cork should be pushed slightly down from the top of the pipe and sealant used to keep water out. Reflectors will be needed at the base of the antenna to provide a ground plane and these will need to connect to the braid of the feeder. The reflectors must be at least a quarter wave in length but it is not necessary for them to be in physical contact with the actual screen of the feeder; a single wire connecting the two is adequate. The length of the pipe should be slightly longer than the internal antenna so that all of the antenna element is clear of whatever mounting pole the plastic pipe is clamped to. If the top of the mounting pole is aligned flush with the bottom of the antenna proper then the reflectors can be bolted to the mounting pole (which should be aluminium or copper).

## Water antenna

No I joke not. I spotted this idea in the excellent 'Technical Topics' column by Pat Hawker G3VA in the RSGB's magazine, Radcom. It's

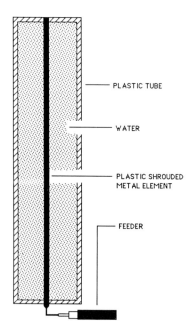

**Figure 9.8** Water-jacket antenna — Plessey patent GB 2001 804

an idea patented by Plessey and makes use of the dielectric loading effect to reduce the resonant length of an antenna. In their patent application Plessey say it is not practical to just put the metallic element of the antenna into water as the liquid will become contaminated. The idea, invented by G. J. Brett, is to create a water jacket so that the element sits in a sleeve surrounded by water although there is no physical contact. It is claimed that using such an antenna, a 15 cm rod gave a 200 percent increase in received signal strength at 100 MHz over a comparable rod in free air.

No dimensions of any kind are given but there is a warning that the water should be free of contamination and can contain anti-freeze. I suggest the water could be distilled water of the type sold for car batteries and steam irons. The plastic tube can be UPVC waste pipe and the element just a stiff wire enclosed in plastic insulation. Quite how you will seal the ends will depend on what materials you can lay your hands on but plastic sheet (even cut from old washing-up liquid bottles) can be used together with suitable glue or epoxy resin, car body filler, etc.

My own version actually used an old 40 cm length of 6 inch drain piping which was bonded with epoxy onto a sheet of aluminium acting as a ground plane. The results were quite surprising and although the antenna has to be considered as a monobander I really cannot see any serious application for as far as the scanner owner is concerned. I have included it here simply for those souls like myself who once in a while on a rainy week-end afternoon get the urge to do something different with a few old bits of wire, feeder and household scrap materials.

### Antenna materials
A range of materials for home construction of antennas has already been mentioned and details are given here of a few more.

By and large mounting poles can be made from virtually anything, including wood. The actual elements of aerials though should be fairly carefully selected. Not only is weight an important factor but the resistance of some metals as well makes them unsuitable for use. For instance I have noticed that certain types of coat-hanger wire make very poor antennas particularly at UHF. We also have to consider what is known as 'skin-effect'. As we progress higher in frequency so more of the actual outer layer of the antenna element conducts the current. Obviously metals that corrode quickly in air, such as iron, are not suitable. Having said that there is of course nothing to stop you using such metals as long as they are given a coating of outdoor-grade varnish. One good source of steel wire for instance is model shops. Many sell this wire in a variety of thicknesses and lengths and the metal is ideal for making up whip antennas as it is far more rigid than copper or brass. Aluminium is the first choice for any base antenna project and scrap lengths of old FM radio or Band 1 television antennas can often be used effectively. Cleaned up and varnished this metal has low resistivity and is very light in weight.

Insulation presents no great problem. Epoxy resin and car body filler paste are useful as are certain types of sealants available by the tube from hardware stores. The only one to avoid is the silicone rubber type which has a smell of vinegar. This product is acid based and will corrode certain metals and wire. Mastics, potting compound or similar materials are all useable and you can purchase silicone grease which can be smeared over antenna connections to protect them (normal engineering grease is not suitable). One product that is very handy is the waxy type of cavity filler sold for automobiles. In Britain this is sold under the brand name 'Waxoyl' and is available in aerosol cans. Sprayed onto connector blocks it will keep moisture out and used on the bolts of pole mounting brackets it will stop them rusting-up.

One final material that is useful to get hold of is heat-shrink plastic tubing. It is available in a variety of bores from components suppliers and is useful for weather-sealing such things as loading coils. The tubing shrinks considerably when heat is applied which can either be from something like a hot-air paint-stripper or it can be simply held close to an electric cooker ring whilst rolling to get an even shrink-wrap. When cutting a section of the tubing always allow for the fact that it shrinks lengthwise as well. I normally allow plenty of extra length and trim with a sharp knife once the shrinking is complete.

**Safety**
Always take great care when mounting antennas outdoors. Remember that many overhead mains power lines are not insulated and anyone holding a metal assembly that comes into contact with such a line can receive a lethal shock. Tragically there have been many recorded cases of amateurs, CBers and similar hobbyists being killed in this way.

# Satellites 10

## Satellite reception

When you have occasionally tired of hearing the usual stations within a thirty or forty mile radius of your scanner and want to hear something new then point your antenna to the skies because there is a host of signals beaming down your way.

Satellite watching is now a fast growing hobby possibly because there is a lot of detective work involved and searching for satellite signals requires a lot more patience and skill than merely tuning into your local radio communication networks. Your scanner is an ideal instrument for searching out satellite signals. If you are lucky enough to own the Icom R7000 then even more satellite signals are there waiting for you to find them. The thrill of Satellite hunting is discovering new frequencies and being rewarded for hours of painstaking detective work. Why so difficult? There are two reasons. With only a few exceptions governments rarely give out lists of frequencies and some do not even publicly announce that they have launched a satellite. In comparison with the number of scanner owners, satellite 'freaks' are few and far between and so information on new frequencies is rarely passed on by word of mouth. Adding to the difficulties is the fact that satellites may only be heard for a few minutes during every few hours as they pass overhead and some may only be switched on occasionally by telecommand from the ground station.

It must be stressed from the outset that you are unlikely to hear much in the way of scintillating conversation on the satellite bands. The vast majority of satellite signals are in the form of data transmissions. Weather satellite pictures, radar pictures of even just strings of numbers from on-board sensors and instruments make up the majority of signals. Even so, some voice traffic can be heard. In Europe the MIR space station, UOSATs (Oscars), Russian amateur RS series and some VHF weather satellites are very strong on overhead passes. I have often received the MIR, UOSAT and NOAA weather satellites on my AOR 2002 just using a telescopic antenna. Other transmissions of interest have been the NASA shuttle communications on UHF.

## Further information

UoSAT Spacecraft Control Centre
University of Surrey
Guildford
England
Telephone numbers 0483–61707 & 0483 61202 give recorded update information on UoSATs 1 and 2 respectively.

AMSAT–UK
94 Herongate Road
Wanstead Park
London E12 5EQ

AMSAT–USA
P.O. Box 27
Washington DC
20044, USA

Remote Imaging Group
c/o Phil Seaford
14 Nevis Close
Leighton Buzzard
Beds LU7 7XD

## Recorded telephone information

**British Telecom Spaceline:** 01–246 8055
**Lasham Ground Station NOAA data (after 6 pm only):** 025 683 448
**US Dial a Shuttle:** 010 1 900 410 6272
**US Naval Observatory Hotline:** 010 1 202 653 0258
**UoSATs:** see above.

## Satellite frequencies

| Frequency | Mode | Name | Type/Details |
| --- | --- | --- | --- |
| 29.330 | DATA | RS-5 | Codestore/Robot on Russian amateur satellite |
| 29.350 | DATA | RS-5 & 7 | Command transponder |

## Satellite frequencies *continued*

| Frequency | Mode | Name | Type/Details |
|---|---|---|---|
| 29.401 | CW | RS-1 | Russian amateur beacon satellite. Send '55' or '5051' in morse |
| 29.410 | Mixed | RS-5 | Downlink 29.410 — 29.450 MHz. Morse and voice traffic |
| 29.430 | DATA | RS-7 | Codestore/Robot |
| 29.460 | Mixed | RS-7 | Downlink 29.460 — 29.500 MHz. Morse and voice traffic |
| 121.750 | FM | Soyuz | Manned 'T' flights |
| 136.320 | | Geos-3 | Radar Sat |
| 136.350 | | CAS-A/EOLE-1 | French Sats |
| 136.380 | | OV5-3 | (ERS-26) |
| 136.590 | | Alouette 2 | Canadian Sat and Isis-2 |
| 136.610 | | Ariane | Telemetry |
| 136.650 | | Transit | |
| 136.694 | | Shinsei | |
| 136.695 | | Jiki'Ken | |
| 136.725 | | Various | |
| 136.800 | | Various | EGRS-1, 7 and 13, Symphonie-B and Dodge |
| 136.830 | | EXP-45 | |
| 136.980 | | Alouette 1/2 | Canadian Sats |
| 136.980 | | Diademe 1 | French Sat also on 149.70/ 399.92 MHz |
| 137.020 | APT | Meteor 30 | Weather satellite |
| 137.049 | | Comsat | General Comsat |
| 137.056 | | ATS-F | US Sat |
| 137.060 | APT | Met 1/30 | Weather satellite |
| 137.080 | | Meteosat | Weather (geostationary) and US DoD |
| 137.110 | | ATS-F | US Sat |
| 137.140 | | ECS-2 | |
| 137.050 | | Met-30 | Weather |
| 137.169 | | Comsat | Marine Comsat |
| 137.170 | | Marecs-A | |
| 137.230 | | Bhaskara-2 | |
| 137.300 | APT | Meteor 2/14 | Weather |

## Satellite frequencies *continued*

| Frequency | Mode | Name | Type/Details |
|---|---|---|---|
| 137.380 | | Various | Timation 2 and OVS-3 |
| 137.400 | WEFAX | Meteors | Meteors 3/1 and 2/13. Weather |
| 137.400 | | Rohini-3 | |
| 137.400 | | Cosmos | Cosmos 1602 and 1766 (Russian oceanographic radar satellite |
| 137.410 | | S69-4 | |
| 137.440 | | Ariabat | |
| 137.500 | APT | NOAA-10 | Weather |
| 137.530 | | SRET-2 | |
| 137.620 | APT | NOAA-9 | Weather |
| 137.850 | | Meteors | Meteors 2/12, 2/15 and 3/1. Weather |
| 137.850 | | Intercosmos | Intercosmos-18 |
| 137.860 | | Landsats | Landsat 3 |
| 137.770 | DSB | NOAA-9 | Weather |
| 137.980 | | Explorer-50 | |
| 140.056 | | ATS-F | US Sat |
| 141.056 | | ATS-F | US Sat |
| 142.400 | FM | Soyuz/MIR | Comms. Prime frequency over Europe |
| 142.420 | FM | Salyut | Comms |
| 142.417 | FM | Soyuz/MIR | Comms |
| 142.600 | FM | Soyuz/MIR | Comms |
| 143.144 | FM | Soyuz/MIR | Comms |
| 143.825 | FM | Soyuz/MIR | Comms |
| 143.625 | FM | MIR | Manned Space Station (USSR). Very strong signal on overhead passes |
| 145.810 | FM | Oscar-10 | Amateur (beacon). Satellite unstable |
| 145.825 | FM | Oscar-9 | Amateur (beacon) 'UOSAT'. Data or Robot voice |
| 145.826 | FM | Oscar-11 | Amateur (beacon). UOSAT 2 |
| 145.930 | SSB | Oscar-10 | Amateur transponder 145.83–145.97 X-pond. Satellite now unstable |

## Satellite frequencies *continued*

| Frequency | Mode | Name | Type/Details |
|---|---|---|---|
| 149.000 | AM | CICADA | Navigation beacons. Spot frequencies 149.910, 149.940, 149.970, 150.000, 150.030 (paired with 400 MHz beacons). CICADA, COSNAV, TRANSIT |
| 149.700 | | D-1A | French Beacon |
| 150.000 | | MIR | MIR/Salyut 7 docking module |
| 162.00 | | Various | |
| 166.00 | | Various | Cosmos, Elint, Ocean Recon, Soyuz, MIR, Ocean Radar, etc |
| 192.040 | FM | Soyuz/MIR | |
| 216.000 | | Anna 1-B | US Sat |
| 225.000 | | | Military comms 225.00– 400.00. Telemetry but voice occasionally |
| 259.700 | AM | Shuttle NASA | Shuttle comms |
| 296.800 | AM | Shuttle NASA | Shuttle comms |
| 324.000 | | Various | |
| 360.044 | | ATS-F | US Sat |
| 360.144 | | ATS-F | US Sat |
| 360.244 | | ATS-F | US Sat |
| 361.144 | | ATS-F | US Sat |
| 399.726 | | Various | Transit(US), Cosnav(USSR), Nav beacons paired with 150 MHz. Spot frequencies: 399.726, 399.842, 399.927. 400.002, 400.082 |
| 399.920 | | D-1A | French Sat |
| 399.968 | | Unknown | Unknown but sends 400 MHz note (usually rough). Often strong signal |
| 400.550 | | Copernicus | OAO-C US Sat |
| 412.050 | | ATS-3 | US Sat |
| 435.025 | CW | Oscars 9/11 | Beacons on UOSATS 1& 2 |
| 435.797 | CW SSB | Fuji | Japanese amateur satellite also designated FO-12, JAS-1, Oscar 12. Downlink 435.797– 435.910 |

## Satellite frequencies *continued*

| Frequency | Mode | Name | Type/Details |
|-----------|------|------|--------------|
| 436.055 | CW | Oscar 10 | Amateur satellite. Beacon. Unstable |
| 464.000 | | Various | US Beacons 1963-22A, 49B, 1964-26A |
| 464 | | CAS-A/EOLE-1 | French Sats |
| 466.00 | | Ocean Recon | Various |
| 702 | TV | | Soviet Direct Broadcast Television 702.00-726.00 MHz WBFM |
| 800.00 | | DATA VOICE | Molniya Soviet Communication satellites 800-1000 MHz |
| 922.75 | FM/TV | | Soviet Cosmonauts MIR/ Salyut and Salyut TV picture downlink |
| 926.06 | FM | MIR | Cosmonauts voice traffic/ Telecommand |
| 928.40 | DATA | Venera | Deep Space Planetary Probe |
| 1227.40 | | NavStar | Eliptical orbit navigation sat |
| 1675.280 | APT | Meteosat 2 | Geostationary weather satellite |
| 1681.60 | APT | Geos 3/4/5 | Weather satellite |
| 1683.833 | APT | Meteosat | Weather satellite |
| 1687 | APT | Geos 3/4/5 | Weather satellite |
| 1691.00 | APT | Meteosat 2 | Weather satellite. Channel 2 |
| 1694.00 | APT | Geos | Weather satellite |
| 1694.30 | APT | Geos | Geostationary weather satellite |
| 1694.50 | APT | Meteosat 2 | Weather satellite. Channel 1 |
| 1698.00 | APT | Various | NOAA/OPS9845 Circular orbit High resolution radiometer Data |
| 1707.020 | APT | NOAA9 | Weather Satellite linked with output on 137.62 MHz as well. High resolution Radiometer Data |
| 2205.00 | FM | Shuttle | NASA shuttle comms |

## US military communication satellites
Known transmit frequencies

---

### Fltsatcom — Atlantic
*23 West Longitude*

---

| | |
|---|---|
| US Navy | 252.05, 253.75, 255.45, 257.050, 258.55, 265.45, 266.95, 268.35, 269.85 |
| Dept of Defence | 261.45, 261.475, 261.50, 261.525, 261.55, 261.575, 261.60, 261.625, 261.675, 261.70, 261.725, 261.75, 261.775, 261.80, 261.85, 261.90, 261.925 |

---

### Fltsatcom — Pacific
*100 West Longitude*

---

| | |
|---|---|
| US Navy | 251.95, 253.65, 255.35, 256.95, 258.45, 265.35, 266.85, 268.25, 269.75 |
| Dept of Defence | 260.35, 260.375, 260.40, 260.425, 260.45, 260.475, 260.50, 260.525, 260.55, 260.575, 260.60, 260.625, 260.65, 260.675, 260.70, 260.725, 260.80, 260.825 |

---

### Fltsatcom — Indian Ocean
*75 East Longitude*

---

| | |
|---|---|
| US Navy | 252.15, 253.85, 255.55, 257.15, 258.65, 265.55, 267.05, 268.45, 269.95 |
| Dept of Defence | 263.35, 263.375, 263.40, 263.425, 263.475, 263.50, 263.525, 263.55, 263.575, 263.60, 263.45,263.625, 263.65, 263.675, 263.70, 263.725, 263.750, 263.775, 263.80, 263.825 |

---

### Fltsatcom — Pacific
*172 East Longitude*

---

| | |
|---|---|
| US Navy | 252.05, 253.75, 255.45, 257.05, 258.55, 265.45, 266.95, 268.35, 269.85 |
| Dept of Defence | 261.45, 261.475, 261.50, 262.525, 261.55, 261.575, 261.60, 261.625, 261.65, 261.675, 261.70, 261.725, 261.75, 261.775, 261.80, 261.825, 261.85, 261.875, 261.90, 261.925 |

---

# 11 Major world airports

This section includes a list of 230 of the world's major international airports. For the sake of clarity, the list has been split into two sections; Europe, Asia, Africa and the Pacific with North and South America listed separately.

The list will not only be of interest to international readers but also provide a reference source for the many people who now travel a lot and take their hand-held scanner with them. However, a word of caution. Whilst the governments of many countries take a liberal view of enthusiasts listening-in to the airbands, this activity can be viewed with great suspicion by many communist and third world countries. Arrest, fines and even jail sentences are not unknown.

The lists only include basic information. The first column covers the Automatic Terminal Information Service (ATIS) as this can contain much useful information. The second and third column contain Approach and Tower details and the fourth column clearance or departure frequencies. The fifth column contains ground control information whilst the final column contains miscellaneous frequencies covering such things as radar, information, additional approach frequencies, etc.

## Table 11.1 Europe, Africa, Asia and the Pacific

| Airport | ATIS | App | Tower | Clr/Dep | GND | Rad/Mix |
|---|---|---|---|---|---|---|
| Aberdeen | 121.850 | 120.400 | 118.100 | | 121.700 | 120.400 |
| Accra Kotoka International | | 118.100 | 118.100 | | | 119.500 |
| Addis Ababa Bole International | | 119.700 | 118.100 | | | |
| Adelaide | 116.400 | 124.200 | 120.500 | 126.100 | 121.700 | |
| Aden International | | 119.700 | 118.700 | 124.500 | 121.900 | 119.700 |
| Ajaccio Campo de Oro | 121.050 | 121.050 | 118.100 | | 121.700 | 118.100 |
| Akrotiri | | 122.100 | 122.100 | | | 123.300 |

## Table 11.1  Europe, Africa, Asia and the Pacific *continued*

| Airport | ATIS | App | Tower | Clr/Dep | GND | Rad/Mix |
|---|---|---|---|---|---|---|
| Algiers Houari Boumediene | | 121.400 | 118.700 | 125.700 | | 119.700 |
| Alicante | | 118.800 | 118.150 | | 121.700 | |
| Alma Ata | 135.100 | 124.800 | 119.400 | 135.400 | 121.700 | 120.800 |
| Amsterdam Schipol | 132.975 | 121.200 | 118.100 | 121.800 | 121.700 | 118.800 |
| Ankara Esenboga | 114.300 | 119.100 | 118.100 | 119.600 | 121.900 | 119.600 |
| Athens Central | 123.400 | 119.100 | 118.100 | 122.400 | 121.700 | 121.400 |
| Auckland International | 127.800 | 120.500 | 118.700 | 118.500 | 121.900 | 126.000 |
| Baghdad Saddam International | | 119.400 | 118.700 | 127.100 | | 120.400 |
| Bahrain | | 122.300 | 118.500 | 126.700 | | 124.300 |
| Bali International | 126.200 | 119.700 | 118.100 | 128.300 | | 120.700 |
| Bangkok | 126.400 | 119.100 | 118.100 | 121.800 | 121.900 | 120.500 |
| Barcelona | 118.650 | 119.100 | 118.100 | | 121.700 | 127.700 |
| Basle Mulhouse | 127.875 | 119.350 | 119.700 | 121.250 | 121.600 | 119.700 |
| Beijing (Peking) | | 129.000 | 118.100 | 125.900 | 121.700 | 132.700 |
| Beira | | 119.700 | 118.100 | | | |
| Beirut International | | 119.300 | 121.900 | 120.300 | | |
| Belfast Aldergrove | | 120.000 | 118.300 | | | 120.000 |
| Belgrade Surcin | | 119.100 | 118.100 | | | 119.100 |
| Benghazi Benina | | 121.300 | 121.300 | | 121.900 | |
| Bergen Flesland | 125.250 | 121.000 | 119.100 | | 121.700 | 125.000 |
| Berlin Gatow | | 125.800 | 123.850 | | | 130.800 |
| Berlin Schoenefeld | 125.900 | 119.500 | 121.300 | | 121.600 | 119.500 |
| Berlin Tegel | 112.300 | 125.800 | 118.700 | | 121.750 | |
| Berlin Tempelhof | 114.100 | 125.800 | 118.100 | 119.300 | 121.900 | 120.850 |
| Bilbao | | 118.500 | 118.500 | | 121.700 | |
| Birmingham International | 112.900 | 120.500 | 118.300 | | 121.800 | 120.500 |
| Bombay | 126.400 | 127.900 | 118.100 | 119.300 | 121.900 | 119.300 |
| Bordeaux Merignac | 131.150 | 118.600 | 118.300 | | 121.900 | 121.200 |
| Bratislava Ivanka | 128.650 | 120.900 | 118.300 | 125.700 | | 120.000 |
| Bremen | 117.450 | 125.650 | 118.500 | | 121.750 | 125.650 |
| Brisbane | 113.900 | 124.700 | 120.500 | 118.900 | 121.700 | 130.400 |
| Brunei International | 112.000 | 121.300 | 118.700 | | 121.900 | 121.300 |
| Brussels National | 114.600 | 118.250 | 118.600 | 121.600 | 121.875 | 120.100 |
| Bucharest Baneasa | 126.800 | 120.600 | 120.800 | | 121.950 | 125.200 |
| Bucharest Otopeni | 118.500 | 120.600 | 120.900 | | 121.700 | 118.800 |
| Budapest Ferihegy | 117.300 | 129.700 | 118.100 | 121.000 | 121.900 | 119.500 |
| Cairo | 121.700 | 119.550 | 118.100 | 130.900 | 121.900 | 118.700 |
| Calcutta | 126.400 | 127.900 | 118.100 | 120.100 | 121.900 | 127.900 |
| Canberra | 116.700 | 124.500 | 118.700 | 125.900 | 121.700 | |
| Cape Town D.F. Malan | 115.700 | 119.700 | 118.100 | 125.100 | 121.900 | 126.500 |
| Casablanca | 125.100 | 118.100 | 118.100 | | | |
| Christchurch International | 112.100 | 120.900 | 118.300 | 126.500 | 121.900 | |
| Cologne-Bonn | 119.025 | 120.250 | 118.900 | | 121.850 | 126.325 |
| Copenhagen Kastrup | 122.750 | 119.800 | 118.100 | 128.150 | 121.900 | 120.250 |
| Damascus International | | 120.000 | 118.500 | 121.300 | 121.900 | 121.300 |
| Dar-es-Salaam | | 119.600 | 118.300 | 119.300 | | 120.000 |
| Darwin | 113.700 | 120.500 | 118.300 | 126.800 | 121.700 | 120.000 |

## Table 11.1 Europe, Africa, Asia and the Pacific *continued*

| Airport | ATIS | App | Tower | Clr/Dep | GND | Rad/Mix |
|---|---|---|---|---|---|---|
| Delhi Indira Gandhi | 126.400 | 127.900 | 118.100 | 129.200 | 121.900 | 127.900 |
| Dhahran | 112.700 | 120.300 | 118.700 | 121.600 | 121.700 | 118.400 |
| Dubai | 115.700 | 124.900 | 118.750 | | 118.350 | 124.900 |
| Dublin | 127.000 | 121.100 | 118.600 | | 121.800 | 119.550 |
| Dubrovnik | | 123.600 | 118.500 | | | |
| Durban Louis Botha | 112.500 | 119.100 | 118.700 | 120.500 | 133.450 | 119.100 |
| Dusseldorf | 115.150 | 119.400 | 118.300 | 128.850 | 121.900 | 119.400 |
| Edinburgh (UK) | | 121.200 | 118.700 | | 121.750 | 121.200 |
| Entebbe Dr A.M. Obote Intl. | | 119.100 | 118.100 | | | 128.500 |
| Fairbanks International | 124.400 | 118.100 | 118.300 | 118.600 | 121.900 | 122.200 |
| Frankfurt Main | 118.025 | 120.800 | 119.900 | 124.025 | 121.900 | 118.500 |
| Geneva Cointrin | 127.550 | 120.300 | 118.700 | 127.300 | 121.900 | 118.700 |
| Gibraltar | | 122.800 | 123.300 | | | 130.400 |
| Glasgow | 113.400 | 119.100 | 118.800 | | 121.700 | 119.100 |
| Hamburg | 113.100 | 120.600 | 126.850 | | | 121.650 |
| Harare International | 113.100 | 119.100 | 118.100 | 125.100 | | 119.100 |
| Helsinki Vantaa | 114.200 | 119.100 | 118.600 | | 121.800 | 119.900 |
| Hong Kong International | 128.200 | 119.100 | 118.700 | 124.650 | 121.600 | 119.100 |
| Honolulu International | 127.900 | 118.300 | 118.100 | 121.400 | 121.900 | 118.300 |
| Instanbul Ataturk (Yesilkoy) | 112.500 | 121.100 | 118.100 | 122.100 | 121.900 | 120.500 |
| Jakarta Halim Perdanakusuma | 128.800 | 120.000 | 118.300 | | | |
| Jakarta Soekarno—Hatta Intl. | 126.86 | 135.900 | 118.200 | 121.950 | 121.750 | |
| Jeddah King Abdul Aziz | 114.900 | 124.000 | 124.300 | 123.800 | 121.600 | 121.600 |
| Jersey | 112.200 | 120.300 | 119.450 | 125.200 | 121.900 | 118.550 |
| Johannesburg Jan Smuts | 116.100 | 125.300 | 118.100 | 119.500 | 121.900 | 124.500 |
| Kagoshima | 127.050 | 126.000 | 118.200 | | 121.700 | 126.000 |
| Karachi | 126.700 | 121.300 | 118.300 | 127.300 | | 125.500 |
| Khartoum | | 120.300 | 120.900 | 124.700 | | 120.300 |
| Kiev Borispol | 126.700 | 130.600 | 119.300 | 135.400 | 119.000 | 120.900 |
| Kuala Lumpur International | 127.600 | 118.200 | 118.200 | 132.200 | 121.900 | 125.100 |
| Kuwait | | 121.300 | 118.300 | 125.200 | 121.700 | 118.300 |
| Larnaca | | 121.200 | 119.400 | | | 119.400 |
| Las Palmas Grand Canaria | | 124.300 | 118.300 | | 121.700 | 118.300 |
| Leningrad Pulkovo | 127.400 | 129.800 | 118.100 | 129.000 | 121.700 | 125.200 |
| Lisbon | 126.400 | 119.100 | 118.100 | 128.900 | | 127.900 |
| London Gatwick | 121.750 | 125.875 | 124.225 | 121.950 | 121.800 | 125.875 |
| London Heathrow | 121.850 | 119.200 | 118.700 | 121.700 | 121.900 | 119.200 |
| Lusaka International | 113.500 | 121.300 | 118.100 | 128.900 | | 120.100 |
| Luton (UK) | | 129.550 | 120.200 | | 121.750 | 128.750 |
| Luxembourg | 112.250 | 118.450 | 118.100 | | | |
| Madras | | 127.900 | 118.100 | | 121.900 | 119.300 |
| Madrid–Barajas | 118.250 | 139.500 | 118.150 | 121.900 | 121.700 | 119.900 |
| Malaga | 118.050 | 118.450 | 118.150 | | 121.700 | 119.300 |
| Manchester International | 128.175 | 119.400 | 118.700 | | 121.700 | 119.400 |
| Manilla International | 126.600 | 121.100 | 118.100 | 125.100 | 121.900 | 119.300 |
| Marseille Marignane | 125.350 | 120.200 | 119.500 | 123.800 | 121.700 | 118.100 |
| Melbourne Essendon | 119.800 | 124.700 | 125.100 | 127.700 | 121.900 | 126.600 |

## Table 11.1  Europe, Africa, Asia and the Pacific *continued*

| Airport | ATIS | App | Tower | Clr/Dep | GND | Rad/Mix |
|---|---|---|---|---|---|---|
| Melbourne International | 114.100 | 124.700 | 120.500 | 118.900 | 121.700 | 128.500 |
| Milan Linate | | 126.700 | 118.100 | 126.300 | 121.800 | 132.900 |
| Milan Malpensa | | 126.750 | 119.000 | | 121.600 | 132.900 |
| Minsk | 124.800 | 125.900 | 128.000 | 129.600 | 119.000 | 120.000 |
| Moscow Sheremetievo | 126.375 | 119.300 | 118.550 | 121.800 | 123.700 | 129.000 |
| Moscow Vnukovo | | 122.300 | 118.300 | | 119.000 | 118.300 |
| Munich | 118.375 | 120.650 | 118.700 | 129.100 | 121.900 | 127.950 |
| Nairobi Jomo Kenyatta | | 119.700 | 118.700 | 118.500 | 121.900 | 121.300 |
| Naples | 135.975 | 124.350 | 118.500 | 120.950 | 121.900 | 124.350 |
| Nice | 129.600 | 120.250 | 118.700 | | 121.700 | 120.250 |
| Odessa Central | 124.800 | 133.100 | 125.500 | 131.500 | 121.800 | 125.500 |
| Okinawa Kadena | 124.200 | 119.100 | 126.200 | 123.300 | 118.500 | 119.100 |
| Okinawa Naha | 127.800 | 119.100 | 126.200 | 126.500 | 121.800 | |
| Osaka International | 128.600 | 124.700 | 118.100 | 119.500 | 121.700 | 125.100 |
| Oslo Fornebu | 123.700 | 120.450 | 118.100 | 119.650 | 121.700 | 129.050 |
| Palma Son San Juan | 119.250 | 119.400 | 118.300 | 119.150 | 121.700 | 118.950 |
| Paris Charles de Gaulle | 128.000 | 121.150 | 119.250 | 126.650 | 121.600 | 119.850 |
| Paris Le Bourget | 120.000 | 119.850 | 119.100 | 121.900 | 121.900 | 121.150 |
| Paris Orly | 126.500 | 120.850 | 118.700 | 127.750 | 121.700 | 124.450 |
| Perth (Australia) | 117.200 | 118.700 | 120.500 | 133.000 | 121.700 | 133.200 |
| Prague Ruzyne | 122.150 | 121.400 | 118.100 | | 121.900 | 119.000 |
| Rangoon Mingaladon | | 119.700 | 118.100 | 118.700 | 121.900 | 125.700 |
| Rhodes Paradisi | 126.350 | 120.600 | 118.200 | | | 119.700 |
| Riyadh King Khalid Intl. | 126.400 | 126.000 | 118.600 | 121.800 | 121.700 | |
| Rome Fiumicino | 114.900 | 119.200 | 118.700 | 121.700 | 121.900 | 119.200 |
| Rotterdam | 110.400 | 121.200 | 118.200 | | | 119.700 |
| Seoul Kimpo International | 126.400 | 119.100 | 118.100 | 124.800 | 121.900 | 127.100 |
| Seychelles International | | 119.700 | 118.300 | | 121.900 | |
| Singapore Changi | 128.600 | 119.300 | 118.600 | 121.650 | 118.050 | 127.300 |
| Sofia | 118.900 | 123.700 | 118.100 | | | 123.700 |
| Shannon | | 121.400 | 118.700 | 121.700 | 121.800 | 121.400 |
| Stockholm Arlanda | 119.000 | 119.400 | 118.500 | 121.700 | 121.950 | 120.500 |
| Stockholm Bromma | 122.450 | 120.150 | 119.400 | | 121.600 | |
| Stuttgart | 109.200 | 119.200 | 118.800 | | 121.900 | 119.850 |
| Sydney Kingsford Smith | 115.400 | 126.100 | 120.500 | 127.500 | 121.700 | 126.900 |
| Taipei Chiang Kai Shek | 127.600 | 125.100 | 118.700 | 121.800 | 121.700 | 125.500 |
| Tehran Mehrabad | | 119.700 | 118.100 | 125.100 | 121.900 | 119.700 |
| Tel Aviv Ben Gurion Intl. | 113.500 | 119.500 | 118.300 | | 121.800 | 120.500 |
| Tokyo Haneda | 128.800 | 119.100 | 118.100 | 121.800 | 121.700 | 119.500 |
| Tokyo Narita International | 128.200 | 125.800 | 118.200 | 124.400 | 121.800 | 120.200 |
| Tokyo Yokota | 128.400 | 123.800 | 120.300 | 122.100 | 133.200 | 120.700 |
| Toulouse Blagnac | 119.900 | 121.100 | 118.100 | 129.300 | 121.900 | 121.100 |
| Tripoli | | 124.000 | 118.100 | | 120.100 | 120.900 |
| Tunis Carthage | 126.600 | 121.200 | 118.100 | 132.550 | 121.900 | |
| Vienna Schwechat | 108.800 | 128.200 | 118.100 | 129.200 | 121.600 | 128.200 |
| Warsaw Okecie | 118.700 | 128.800 | 121.600 | 134.175 | 121.900 | 118.300 |
| Wellington International | 112.300 | 119.300 | 118.800 | 123.700 | | 123.700 |

## Table 11.1  Europe, Africa, Asia and the Pacific *continued*

| Airport | ATIS | App | Tower | Clr/Dep | GND | Rad/Mix |
|---|---|---|---|---|---|---|
| Zagreb | 120.800 | 118.500 | 118.300 | 128.375 | | 118.500 |
| Zurich | 114.300 | 118.000 | 118.100 | 121.800 | 121.900 | 128.050 |

## Table 11.1  North and South America

| Airport | ATIS | App | Tower | Clr/Dep | GND | Rad/Mix |
|---|---|---|---|---|---|---|
| Anchorage International | 118.400 | 118.600 | 118.300 | 119.400 | 121.900 | 122.200 |
| Atlanta William B. Hartsfield | 119.650 | 118.100 | 119.100 | 125.000 | 121.750 | 127.900 |
| | 125.550 | 127.900 | 119.500 | 121.650 | 121.900 | 123.850 |
| Atlantic City | 108.600 | 118.350 | 120.300 | | | |
| Austin R.E. Meuller Municipal | 119.200 | 118.800 | 121.000 | 125.500 | 121.900 | 124.900 |
| Baltimore Washington Intl. | 115.100 | 119.700 | 119.400 | 125.300 | 121.900 | 119.000 |
| Bangor | 125.600 | 124.500 | 120.700 | 125.300 | 121.900 | |
| Bermuda | | 119.100 | 118.100 | 126.200 | 124.500 | 133.000 |
| Birmingham Municipal | 119.400 | 132.200 | 119.900 | 120.900 | 121.700 | |
| Bogata Eldorado | 114.700 | 119.500 | 118.100 | 121.600 | 121.900 | 121.300 |
| Boston Logan International | 135.000 | 120.600 | 119.100 | 127.200 | 121.900 | 118.250 |
| Buenos Aries Ezieza | 116.500 | 119.900 | 119.100 | 124.100 | 121.700 | 125.900 |
| Buffalo International (NY) | 135.350 | 123.800 | 120.500 | 124.700 | 121.900 | 126.500 |
| Calgary International | 114.800 | 125.900 | 118.400 | 119.800 | 121.900 | 128.700 |
| Caracas | 114.800 | 120.100 | 118.100 | 118.400 | 121.900 | 120.400 |
| Charlotte Douglas International | 121.800 | 125.350 | 118.100 | 121.800 | 121.900 | 126.150 |
| Chicago O'Hare | 135.400 | 119.000 | 118.100 | 119.850 | 121.900 | |
| | | 125.700 | 120.750 | 121.600 | 121.750 | |
| | | 127.400 | | 129.050 | | |
| Cincinnati | 135.300 | 119.700 | 118.300 | 124.700 | 121.700 | 121.300 |
| Cleveland Hopkins International | 127.850 | 124.500 | 120.900 | 118.150 | 121.700 | 125.050 |
| Colorado Springs Municipal | 125.000 | 118.500 | 119.900 | 124.000 | 121.700 | 120.600 |
| Columbus (Port Columbus) | 124.600 | 124.200 | 120.500 | 125.950 | 121.900 | 126.200 |
| Dallas Fort Worth Intl. | 117.000 | 119.050 | 126.550 | 127.750 | 121.800 | 127.500 |
| | 135.500 | 125.800 | 124.150 | 118.550 | 121.650 | 128.250 |
| Denver Stapleton | 125.600 | 120.800 | 118.300 | 128.050 | 121.900 | 125.300 |
| Des Moines | 119.550 | 118.600 | 118.300 | 134.150 | 121.900 | |
| Detroit Wayne Metropolitan | 124.550 | 124.050 | 118.400 | 120.650 | 121.800 | 125.150 |
| Fairfield International | 124.400 | 118.100 | 118.300 | 127.600 | 121.900 | 126.600 |
| Fort Lauderdale | 135.000 | 127.650 | 119.300 | 119.700 | 121.400 | 128.600 |
| Halifax International | 121.000 | 119.200 | 118.400 | 122.200 | 121.900 | 126.700 |
| Havana Marti | | 120.300 | 118.100 | 135.100 | | 128.700 |
| Honolulu | 127.900 | 118.300 | 118.100 | 121.400 | 121.900 | 131.950 |
| Houston Intercontinental | 124.050 | 124.350 | 118.100 | 119.700 | 121.700 | 127.250 |

## Table 11.1 North and South America *continued*

| | | | | | | |
|---|---|---|---|---|---|---|
| Indianapolis International | 125.350 | 121.100 | 120.900 | 128.750 | 121.900 | |
| Jacksonville International | 125.850 | 119.000 | 118.300 | 127.000 | 121.900 | 118.000 |
| Kansas City International | 128.350 | 132.950 | 128.200 | 126.600 | 121.800 | 126.600 |
| Kingston (Jamaica) | 125.400 | 120.600 | 120.600 | 124.000 | 121.700 | 128.100 |
| Las Vegas | 125.600 | 127.150 | 119.900 | 133.950 | 121.900 | 121.100 |
| Los Angeles International | 133.800 | 124.900 | 120.950 | 125.200 | 121.650 | 124.500 |
| | 135.650 | 128.500 | 133.900 | 124.300 | 121.750 | 121.400 |
| Memphis International | 121.000 | 119.100 | 118.300 | 124.650 | 121.900 | 125.200 |
| | 119.450 | 125.800 | 119.700 | 124.150 | | |
| Mexico City | 127.700 | 121.200 | 118.100 | 119.700 | 121.900 | 121.100 |
| Miami International | 117.100 | 126.850 | 118.300 | 119.450 | 121.800 | 125.700 |
| | 119.150 | | 123.900 | 118.100 | 127.500 | 128.750 |
| Milwaukee General Mitchell | 126.400 | 126.500 | 119.100 | 125.350 | 121.900 | 120.000 |
| Minneapolis St Paul Intl. | 135.350 | 119.300 | 126.700 | 124.700 | 121.900 | 126.950 |
| Montevideo Carrasco | | 119.200 | 118.100 | 119.200 | | 126.500 |
| Montreal Dorval | 128.000 | 125.150 | 119.900 | 124.650 | 121.900 | 135.025 |
| Montreal Mirabel | | | | | | |
| International | 125.700 | 125.150 | 119.100 | 124.650 | 121.800 | 120.500 |
| Nashville Metropolitan | 120.000 | 120.600 | 119.100 | 118.400 | 121.900 | 124.000 |
| Nassau International | 118.700 | 121.000 | 119.500 | 124.200 | 121.700 | 118.300 |
| Newark | 115.700 | 128.550 | 118.300 | 119.200 | 121.800 | 132.450 |
| New Orleans Moisant | 126.700 | 120.600 | 119.500 | 127.200 | 121.900 | 122.200 |
| New York Kennedy | 111.200 | 127.400 | 119.100 | 135.900 | 121.900 | 124.750 |
| | 115.400 | 132.400 | 123.900 | 123.700 | 121.650 | 135.050 |
| New York La Guardia | 125.950 | 118.800 | 118.700 | 120.400 | 121.700 | 134.900 |
| | 127.050 | 132.700 | 126.500 | 128.800 | 121.850 | 124.950 |
| Norfolk International | 127.150 | 118.900 | 120.800 | 124.900 | 121.900 | 127.350 |
| Oakland | 128.500 | 120.900 | 118.300 | 135.100 | 121.750 | 122.000 |
| | | 127.000 | 127.200 | 135.400 | 125.800 | 122.200 |
| Oklahoma City (Rogers) | 125.850 | 119.300 | 118.300 | 123.700 | 121.900 | |
| Ontario International | 124.250 | 125.500 | 120.600 | 135.400 | 121.900 | 127.000 |
| Orlando | 121.200 | 124.800 | 124.300 | 120.150 | 121.850 | 134.700 |
| Ottowa International | 121.150 | 135.150 | 118.800 | 128.175 | 121.900 | 119.400 |
| Panama City (Torrijos) | | 119.700 | 118.100 | 125.500 | 121.900 | 119.700 |
| Philadelphia International | 133.400 | 128.400 | 118.500 | 119.750 | 121.900 | 124.350 |
| Pittsburgh Greater Intl. | 127.200 | 123.950 | 119.100 | 124.750 | 121.900 | 126.750 |
| | 111.000 | | 128.300 | 123.950 | 127.800 | |
| Portland International | 128.350 | 119.800 | 118.700 | 124.350 | 121.900 | 119.000 |
| Port of Spain (Piarco) | | 119.000 | 118.100 | 126.900 | 121.900 | 118.100 |
| Quebec | 119.800 | 127.850 | 120.300 | 123.550 | 121.900 | 126.700 |
| Rio de Janeiro Galeao | 127.600 | 119.000 | 118.000 | 121.000 | 121.900 | 119.900 |
| Sacramento Metropolitan | 126.750 | 125.600 | 125.700 | 124.500 | 121.700 | 124.500 |
| St John's Newfoundland | 128.000 | 133.150 | 119.300 | 134.700 | 121.900 | 122.200 |
| St Louis Lambert Intl. | 120.450 | 126.500 | 118.500 | 118.950 | 121.900 | 127.200 |
| Salt Lake City | 124.750 | 124.300 | 118.300 | 127.300 | 121.900 | |
| San Antonio International | 118.900 | 125.100 | 119.800 | 125.700 | 121.900 | 127.100 |
| San Francisco International | 115.800 | 134.500 | 120.500 | 120.900 | 121.800 | 118.200 |
| | 113.700 | 135.650 | 125.600 | 135.100 | 121.650 | 118.200 |
| San Juan International | 125.800 | 120.900 | 118.300 | 119.400 | 121.900 | 126.400 |
| Sau Paulo Guarulhos | 127.750 | 129.750 | 118.100 | 119.100 | 121.700 | 129.200 |
| Seattle King/Boeing | 127.750 | 123.900 | 118.900 | 118.900 | 121.900 | 121.650 |

**Table 11.1  North and South America** *continued*

| | | | | | | |
|---|---|---|---|---|---|---|
| Seattle Tacoma | 118.000 | 123.900 | 119.900 | 118.900 | 121.900 | |
| Syracuse Hancock | | | | | | |
| International | 120.750 | 124.200 | 120.300 | 125.050 | 121.700 | 124.600 |
| Tampa International | 126.450 | 118.800 | 119.500 | 120.250 | 119.050 | 126.000 |
| Toronto | 114.500 | 127.575 | 118.000 | 128.800 | 121.900 | 121.300 |
| | 114.800 | 125.400 | 118.350 | 124.475 | 121.650 | 133.100 |
| Vancouver | 124.600 | 120.800 | 118.700 | 120.500 | 121.700 | 121.400 |
| Washington Dulles | 134.850 | 120.450 | 120.100 | 125.050 | 121.900 | 126.100 |
| | | 126.100 | | 126.650 | 125.800 | 124.650 |
| Wichita Mid—Continental | 121.150 | 126.700 | 118.200 | 120.600 | 121.900 | 134.450 |
| Windsor Locks (Bradley) | 118.150 | 125.800 | 120.300 | 125.350 | 121.900 | 123.850 |
| | | 121.750 | 119.100 | 125.650 | | 121.750 |
| Winnipeg | 114.800 | 119.500 | 118.300 | 119.900 | 121.900 | 121.300 |

### Scanner kit

The VHF/FM scanner described in Chapter 3 is available as a complete kit (less crystals) and is supplied by:

Cirkit Holdings
Park Lane
Broxbourne
Hertfordshire
Telephone: (0992) 444111
Available early 1988.

Crystals can be ordered from any of the several suppliers who advertise in the Amateur Radio magazines. Marine and amateur 2 metre crystals are relatively inexpensive but should you need a crystal cut to a specific frequency then the formula is:

$$\text{Crystal frequency} = \frac{\text{Required frequency} - 10.7 \text{ MHz}}{3}$$

### Scanners 1

Readers who enjoy this book may be interested to know that it is the second in the series on Scanners by Peter Rouse, published by Argus Books.

Scanners 1 was so successful that a second edition was printed just a year after the book was first published. Although several publishers have produced frequency lists none have given the in-depth explanations that are needed to fully understand some of the more complex aspects that are explained in Scanners 1.

The book starts by explaining radio theory in non-technical terms and covers receivers, transmitters, frequency, wavelength, spectrum, distances transmissions cover, modes of modulation, channelising and simplex/duplex operation. The explanations are aimed at the layman and answers the many queries raised by non-technical scanner owners.

Equipment is described in detail, what all the controls do and what all the input and output sockets are for. Operation of scanners covers portable, mobile and base use and how to order crystals. One section even describes how to get some scanners to cover frequencies outside their normal range.

The book has a section on antennas describing how they work, why they are important and how to choose the right type. Accessories such as antenna amplifiers are described together with computer interfaces, weather satellite decoders and similar extras.

Scanners has a detailed section on the full British band plans from 25 to 1300 MHz, not just frequency listings but complete sections broken down and described in detail. The Chapter is so comprehensive that the average scanner user will have little difficulty in using the information to track down allocations which cannot legally be published. Specific details are given of aviation, marine, amateur, military, emergency services, private mobile radio, radio telephones (including cellular), cordless telephones, pagers, beacons, radiomicrophones, telemetry and similar allocations. A range of frequencies are given for satellites including weather, navigation, the MIR Space Station, NASA shuttle and military.

Another section of Scanners covers RT Procedure and describes how the language of the airways is used and why and how frequencies or channels are changed or used at certain times.

The book also features a full review of Scanners and accessories from the different manufacturers. Although Scanners has one chapter devoted to the British band plans the rest of the book will provide a valuable reference source for any scanner owner.

**What the UK radio press said:**

*Shortwave Magazine* In a review of the PRO 2004 said: 'If this is to be your first scanner then it will pay you to obtain a good book on what scanners are all about, such as *Scanners* by Peter Rouse.

*Radio & Electronics World* carried a review by Duncan Leslie which said: 'The book is written to his usual high standard. It begins with radio theory, covering this in an elementary, non-technical manner, in sufficient depth to allow a newcomer to understand what's going on. All in all a rather good book'.

*Radio & Electronics World's* 'Spectrum Watch' by Nigel Cawthorne said: 'The book fills a gap in scanner reading material in the UK . . . The book contains plenty of information on what equipment is available on the scanner market, as well as some useful frequency tables and other general information'.

The latest edition of Scanners 1 has been updated with changes recently made to the British bandplanes and includes new satellite frequencies and more comprehensible lists of both civilian and military airfields.

# Index